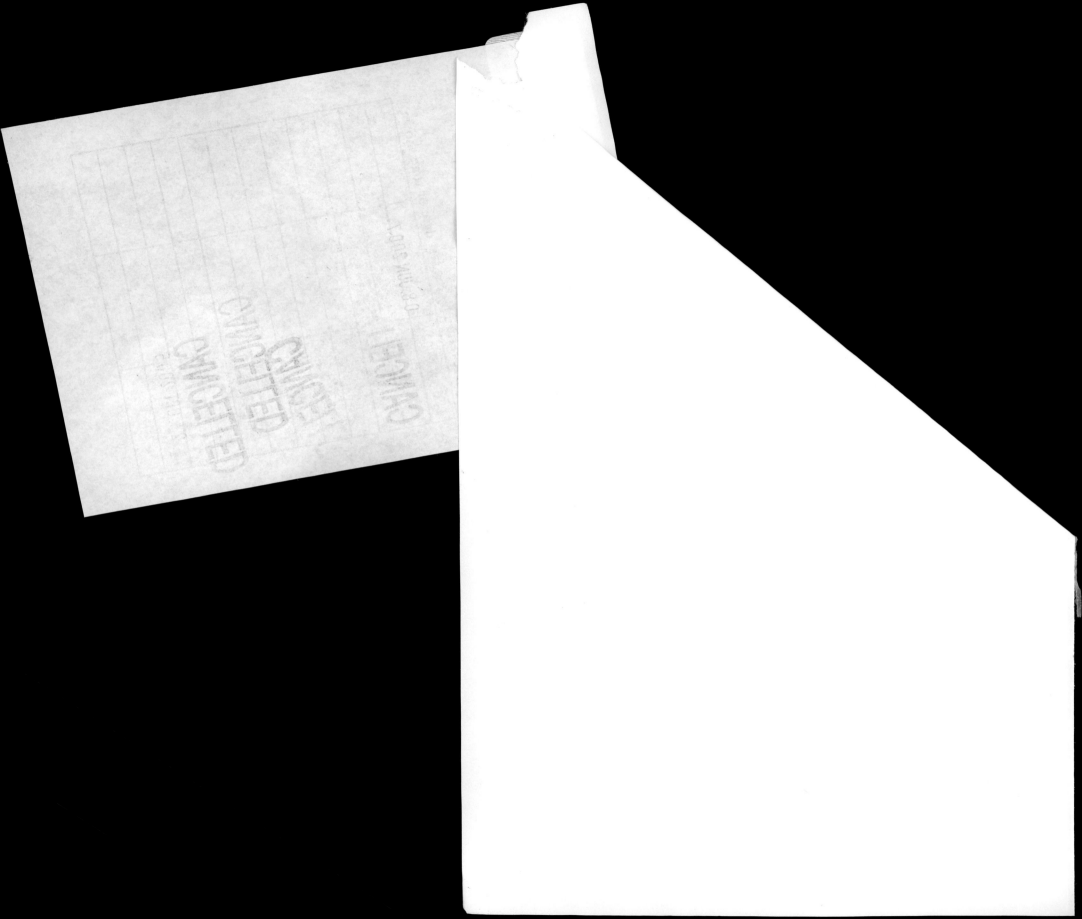

Spatial Representation in Animals

edited by
Sue Healy
Department of Psychology,
University of Newcastle

OXFORD NEW YORK TOKYO
OXFORD UNIVERSITY PRESS
1998

Oxford University Press, Great Clarendon Street, Oxford OX2 6DP

Oxford New York
Athens Auckland Bangkok Bogota Bombay
Buenos Aires Calcutta Cape Town Dar es Salaam
Delhi Florence Hong Kong Istanbul Karachi
Kuala Lumpur Madras Madrid Melbourne
Mexico City Nairobi Paris Singapore
Taipei Tokyo Toronto Warsaw
and associated companies in
Berlin Ibadan

Oxford is a trade mark of Oxford University Press

Published in the United States
by Oxford University Press, Inc., New York

© Oxford University Press, 1998

A catalogue record for this book is available from the British Library

Library of Congress Cataloging in Publication Data
Data available

ISBN 0 19 850007 6 (Hbk)
       0 19 850006 8 (Pbk)

Typeset by Hewer Text Composition Services, Edinburgh

Printed in Great Britain by Bookcraft (Bath) Ltd
Midsomer Norton, Avon

Preface

How do animals find breeding grounds after migrating many kilometres? How do they return to their nest with food? Which environmental features might animals use to find their way? How and where does the processing and storing of spatial information occur in the brain? Our understanding of the way in which animals know how, when and where to orient and navigate around their environment has grown considerably over the last few decades. Animals' use of different sensory capacities to detect changes in environmental cues, the innate bases and/or learning to use such cues as well as the neurobiological underpinnings of the perception of and memory for their movement through space have been investigated by many people, often working on very different animals.

It was not my aim here to attempt a collation or a comprehensive survey of all of this work. Indeed, something of the kind has recently been produced and with 33 contributions comprises the whole of the January 1996 issue of the *Journal of Experimental Biology*. Rather, I had in mind an introduction to the current state of our knowledge of the ways in which animals represent space in the hope that advanced undergraduate and graduate students might find this field accessible, interesting and challenging. Although this compilation has a strong behavioural bias, each of the chapters demonstrates in its own way the interdisciplinary nature of current investigations into the essence of spatial representation. Delighting in the arrival of hummingbirds in late spring at the feeders in your garden, marvelling at stories of pets travelling thousands of miles to return to a former home or watching with despair as trails of ants march in and out of your larder is only the beginning. Understanding the psychological, neurobiological and even genetic bases of these behaviours is now possible and made more accessible through recent theoretical, experimental and technical advances. The broad taxonomic range across which spatial representation is investigated offers opportunities for discovering similarities and differences in the ways in which animals move around their environment. Unfortunately, this book covers only a smattering of the species studied to date, reflecting a somewhat personal preference.

Returning home is a problem faced by most animals and how they view the world is crucial to this way finding. The animal must determine whether the world looks (for many animals use visual landmarks of some kind) sufficiently appropriate for the goal to have been reached. If not, the animal must determine how to move from its current location to the preferred goal. The book begins with two chapters, by Cheng and Spetch on birds and mammals, and by Zeil and Collett on arthropods, which both examine the ways in which these animals may, and do, use landmarks to find their way. These two chapters demonstrate the value gained by investigating the nature of landmark use in a wide variety of different species. Dead reckoning is a navigational technique that humans have employed to explore the world beyond the horizon for thousands of years and as Etienne *et al.* explain, probably also underpins much exploration and navigation in other animals. The homing pigeon *Columba livia* is one of the icons in spatial navigation. It has not only provided us with a model system for such studies but also some insight into the way in which scientific investigations progress. The debate over the role of olfaction in pigeon homing has both amused and bemused those standing on the sidelines by its intensity and duration. Bingman offers us a view of the homing pigeon literature coincident with the death throes of the olfaction controversy. In contrast to the homing pigeon, the chapter by Braithwaite on fish shows us how much we have yet to learn about the movements of this large group of animals. As with terrestrial animals, fish vary enormously in the ways in which they utilise space. The often-remarked abilities of salmon to home and of gobies to leap from one pool to another are only two of many examples of spatial orientation and navigation in fish. Further, more extensive investigation is now being permitted by several recent technological advances. How does a brood parasite like a cuckoo 'know' in which direction to migrate and, having embarked, 'know' when to stop? A flavour for the vast body of literature on avian long-distance migration is provided in the chapter by Berthold. The 'cognitive map', a pervasive concept in spatial representation since 1978, and the kinds of cues that rats use for moving about the environment are addressed in the chapter by Save *et al.* These authors underline the experimental difficulties of determining the nature of the cues used as well as the relative value of different cues to the rat. The role of the hippocampus in the representation of space is addressed by Sherry and Healy. While both experimental and comparative evidence point to involvement by the hippocampus in spatial representation in birds and mammals (as proposed by O'Keefe and Nadel 1978), it remains far from clear whether this is its sole or even prime function.

The 1995 winter meeting of the Association for the Study of Animal Behaviour (ASAB) served to bring together most of the book's contributors and I should like to thank the Council of ASAB for supporting that conference. I thank Robert Biegler and Jackie Chappell for their help in reviewing some of the chapters and Tim Guilford, Andy Hurly, John Krebs and Sara Shettleworth for the many stimulating discussions we have shared on the nature of spatial representation in animals.

Newcastle upon Tyne   S.H.
April 1997

Contents

Contributors

Joëlle Berlie Laboratoire d'Ethologie, University of Geneva, 54 rte des Acacias, Carouge, Switzerland CH 1227.

Peter Berthold Research Unit for Ornithology of the Max Planck Society, Vogelwarte Radolfzell, Schloss Moeggingen, D-78315 Radolfzell, Germany.

Verner P. Bingman Department of Psychology, Bowling Green State University, Bowling Greeen, Ohio 43403, USA.

Victoria A. Braithwaite ICAPB, King's Building, University of Edinburgh, West Mains Road, Edinburgh, EH9 3JT, UK.

Ken Cheng School of Behavioural Sciences, Macquarie University, Sydney, NSW 2109, Australia.

Tom S. Collett Sussex Centre for Neuroscience, School of Biological Sciences, University of Sussex, Brighton BN1 9QG, UK.

Ariane S. Etienne Laboratoire d'Ethologie, University of Geneva, 54 rte des Acacias, Carouge, Switzerland CH 1227.

Joséphine Georgakopoulos Laboratoire d'Ethologie, University of Geneva, 54 rte des Acacias, Carouge, Switzerland CH 1227.

Sue Healy Department of Psychology, Ridley Building, University of Newcastle, Newcastle upon Tyne NE1 7RU, UK.

Roland Maurer Laboratoire d'Ethologie, University of Geneva, 54 rte des Acacias, Carouge, Switzerland CH 1227.

Bruno Poucet CNRS, Centre de Recherche en Neurosciences Cognitives, 31 chemin Joseph-Aiguier, 13402 Marseilles cedex, France.

Etienne Save CNRS, Centre de Recherche en Neurosciences Cognitives, 31 chemin Joseph-Aiguier, 13402 Marseilles cedex, France.

Marcia L. Spetch Department of Psychology, University of Alberta, Edmonton, Alberta T6G 2E9, Canada.

David Sherry Department of Psychology, University of Western Ontario, London, Ontario N6A 5C2, Canada.

Catherine Thinus-Blanc   CNRS, Centre de Recherche en Neurosciences Cognitives, 31 chemin Joseph-Aiguier, 13402 Marseilles cedex, France.

Jochen Zeil   Centre for Visual Sciences, Research School of Biological Sciences, Australian National University, Canberra, ACT 2601, Australia.

1 Mechanisms of landmark use in mammals and birds

Ken Cheng and Marcia L. Spetch

Many animals face the problem of returning to a place that they have visited before. The place may be a home, a food site or a nest for one's offspring. The female digger wasp, for example, digs nests in the ground in which she lays eggs. The future larvae must be provisioned with food, and thus the wasp faces the problem of returning to her nests after foraging for food. For the digger wasp, reproductive success depends heavily on place finding. Food-storing birds must return to a number of places at which they have stored food (see Sherry and Healy, Chapter 8). And any home-based animal that ever ventures forth faces the problem of returning home. Diverse place-finding mechanisms are thus commonly found in the animal kingdom.

One common mechanism is the use of landmarks surrounding the goal one is returning to. This is also called piloting or mnemotaxis, a mechanism that is especially useful in the final stages of navigation, when one tries to pin-point one's goal. Most species use visual landmarks, and most experiments have manipulated visual landmarks. Our review will summarise work on landmark-based spatial memory in several species of vertebrates that we and others have studied. Reviews of other mechanisms of wayfinding, and other species, are found in this book, and in the entire January 1996 issue of the *Journal of Experimental Biology*.

Cheng (1995) characterised wayfinding as servomechanisms. At the heart of a servomechanism is the comparator. This device compares a reading of the world, delivered from the senses, with an internal standard specifying how the world should read. The discrepancy between the actual reading and the ideal reading generates action, and the action generated, under normal circumstances, reduces this discrepancy, completing a negative feedback loop. A servomechanism thus tracks a standard level on some variable(s).

Servomechanisms keep many physiological variables within the narrow range necessary for life, with examples such as blood acidity level and body temperature. In the case of wayfinding, the standard is some specification of a goal. In landmark-based spatial memory, that goal is specified in terms of where surrounding visual landmarks should appear. When an animal is not at the goal, the perceived world looks different from the standard specifications. Then action, movement in this case, is generated to bring the perceived world to the way it should look. When the world looks like what is specified for the goal, the creature is at the goal and the problem is solved. Working out what the specifications are and what gets compared is a key task for the researcher.

The transformational approach

Many results to be reviewed rely in common on an experimental technique that we call the transformational approach. This technique was pioneered by Tinbergen (1972), and is used to show that the animal does in fact rely on landmarks to find a place as well as to elucidate the mechanisms of landmark use. Tinbergen placed pine cones around the nests of digger wasps. As the wasps left the nest, they apparently learned the configuration of pine cones around it. When Tinbergen subsequently displaced the pine cones, the returning wasps searched in the middle of the pine cones, and not where their nests actually were. This fact convincingly shows that the wasps relied on the pine cones in relocating their nests. Subsequently, Tinbergen changed various aspects of the pine cones to see which cues they relied on. The displacement technique has been used to show that many species use landmarks, including rodents (Suzuki *et al.* 1980; Cheng 1986; Collett *et al.* 1986; Etienne *et al.* 1990, 1995a,b), birds (Vander Wall 1982; Balda and Turek 1984; Cheng 1988, 1989, 1990, 1994, 1995; Spetch and Edwards 1988; Vallortigara *et al.* 1990; Cheng and Sherry 1992; Spetch *et al.* 1992, 1996, 1997; Bennett 1993; Spetch and Mondloch 1993; Spetch 1995; Gould-Beierle and Kamil 1996), cephalopods (Mather 1991) and insects (von Frisch 1953; Tinbergen 1972; Wehner and Räber 1979; Cartwright and Collett 1982, 1983; Dyer and Gould 1983; Cheng *et al.* 1986; Collett and Kelber 1988; Collett 1992; Collett and Zeil, Chapter 2).

In the experiments we describe, a participant is first trained to find a goal located at a fixed place with respect to a set of experimental landmarks. The entire array of goal and landmark may be displaced from trial to trial within the search arena in order to ensure that participants use the experimental array. After being trained, participants are occasionally tested with the goal absent. As the surface on which the participant is searching is uniform and gives no hint of where the goal is, the participant is forced to rely on the landmarks provided. The landmarks provided might be transformed in some way to find out something about how participants use landmarks. We will describe these transformations, the resulting data, and what they imply. Three themes are discussed: (1) the use of metric properties of distance and direction; (2) principles in the use of multiple cues; and (3) the ways in which configurations of landmarks are used.

Use of metric properties

Metric properties are the ones we intuitively think of when we think of geometric properties, such as measures of distances, angles and directions. They can be formally defined in terms of transformations (Cheng and Gallistel 1984; Gallistel 1990, chapter 6), but intuitive notions will suffice here. Metric properties need not necessarily be relied on, but empirically, in any species in which the mechanisms of landmark use have been elucidated, metric properties are used. It may be a universal law that piloting relies on metric relations among landmarks and target sought.

As an example of a possible solution not using metric properties, consider Cheng and Gallistel's (1984) hypothetical example of using the betweeness relation. The goal that the animal wishes to return to is encoded as lying between identifiable landmarks. At least two such pairs are needed. The goal lies at the intersection of the straight lines defined by these pairs of corresponding landmarks. In using this strategy, some geometric notions are required. These include straight line, collinearity and betweeness, entities and relations in affine geometry. However, distances and directions need not be measured. In terms of the transformational approach, any transformation of the search space that preserves collinearity should leave this strategy, and its user, unperturbed. However, research has failed to reveal the use of such a non-metric strategy.

The geometric module

One intriguing finding, and one of the first attempts to show that rats use metric properties, is a systematic error found in search tasks in a rectangular search space (Cheng 1986; Margules and Gallistel 1988; Gallistel 1990, chapter 6). In one trial, the rat was shown the location within the arena of some highly desired food. After eating some but not all of the provided food, the animal was removed from the arena. The food was buried at the same location (actually in a replica of the search arena that looks the same), and the rat's task was to find the food again 90 s later. The arena was rotated at random during the delay period, so that the participant could not rely on an inertial sense of direction to solve the task. The target location varied from trial to trial, so that the task was, operationally, a working memory task.

It is important to note that many discriminable cues were found on the walls of the rectangular space. A different pattern of high-contrast stripes was in each corner. A different number of small lights shone at each corner. Distinctive smells emanated from two of the corners. And in one experiment, one entire long wall was white while the other walls were black. Despite these dramatic cues, the rat often made a rotational error, sometimes as often as it searched at the correct location (Margules and Gallistel 1988). This error is shown in Fig. 1.1a. One arrives at the location of the rotational error by rotating the correct location by 180° around the centre of the space.

This is a remarkable error. The rat is mixing up locations that differ in many characteristics. It might have been shown food near a white wall smelling of peppermint, and later be searching near a black wall smelling of anise! To make this error, the rats must have encoded the target location with respect to the overall shape of the arena, a rectangle, and not with respect to individual features such as vertical stripes, smells or even a whole wall of white (Fig. 1.1B). Note that in making the rotational error, the rat got all the metric properties right: the location is at the correct distance and direction from the nearest corner. Only, the 'map' is misaligned with the world by 180°. The rat also kept track of left and right, more specifically, whether the long wall is to the right or left of the short wall when the rat faces the corner nearest the place of search. Technically, this geometric property is called sense. It distinguishes mirror reflections of the same object. In other words, the rat did not make any systematic reflectional errors.

What the rotational error means is that the rat has one record that encodes only the overall shape of the arena, and this record contains the metric properties of space and sense because all the metric relations, plus sense, are correct in the rotational error. It shows the primacy of metric properties in locating a place by landmarks. This record was called the geometric module.

A. Performance on task

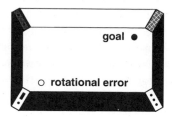

B. Geometric module

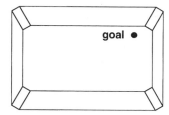

Fig. 1.1 Schematic illustration of the geometric module in the rat (Cheng 1986). (a) Rats were trained on a working memory task of spatial search in which they were shown the location of food (goal) on each trial and later required to go back to the same location. They sometimes searched at the goal and sometimes made a rotational error by searching at the location rotated 180° from the goal through the centre. (b) To commit the rotational error, the rat must have encoded the location of the goal with respect to the overall shape of the environment, and not with respect to the locations of featural cues such as smells and visual patterns on walls.

One theoretical proposal for the geometric module is that it encodes the principal axes of space (e.g. the long and short mid-lines in a rectangular space; Gallistel 1990, chapter 6). The animal lines up the principal axes of the record with that of the perceived space in order to figure out which direction in the world corresponds with which direction on the record. This process is known as determining heading.

When the target location stayed the same trial after trial, the rats learned to discriminate the target location from the rotational error. This shows that the features provided experimentally were discriminable. But the rats still made rotational errors systematically, again showing the use of the geometric module.

Such a record is found in human children as well, because 2-year-olds also commit this rotational error (Hermer and Spelke 1994). Like rats, the young children committed many rotational errors in retrieving a desired object from the corner of a rectangular room. They did so even in a reference memory task in which the target location was the same for a number of trials.

Just how widespread the geometric module is among the vertebrates has yet to be ascertained. Vallortigara *et al.* (1990) conducted experiments on chicks in rectangular boxes, in paradigms based on Cheng's (1986) experiments on rats. The chicks were tested in a reference memory task, in which the target location remained the same from trial to trial. When tested in a featureless rectangular box, featureless, that is, except for the rectangular shape, the chicks searched at the correct location or made the rotational error, but did not make any other systematic errors. Like the rats, the chicks were deprived of any sense of direction other than the box. They could not see outside the box, and they were rotated during the delay period so that they could not keep track of direction internally. Without a sense of direction, the correct location and the rotational error could not in principle be distinguished, so that the chicks' performance was the best possible. The performance again requires encoding both metric properties and sense, and strongly suggests a geometric module. When provided with added visual features in the corners, however, the rotational errors disappeared. It is not known whether chicks would commit the rotational error in a working memory paradigm, as that was not done.

Other evidence for the use of metric properties

Other kinds of evidence for the use of metric properties come from the transformational approach. When an array of landmarks is transformed in some way on a test, the participant searches most at a location that preserves the metric relations to some subset of the array (Collett *et al.* 1986; Spetch *et al.* 1992, 1996, 1997). We discuss these experiments on pp. 13–15.

More indirect evidence for the use of metric properties comes from the theories and models that have been formulated to account for data. Basically, we cannot make sense of the data without assuming that the animals have encoded metric relations between the goal and surrounding landmarks (Cheng 1988, 1989, 1990, 1994, 1995; Cheng and Sherry 1992; Bennett 1993; Gould-Beierle and Kamil 1996).

Measuring distance

How is distance to a landmark measured? The mammalian and avian visual systems can gauge distance from a number of cues. They include accommodation, motion parallax, binocular cues such as convergence and binocular disparity, and the retinal size projected by a familiar landmark. Little systematic work has been done on this topic. The experimental manipulations have focused primarily on the projected retinal size. The key transformation here is changing the size of a landmark on a test. If projected retinal size is used, making the landmark smaller ought to make the subject search nearer to the landmark, when compared with search distance on control tests with the standard landmark size. Making the landmark larger ought to make the subject search farther away. In vertebrates, the results differ between species.

Collett *et al.* (1986) tested gerbils trained with a single cylinder as landmark. The goal was at a constant distance from the training landmark. On tests, the landmark was made smaller, larger, or the same size as in training. When the landmark was made larger, the gerbils still searched at about the same distance from it as on control tests. But when the landmark was made smaller, they searched closer to the landmarks. This indicates that both retinal size and other distance cues are used. Goodale *et al.* (1990) trained gerbils to jump a gap from one platform to another. During training, the target platform was a constant size, but target distance varied from trial to trial. On crucial tests, the target platform was made larger or smaller. The gerbils jumped longer distances when the platform was made smaller, and shorter distances when the platform was made bigger, thus indicating the use in part of retinal size to determine distance.

In an experiment on humans tested with a single landmark on a computer monitor (Spetch *et al.* 1996), results resembled those shown by Collett *et al.*'s gerbils. Making the landmark smaller resulted in searches closer to the target. Making the landmark larger resulted in searches farther from the target, but the magnitude of this shift was smaller than would be expected if distance was judged solely on the basis of landmark size.

In pigeons, in contrast, no evidence has been found for the use of retinal size to determine distance (Cheng 1988). In the size manipulation experiments, the key landmark was either a strip of blue cardboard paper on an arena wall, or a block against an arena wall. Changing the width of the cardboard strip or the height of the block produced no systematic change in the place of peak searching.

Caution should be taken in interpreting such comparative differences because the landmark set-ups were different. In the case of gerbils and humans, an isolated landmark (computer drawn object, cylinder or platform) was used, while in the case of pigeons, many other cues, such as the walls of the arena, were also present. We have tried to train and test pigeons with single bottles as landmarks. This has failed on methodological grounds: When the size of the bottle changed, especially when it was larger than the training bottle, the birds appeared to fear the new landmark. Their search was sparse and scattered.

The use of multiple cues

Landmarks are not isolated in the world. Locations in the real world, unlike the laboratory, are defined by multiple landmarks. Not surprisingly, mammals and birds use multiple landmarks in experimental situations. Perhaps surprisingly, pigeons sometimes have been found to use only a single landmark when multiple landmarks indicate the goal's location. Experiments with multiple cues also show the use of metric properties, and illustrate some principles of learning.

Averaging

Consider an experimental situation in which two identical landmarks define a goal's location during training (Fig. 1.2a). Take the top of the figure to be north. One landmark is to the northwest, one to the northeast. On a test the landmark array is transformed by moving the landmarks farther apart (Fig. 1.2b). On this test, one can maintain the correct direction and distance to either of the two landmarks, and that is what gerbils do (Collett *et al.* 1986). One can match the compass directions to both landmarks, but search at the wrong distances, and that is what adult humans do (Spetch *et al.* 1996, 1997). One can also attempt to match both direction and distance to the landmarks, but average the dictates of the two landmarks. In this case, the distance maintained is the perpendicular distance to the line segment connecting the two landmarks (solid line segment in Fig. 1.2b). Averaging the dictates of the two landmarks then means searching somewhere along the dashed line segment that connects the two locations where gerbils search. Pigeons show this search pattern. They do so with computer drawn stimuli on the surface of a monitor (Spetch *et al.* 1996), with two isolated bottles on the floor of a lab room (Spetch *et al.* 1997) and with two blocks at one edge (wall) of a square arena (Cheng 1989).

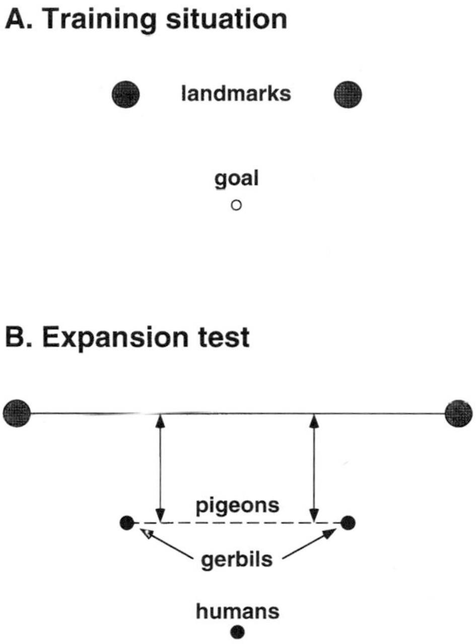

A. Training situation

landmarks

goal

B. Expansion test

pigeons

gerbils

humans

Fig. 1.2 Schematic illustration of the performance of three species when an array of two landmarks was expanded (Collett *et al.* 1986; Spetch *et al.* 1996, 1997). (a) Set-up of landmarks during training. (b) Performance on expansion tests. Pigeons searched most somewhere along the dashed line. Gerbils searched most at the two locations the arrows are pointing to. Pigeons and gerbils maintained the same perpendicular distance to the line joining the two landmarks. Humans searched most at the point that maintains the same directions from the goal to both landmarks.

What this means is that pigeons maintain the perpendicular distance to an edge, including an invisible edge defined by a line segment connecting two bottles. Further evidence of this is found in other transformational experiments on pigeons, chickadees (Cheng and Sherry 1992) and on Clark's nutcrackers (Gould-Beierle and Kamil 1996). In the training set-up in those experiments, the goal was near an edge of an arena and one additional nearby landmark was provided. On crucial tests, the landmark was translated both parallel and perpendicular to the edge (in a diagonal direction). The birds' searching followed the parallel shift of the landmark but not the perpendicular shift. That is, they maintained about the same distance from the edge of the arena in searching. Pigeons, in addition, have been tested on the computer monitor with this manipulation and the results showed the same pattern (Spetch *et al.* 1992).

Independent averaging of distance and direction

What do the birds average? A distance plus a direction from a landmark amounts to a vector from that landmark. Do they average entire vectors or do they average the components of the vector, distance and direction, separately? Figure 1.3 casts this question into concrete experimental situations. Imagine that on a transformed set-up, an animal encounters conflicting directional cues for the location of the goal. One cue indicates the goal as lying to the north (from a place that can be considered the centre of the search space), while another cue indicates the goal as lying to the east. The distance in both cases is the same, 20 cm in the example. Averaging the two vectors (20 cm N and 20 cm E) in their entirety means searching somewhere on the line segment connecting the two endpoints of the vectors. Where one searches along this line segment is determined by the relative weights given to the vectors. Averaging distances and directions separately means searching somewhere along the arc connecting the two endpoints of the vectors. Averaging the distance components yields 20 cm, the same measure as the component distances, while averaging the directions yields some direction between N and E. The result lies on the arc from 20 cm N to 20 cm E, and again, the relative weights given to the two vectors determine the location along the arc.

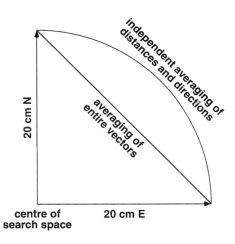

Fig. 1.3 Testing the independence of calculations of distances and directions (Cheng 1994). Situations are created in which different landmarks point to goal locations differing in direction from the centre of the search space, as exemplified by the two vectors (20 cm E and 20 cm N) shown. If entire vectors are averaged, place of peak searching should lie on a straight line connecting the two endpoints of the vectors. If distances and directions are independently averaged, place of peak searching should lie on the arc connecting the two endpoints of the vectors.

Cheng (1994) subjected pigeons to a number of such experiments. The results clearly support the independent averaging of distances and directions, and reject the averaging of entire vectors. These experimental paradigms have not been tried on any other species, and further comparative work here would be well worth the effort. In honey-bees, the current model of the use of landmarks suggests that distances and directions are also separately calculated (see Cartwright and Collett 1982, 1983; Collett and Zeil, Chapter 2).

Averaging dictates of different systems

The dictates of landmarks may be averaged with the dictates of other systems of navigation. One example is the averaging of landmark information with inertial information. Inertial information refers to information on direction and distance from a starting point, gathered by keeping track of the vector that one has covered from the beginning of the journey (see Etienne *et al.*, Chapter 3). In experiments on hamsters by Etienne *et al.* (1990, 1995*a,b*), the participant lived just outside a circular arena. A landmark (e.g. light) was permanently over its nest. The hamster was induced to go to the middle of the arena to retrieve food for hoarding. After retrieving the food, the rodent had the task of returning home.

On a crucial test trial, the landmark was rotated by 90° from its usual location. Now the direction home according to the landmark differed by 90° from the direction home according to inertial navigation. Hamsters sometimes struck out in an intermediate direction between the dictates of the landmark and the dictates of inertial navigation, indicating that two different systems of navigation may be averaged.

Learning principles in the use of landmarks

Some aspects of spatial learning point to specialised mechanisms that deal with specifically spatial properties of the world. A geometric module that extracts the shape of the environment is a prime example of such a dedicated device. While much of the learning of landmarks may point to specialised memory systems (Sherry and Schacter 1987), other aspects of the use of landmarks illustrate general principles of learning.

Selective stimulus control

Chapter 2 (pp. 18–53) presents evidence that birds and mammals often use multiple cues in determining where to search. Frequently, however, pigeons seem to use only a subset or a single landmark even when many landmarks are provided. Furthermore, which landmark controls behaviour may vary from individual to individual. These findings seem to parallel selective attention effects sometimes observed in instrumental discrimination training (e.g. Reynolds 1961).

Spetch and Mondloch (1993) presented pigeons with an array of four visually distinct landmarks in a fixed configuration on the touch screen. The goal was roughly in the middle of the array. During training, the landmark array and corresponding goal were translated across trials so that the goal maintained a fixed location with respect to each landmark but occupied varied locations on the touch screen. Subsequent probe tests, in which individual landmarks were removed or shifted, revealed that pigeons' search behaviour was controlled by only a subset of the landmark array. Some pigeons showed exclusive control by only one or two of the landmarks. Although individual pigeons differed in which landmark exerted the most control, results were very consistent across tests for each pigeon. In other words, the pigeons displayed individual but stable patterns of selective landmark control.

Cheng and Spetch (1995) provided pigeons with computer-generated landmarks on the touch screen that replicated the set-up used by Cheng and Sherry (1992) and Spetch *et al.* (1992). A square frame surrounded the target location, with the goal near an edge. Another computer drawn stimulus served as a nearby landmark. The entire configuration was translated on the monitor from trial to trial. Removal and shift tests were again done. In one series of tests, either the frame or the landmark was removed, while in another series, either an edge of the frame or the landmark was shifted. Some pigeons' performance was controlled primarily by the landmark while one pigeon's performance was controlled primarily by the frame.

Predictive value of landmarks: preference for nearer landmarks

In temporal relationships, predictiveness plays an important part in learning. Classic work by Rescorla (1967) shows that the predictive contingency between conditioned and unconditioned stimuli determines the degree of learning in classical conditioning. We believe that this principle is general and applies to spatial predictiveness as well. One piece of evidence consistent with the principle is that a variety of species rely preferentially on nearer landmarks. Landmarks near the goal supply the most precise information in specifying goal location. As one moves from the goal, the compass direction and the relative distance to a nearer landmark change faster than those to a farther landmark. Thus, with a nearer landmark, one is better able to tell when one has deviated from the goal.

In pigeons, evidence for preferential weighting of nearer landmarks comes from tasks on the touch screen and on the laboratory floor. On the floor, when a landmark 20 cm away from the goal and a landmark 60 cm away were both shifted, in opposite directions, the pigeons preferentially shifted in the direction in which the nearer landmark was shifted (Cheng 1989). For landmark shifts in the same direction, moving a nearer landmark again had more effect than moving a farther landmark (Cheng 1989). On the touch screen monitor, Spetch and Wilkie (1994) provided three landmarks with the goal nearest one of the landmarks. When the nearest landmark was removed on a test, accuracy of search dropped, whereas removing the farther landmarks did not affect accuracy. When the nearest landmark was shifted, the pigeons shifted their searching in the direction in which the landmark was shifted. Shifting the farther landmarks had no effect.

European Jays, a food-storing corvid, also rely more heavily on near landmarks than far landmarks. Bennett (1993) trained European Jays to find a peanut that was hidden in sand on the laboratory floor. The location of the peanut was fixed relative to an array of 12 landmarks that surrounded the goal, but the location in the room of the goal and landmark array varied across trials. The landmarks differed in height and distance from the goal. Tests in which subsets of the landmarks were removed indicated that the birds primarily relied on the near, tall landmarks to find the goal.

In chicks, Vallortigara et al. (1990) showed preferential reliance on nearer landmarks. As already described, one experiment provided the chicks with distinct landmarks in the corners of a rectangular box. The target location was at one of the landmarks. Removing the landmark at the goal and at the diagonally opposite corner drastically affected performance. To be specific, the chicks then made as many rotational errors as correct responses. They did not use the landmarks in the remaining corners to differentiate the two geometrically equivalent locations. Rats in Cheng's (1986) experiments showed the same pattern of results with this manipulation. This indicates that both species rely preferentially on landmark features near the goal. On the other hand, when the landmark at the goal was exchanged with its diagonally opposite landmark, both species continued to choose the target landmark. As this manipulation drastically altered the configuration of features around the arena, it indicates that the configural arrangement of far landmarks had little effect on localisation.

In gerbils, evidence comes from a study by Collett *et al.* (1986) in which gerbils were trained to search for a goal at different distances from three distinguishable landmarks on the floor. When the nearest landmark was moved apart from the other two, the gerbils searched most at a location appropriate for the landmark that was nearest the goal.

The predictive value of a landmark also depends on the reliability with which it indicates a goal location. Reliability is manipulable experimentally, but it has not yet been done. For instance, consider two identical landmarks east and west of the goal. Both landmarks are on average 20 cm from the goal, but the west landmark is invariably 20 cm away, while the east landmark varies about a mean of 20 cm. In this case, the west landmark is more reliable and better predicts the goal location. Animals ought to rely preferentially on more reliable landmarks.

Overshadowing in landmark use

In classical conditioning and instrumental learning, it is not only the absolute predictiveness of a stimulus that is important, but also the predictiveness relative to other stimuli that are present (e.g. Wagner *et al.*1968; Kamin 1969). One phenomenon that illustrates this principle is overshadowing (Pavlov 1927), in which learning about a stimulus element is reduced if it is presented in compound with another stimulus element during conditioning. A conditioned stimulus (CS) that supports good conditioning when paired singly with the unconditioned stimulus (US) often shows substantially reduced conditioning if it is presented in compound with a CS that is more intense or temporally closer to the US during conditioning trials (e.g. Mackintosh 1976; Mackintosh and Reese 1979; Kaye *et al.* 1988).

Spetch (1995) used a touch screen task to determine whether control by a landmark in spatial learning is also subject to overshadowing. Pigeon and human participants were trained with a randomly alternating pair of stimulus displays that each contained a landmark at a fixed distance from the goal (Fig. 1.4). The landmark in one pair (non-overshadowed) was the closest member of its set to the goal, whereas the landmark in the other pair (overshadowed) was presented together with another landmark that was closer to the goal. Thus, overshadowed and non-overshadowed landmarks were equal in absolute distance to the goal but differed in their *relative* proximity to the goal. Counterbalancing across participants controlled for featural differences between the overshadowed and non-over-shadowed landmarks. During subsequent probe tests, overshadowed and non-overshadowed landmarks were presented alone, or were presented together in arrangements that put the hypothetical goal locations according to each landmark in conflict. For both pigeons and humans, overshadowed landmarks showed less control than non-overshadowed landmarks, indicating that control by a landmark can be overshadowed by the presence of a closer landmark. Evidence of overshadowing effects also has been found in the spatial learning of rats (March *et al.* 1992). In this case, reciprocal overshadowing was found between intramaze and extramaze cues in a radial maze task.

Other general principles to explore

While landmark-based search may be based on some specialised learning, for example, in the extraction of geometric properties, we have seen that it obeys some general principles of

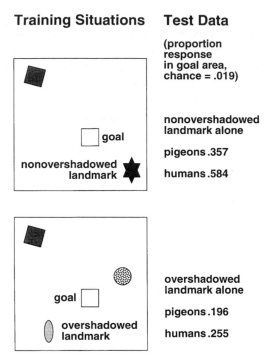

Training Situations   **Test Data**

(proportion
response
in goal area,
chance = .019)

nonovershadowed
landmark alone

pigeons .357

humans .584

overshadowed
landmark alone

pigeons .196

humans .255

Fig. 1.4 Schematic illustration of overshadowing in landmark use in two species (Spetch 1995). Pigeons and humans participated in a spatial search task on the computer monitor. In the training situations, the non-overshadowed landmark was the closest to the goal, while the overshadowed landmark was not, although both were at the same absolute distance from the goal. Landmarks and set-ups were not exactly as shown, and computer drawn objects were counterbalanced across participants. The location of the goal was not shown, except during a few initial training sessions (for pigeons) or a few initial trials (for humans). Both pigeons and humans performed better with a non-overshadowed landmark alone than with an overshadowed landmark alone.

learning as well. Other general principles that might be explored in the spatial domain include blocking, inhibitory conditioning, contingency learning and latent inhibition. If an animal has learned to localise using one landmark, would that hamper learning a spatial relation of the goal to a second, equally predictive landmark? Can an animal learn that a particular location does not contain food, whereas other locations do? Can an animal discriminate a reliable indicator of goal location from an unreliable one? And if a landmark has been an unreliable one, will it subsequently be harder to learn a location with respect to it? These and other questions suggest whole programmes of experiments analogous to those on the temporal relations between events. We refrain from detailing experimental designs here, but we think that such programmes of research are worthwhile for finding out how much this important domain of learning has in common with all other domains of learning.

Use of configurations and elements

Upon looking at an array of landmarks (for example, see Fig. 1.5), we may intuitively think of a configuration. We may solve the task by coding the goal as being in the middle of the array, and even ignore the identities of the individual elements. Yet, Spetch and Mondloch's (1993) results show that this is not how pigeons do the task, and Cheng (1995) has discussed in some detail how the pigeon's landmark-based spatial memory is elementalistic, a term we will shorten to 'elemental' here. We will therefore present evidence that pigeons, rodents and humans all can learn to use configurations, and go on to point out some differences between humans and other vertebrates.

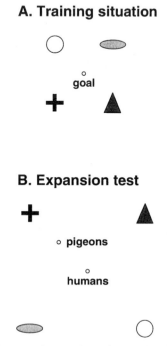

A. Training situation

B. Expansion test

Fig. 1.5 Schematic illustration of the performance of two species on the expansion of an array of four landmarks with the goal in the centre (Spetch *et al.* 1996, 1997). (a) The set-up used in training. Landmarks used were not exactly as shown. Which landmark was in which position varied across trials. (b) Performance on an expansion test. Pigeons typically maintained the correct distance and direction to one landmark, while humans maintained the correct direction to all landmarks. The same patterns of performance were found both on the touch screen monitor, and on the table top, on the floor, and on the ground outdoors.

Evidence for the use of configuration

What does it mean to use a configuration? We mean by the phrase more than the use of multiple cues. In using multiple cues, each element may still be used separately and independently of every other element, even though some final averaging of dictates may be computed. Such a system is elemental through and through (Cheng 1995). In using a configuration, the array as a whole, or some subset of the array including more than one element, must be used either to (1) identify landmarks, or (2) figure out where to search. Something in the system must be coding some relations between two or more elements. We will also say more about distinguishing (1) and (2) below. It is easiest to explain by proceeding with the evidence.

In one of Collett *et al.*'s (1986) experiments with gerbils, participants were trained with an array of two distinct landmarks. The goal was near one of the landmarks, but the direction of the goal from the nearest landmark was defined with respect to the farther landmark. As the entire array, the goal along with it, was rotated from trial to trial, the only way to establish the correct direction was with reference to both landmarks. Thus, the configuration of the array had to be used to solve this problem, which the gerbils did.

A second experiment with gerbils also showed the use of configural information. Gerbils were trained with an array of two distinct landmarks. The array was in the same orientation on each trial, while the starting point from which the participants were released varied from trial to trial. On a critical test trial, the array was rotated by 180°. The gerbils followed the rotation of the array in searching. They thus used the array of two to determine which direction is which.

Pigeons also use the configuration of a landmark array, at least to identify which landmark is which. In one experiment on the touch screen, the goal was in the middle of four distinct landmarks arranged in a square (Spetch *et al.* 1996). Which landmark was placed at which position, however, changed from trial to trial throughout training. Both pigeons and humans solved this task readily. Although we initially assumed that such a task could be solved only by attending to the use of configural information (Spetch *et al.* 1996), we now believe that such a task could, in principle, be solved elementally. That is, participants might learn that the goal sometimes will be found at any one of four vectors from each landmark. They might learn to search in the centre of the array because that is the only place at which they find one of the correct vectors for every landmark.

Although the training task could therefore be solved elementally, undeniable evidence for the use of configural information in pigeons is found on expansion tests, in which the entire array is expanded so that the landmarks are farther apart from one another (Fig. 1.5). Remember that Fig. 1.5 only shows the set-up for one expansion test. On different expansion tests, different landmarks are in each of the positions. And the entire array moves around on the screen from training trial to training trial and from test to test. The typical pattern of results is illustrated in Fig. 1.5. The birds searched at the right distance and direction from one landmark. The landmark, however, was not defined by its individual (elemental) characteristics. Instead, it was defined by its position in the array. In the example in Fig. 1.5, the bird searched at the right distance and direction from the top left landmark.

It is useful to think of two separate processes in solving any problem of landmark-based search. One problem is to identify which landmark is which and pick out landmarks to use, the process of matching a landmark in the world to a landmark recorded in memory. We called this the landmark matching process (Spetch *et al.* 1997). In the example in Fig. 1.5, the landmark identified and selected is the top left one, regardless of its physical appearance. To do this, configural information must be used. To pick out the top left one, the landmark's spatial relations to other landmarks must be used. For example, the landmark must be defined either as the topmost and leftmost of the array, or as the one of four closest to the top left corner of the touch screen.

The other process is figuring out where to search with respect to identified landmarks. We called this search place matching (Spetch *et al.* 1997). As only a single landmark is used in the example in Fig. 1.5, configural information is not used in search place matching. The pattern of results was replicated when the four landmarks in the square were identical rather than distinct, both on the touch screen monitor (Spetch *et al.* 1996) and on the laboratory floor (Spetch *et al.* 1997). The same analysis applies in the case of four identical landmarks.

For humans, evidence for the use of configuration comes from various experiments. One source of evidence is verbal reports. In the same kind of tasks presented to pigeons, humans reported using a middle rule, something to the effect of searching in the middle of an array (Spetch *et al.* 1996, 1997). And the results show that they did search in the middle of the array when it was expanded. Another line of evidence comes from transfer tests on arrays of landmarks. Humans were first trained to search in the middle of an array of four distinct landmarks. The landmarks were in fixed positions with respect to one another throughout training. On one kind of probe test, the relative positions of the landmarks were scrambled. If a participant uses an elemental code, none of the landmarks elementally point to a goal location in the middle of the array. For instance, the landmark usually at the top left might now be at the top right. It would now indicate a goal below it and to the right, and this location would now be outside of the array. Using a configural code, however, the goal can be described as being in the middle of the array. Humans searched in the middle, consistent with the use of the configuration of the array. Pigeons do not transfer in this situation (Spetch *et al.* 1996). They do not seem to use the configuration to do search place matching. We will elaborate on differences between vertebrate species presently.

We have already presented the data on rats in Cheng's (1986) study (Fig. 1.1). The geometric module is one of the clearest cases of the use of configuration. In making the rotational error, the rats were not using any elemental information, but only the broad shape of the environment. Shape formed by surfaces and objects is quintessential configural information. It is not the configuration of elements that was used, but a shape abstracted from the elements. In another way of phrasing this, the elemental information has been thrown out, and the rats relied on pure configuration.

Of comparative interest is the fact that extant data on honey-bees (Cartwright and Collett 1982, 1983; Cheng *et al.* 1986, 1987) as well as unpublished data (Cheng, in preparation) indicate that their performance on landmark-based search can all be accounted for elementally. These species differences, and the entire issue of the use of configurations clearly deserve more theoretical and empirical analysis.

Comparing humans, rodents and birds

The vertebrate species we have been reviewing all use configurations in some way in landmark-based spatial memory. But they differ, and we believe that the biggest differences are between adult humans and the other mammals and birds. Gerbils and pigeons use configurations for landmark matching, but not for search place matching. Instead, they use the correct distance and direction to individual landmarks in searching for a place, while humans use geometric rules that abstract away from individual landmark identities.

The differences are highlighted in the reactions to an array of landmarks that has been expanded or contracted. As reviewed in the previous section, Spetch *et al.* (1996, 1997) trained humans and pigeons with the goal in the middle of a square array of four landmarks. When the array was expanded on a test, humans searched in the middle of the array, whereas pigeons typically searched at the correct distance and direction from one of the landmarks. The pattern is found with the search space on the monitor, on the table top, or on the ground, so that method of testing is not a factor in the species difference. A similar pattern is found with an array of two identical landmarks (Fig. 1.2). In this case, the goal was midway between the two landmarks and at some perpendicular distance from the line joining the two landmarks. When the two landmarks were moved apart, humans searched farther away from the landmarks perpendicularly, whereas pigeons (Spetch *et al.* 1996, 1997) and gerbils (Collett *et al.* 1986) maintained the same perpendicular distance. When the landmarks were moved closer together, humans searched at a shorter perpendicular distance, whereas pigeons again maintained the same perpendicular distance (Spetch *et al.* 1996, 1997). These contraction tests were not performed on gerbils. On the dimension parallel to the landmarks, expansion and contraction also produced different results across species. The humans continued to search exactly at the middle, whereas the pigeons' search was scattered along the parallel dimension. Results again held for experiments both on the touch screen monitor and on the lab floor or table top. On expansion of two landmarks, gerbils searched primarily at two locations in the parallel dimension, one appropriate for each of the landmarks. Most individual participants searched at both locations. For humans and pigeons, performance on a two-landmark array thus paralleled performance on a four-landmark array. And gerbils resemble pigeons more than they do humans.

It is not known how rats would react to a scale transformation of a search space. We assume that they would behave in the pattern of gerbils, and keep the vector distance and direction to nearby landmarks, such as the nearest corner of the arena. If that is the case, we have not been strictly correct in saying that rats use only the shape of the environment. Geometrically, shape is abstracted away from size and absolute distance. The rodents may use shape, perhaps to determine heading as Gallistel (1990) suggests, but they may also use absolute distance in search place matching.

While behavioural reactions of rats to scale transformations of space are lacking, reactions of single hippocampal neurons have been recorded (O'Keefe and Burgess 1996). Patterns of firing rates of hippocampal cells when space is stretched or expanded resemble the patterns of pecking of Spetch *et al.*'s (1996, 1997) pigeons and the search behaviour of gerbils (Collett *et al.* 1986) when space is similarly stretched or expanded. For instance, cells that fire most at a particular distance and direction from a nearby corner tend to maintain high firing rates at the same vector from the same corner when the space is made bigger.

How can we interpret these data patterns? The human pattern parallels how honey-bees respond to expansions of landmark arrays (Cartwright and Collett 1983). Honey-bee performance is characterised by an elemental model (Cartwright and Collett 1982, 1983; Cheng 1995). But we find it unlikely that the same interpretation can be given for humans. For honey-bees, the matching of separate individual elements leads to matching compass directions of landmarks while sacrificing distance to individual landmarks. Humans in their verbal reports do not spell out such a strategy. Rather, they speak of searching in the middle of an array, of following a middle rule. Middle is defined with respect to an array of landmarks. It appears that the problem is solved configurally. Corroborating evidence comes from the fact that individual elements in the array can be scrambled with one another in position or be replaced by totally new ones. We thus think that adult humans are using the shape or configuration of the array to determine where to search, shape in this case abstracting away from distance. Configuration is used in landmark matching and search place matching.

Pigeons and gerbils, on the other hand, use the shape or configuration only to determine which landmark is which. Configuration is only used for landmark matching. When it comes to determining where to search (search place matching) only one element is used (or sometimes two or more elements are averaged), and matching is according to absolute and not relative distance. Landmark matching uses configural information, while search place matching uses elemental information. Or in Collett *et al.*'s (1986) words, 'although landmarks may be used independently for computing trajectories, the process of matching landmarks to the gerbil's representation requires a knowledge of the distances and directions *between* landmarks' (p. 835, emphasis theirs).

Conclusions

We have reviewed the transformational approach to the study of landmark-based spatial memory, and extant data on three themes: (1) the use of metric properties of distances and directions; (2) the use of multiple cues; and (3) the use of configurations of landmarks. In the transformational approach, the participant has the task of locating a target with respect to an experimentally provided set of landmarks. Often the experimental set is moved about from trial to trial to ensure that the target is in a constant location only with respect to the experimental landmarks and not to anything else. On crucial unrewarded tests, the experimental landmarks are transformed in theoretically motivated ways to find out something about how the participants use landmarks in localisation.

Our review indicates that all vertebrate species that have been studied use metric properties in localisation. On transformations of landmark arrays, participants search in locations that preserve some metric properties, although different species might preserve different properties. In pigeons, evidence indicates that distances and directions are computed separately and independently.

With multiple landmarks in the array, participants often use more than one cue or element in searching. However, when other cues provide a stable directional frame of reference, control of searching is sometimes restricted to a single element of a landmark array. We reviewed parallels between landmark learning and other forms of learning in general. Participants prefer to rely on better predictors, those landmarks that are closer to the goal. Moreover, relative distances from goal to landmarks matter. A landmark at a particular absolute distance is overshadowed by a landmark that is nearer to the goal. Testing for other general laws of learning in landmark-based search forms a worthwhile research programme.

By the use of configuration, we mean more than using multiple landmarks. The participant must encode some relationship between landmarks. An elemental solution encodes only relations between the target and single landmarks. Evidence indicates that all vertebrate species use the configuration of landmarks, whereas honey-bees seem to use an elemental system. Adult humans differ from other species in the use of configuration. They use abstract geometric rules such as 'search in the middle of the array'. The entire area of the use of configuration deserves more investigation.

2 Places and landmarks: an arthropod perspective

Thomas S. Collett and Jochen Zeil*

Introduction

Many arthropods lead complex lives in which they need to travel regularly between several familiar places. Significant places for an arthropod include those where it can gather food, water and nest material, sites for mating and aggregation, perching sites, communal sleeping sites and, most importantly, nest sites. The variety of activities and resources associated with these different places emphasises that it is not sufficient to know and to remember topography. In some way there must be an association of particular sites with the resources that they offer. We start with a brief survey of the arthropods' use and knowledge of places. We then go on to consider how arthropods employ landmarks for finding and recognising places.

Journeys between familiar places may involve flying several kilometres before homing in on a small and inconspicuous nesthole. Such feats clearly require sophisticated navigational skills and much learning of detailed visual patterns. One major attraction of studying these skills in arthropods is their relatively tiny nervous system. An animal with a small brain (an estimated 960 000 neurons in the honey-bee, Witthöft 1967) is likely to have been forced to discover an array of tricks that allows it to economise on the neural machinery that it needs to perform a particular task. Simplified solutions will often limit versatility, so raising the hope (which has sometimes been fulfilled!) that navigational mechanisms may emerge clearly in the details of an animal's behaviour. The path that an animal takes provides a wonderfully informative read-out of its behavioural output. When paths are recorded on film or on videotape within a small area of space, the orientation of the animal's body axis can be resolved. In insects, with eyes fixed in their heads and limited head movements, it then becomes possible to calculate where the animal is looking and how the image of its surroundings moves over its eyes. A record of both visual input and motor output makes it possible to get at the workings of at least some of the navigational strategies that arthropods use.

* Both authors contributed equally and are listed alphabetically

Significant places in an arthropod's life

Nests and shelters

Nests and burrows provide places of safety in which to store food, rear young and escape from a hostile world of predators and extremes of weather. Nests take time, energy and sometimes materials to build. The digger wasp *Sphex* spends 20 min in excavating a nesthole in solid ground (Ribi and Ribi 1979) and ghost crabs take some 80 min to construct a mating burrow with a pyramid outside (Linsenmair 1967) (Fig 2.1, top). The potter wasp, *Eumeus*, builds a still more elaborate structure (Fig. 2.1, bottom). It collects balls of clay that must be moistened, if too dry, and it forms these into a small pot in which larvae can overwinter without dehydrating. Natural shelters that do not require construction are often costly

Fig. 2.1 Significant places for arthropods. The photograph at the top is of a male *Ocypode saratan* in Oman standing beside the sand pyramid he has constructed while excavating the mating burrow he makes in order to attract females. Females find mating burrows by walking towards a pyramid and searching for an entrance in its vicinity. Photograph by Jochen Zeil. The potter wasp in the bottom picture builds an elaborate gourd-like nest using moistened balls of clay. Photograph from von Frisch (1974).

because they are scarce and hotly competed for. Lobsters and crabs living at high density on rocky shores or in mangrove swamps spend long periods of time in crevices under stones or among mangrove roots (Vannini and Cannici 1995). Nests and shelters are thus valuable resources on their own account, in addition to the food and young that may be housed within. For this, and for many other reasons, their sites are remembered.

Escape burrows or shelters must be near at foot or claw, if an efficient predator is to be eluded. If you walk, or even run, among a dense colony of crabs, there will be an empty space around you. Within a radius of 5–10 m, the crabs have vanished into their burrows. A crab will have disappeared before you arrive, even if to reach its burrow it has to run towards you. As we will see later, crabs while foraging continually keep track of the location of their burrow (Land and Layne 1995). Lobsters which forage over larger ranges seem to know the locations of several shelters, and, when chased, they will make for the closest one, although the shelter may be hidden from direct view (Karnofsky et al. 1989).

Often animals need only remember the site of a single nest, but sometimes they have to do more. Digger wasps of the genus *Ammophila* care for at least three nests at the same time. Not only must the wasp remember the location of each site, but also which particular nest is in need of provisions (Baerends 1941; Weaving 1989). Honey-bees that have recently swarmed and found a new hive rapidly learn its location. They will continue to forage at old sites (Dyer 1993), but return to the new hive rather than to the old. After a day's foraging from the new hive, only 1–4% of bees that had been marked there were found in the old hive (Robinson and Dyer 1993). However, bees in the new hive do not erase their memory of the location of the old hive for a long time. When the new hive was temporarily hidden, a large proportion of bees returned to the old hive in preference to a control hive placed at an equivalent site elsewhere. Such tests were done weekly. Preference for the old hive remained at about 90% for 4 weeks, dropping abruptly to 50% on week 5. This unexpected persistence, longer than the expected foraging life of a worker bee in summer, makes one wonder whether there might be a slow but continuing exchange of workers between the two hives—a useful safety measure in case either colony suffers an accident. Interchange of workers and brood is known to occur in ant colonies which are dispersed over multiple nests (e.g., Bourke and Franks 1995).

Foraging sites

Animals leave their nest to find water, food, nest materials or mates and their foraging behaviour reveals the sometimes extensive knowledge that arthropods have of their surroundings. To obtain a full load of nectar and pollen, individual orchid bees sample many, very widely spaced and sparsely distributed plants (Janzen 1971). Their foraging trips cover 10 or more kilometres as they fly from flower to flower along fixed routes (Fig. 2.2).

Honey-bee colonies are large so that individuals can specialise on particular tasks. Division of labour allows a single bee to concentrate on collecting a single resource from a single site. Individual bees have been observed to forage from a single flowering tree or rich patch of flowers for many days (Buzzard 1936). Robinson et al. (1984) followed one bee that did nothing but collect water over much of its foraging career. Fidelity to a rewarding site is

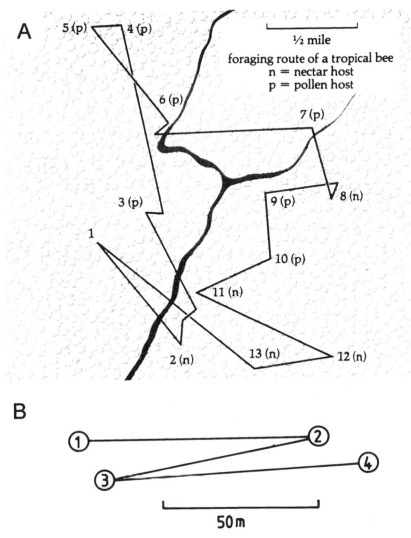

Fig. 2.2 Foraging route of an orchid bee. (a) The inferred daily path of a bee in Costa Rican forest. The nest is 130 m above ground in a tree. Every day the bee flies along the 'trapline' route collecting nectar 'n' and pollen 'p' from the flowers produced by vines, ground plants, bushes and trees. After Janzen (1974). (b) The route above was reconstructed from observing individual bees from a single site from which several plants were visible. A bee arrived on five mornings between 7.00 and 7.15 am to visit the same four flowers in the same order. After Janzen (1971).

worthwhile because it takes time to find new ones. This is true not only for scouts, which search over many hectares, but also for recruits using the information that scouts supply through the waggle dance. The dance and the odour of the dancing bee tells recruits the distance, direction and scent of the food source (von Frisch 1967). However, this information is not precise and using it for finding places seems hard. Seeley and Towne (1992) observed individual bees in the hive as they followed dances. A single bee will sample the dances of several bees and may make a number of abortive trips before returning successfully with forage. Memorising foraging sites and the route to them will thus increase foraging efficiency.

Site fidelity can be surprisingly long lived: wood ants return to the previous year's site after being nestbound during the winter (Rosengren 1971; Quinet and Pasteels 1996;) and anecdotal evidence suggests that honey-bees do the same.

Solitary, nest-building wasps, and those from small colonies, cannot afford to specialise. The need to perform several tasks makes an individual wasp's job more complex than that of an individual honey-bee. On some foraging trips, a wasp may gather pulp for nest construction; on other trips it collects water for temperature control, or liquid or solid food. To add to the wasp's difficulties, these various resources may often be found in different places. Steiner (1932) and Matsuura and Yamane (1984) studied individually marked *Polistes* wasps from small colonies. In a 100 min observation period, the same wasp switched between a variety of tasks. The data of Table 2.1 show that all four wasps engaged heavily in nest construction and all collected pulp, but wasp 6 was almost alone in collecting water. The whole group also gathered food, with wasp 4 emphasising liquid food and wasp 5 solid food.

Table 2.1 Foraging activity of four *Polistes* wasps during 102 min observation. Numbers give percentage of trips of different kinds performed by each wasp. After table 4 in Steiner (1932).

Wasp	4	5	6	7
Collection of				
wood pulp	47	39	36	38
water	7	—	36	—
liquid food	33	18	6	24
solid food	13	39	23	38

This versatile behaviour raises the interesting but largely unresearched question of how insects associate knowledge of geography with that of resource quality, and more broadly whether their behaviour is driven by explicit goals. Do wasps set out in a given direction towards a place expecting to come across a particular resource? For instance, do events during nest construction prime the whole package of linked memories that is needed for finding and collecting pulp? Or are memories concerned with such a behavioural sequence primed piecemeal, requiring external events to trigger them? Thus, a particular environmental or motivational state causes the wasp to leave its nest in a particular direction. This trajectory brings it to where local cues are recognised and lead it to the correct site. From there it has a view of chewable wood and this sight triggers the collection of pulp.

An elegant study by Greggers and Mauelshagen (1997) raises similar questions. Honey-bees were trained to feed at four automatically controlled sucrose dispensers placed on a large table on a flat roof. Each feeder delivered 2 mol/l of sucrose solution at one of four, low flow rates. Individual bees visited all four feeders, and within 15–20 min they had learnt to match the frequency of their visits to the relative flow rates of the feeders, showing that in some way they had associated a reward value with each feeder (Fig. 2.3a).

The positions of the feeders on the table were marked by an array of stones (Fig. 2.3a). When the stones were removed so that the only landmarks were more than 15 m away, bees no longer distinguished the feeders from each other and visited them with equal frequency

(Fig. 2.3b). Cues very close to the feeder are not essential for matching, as it was shown in parallel experiments elsewhere that matching persisted when there were no distinguishing features within a radius of 0.5 m around each feeder. Bees can thus identify the differentially rewarding feeders solely by their position in a nearby landscape. Have bees formed an association between a particular location and a particular reward value, or do they tend to select the feeder with the highest flow because the memory of the route to the most rewarded place clamours the loudest?

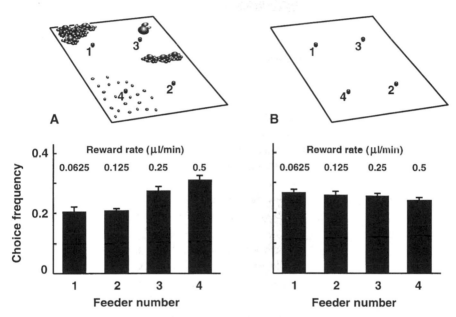

Fig. 2.3 Honey-bees associate places and rewards. (a) Top: the positions of four feeders on a tabletop, 1.5 m by 1.5 m. Each feeder consists of a tube that the bee enters to collect sucrose that accumulates inside and as a drop on the end of a capillary into which it is dispensed at a constant flow rate. Stones provide landmarks. Bottom: bees match their visits to the flow rate of each feeder. This histogram probably underestimates the bees' preference for the more productive feeders. Repeated visits to the same feeder are not counted. The bee must shift to another feeder before a new visit to the same feeder is registered. (b) If the stones are removed, bees no longer match their visits to the flow rate. Modified from a figure kindly supplied by U. Greggers.

Meeting and mating sites

Males of many insect species go to particular places because it increases their chances of encountering females that are attracted there. Males often become territorial at this time and defend places visited by females from incursion by other competing males. Such places may be particular features of the landscape, or food plants, or even warming sunspots. For example, male mason bees (*Hoplitis anthocopoides*) carve out territories that contain food plants and rocks or bare areas on which to perch (Eickwort 1977). The bees take short, patrolling flights within their territory, hunting for females and excluding other males. When males first emerge, competition for territories is intense and a male holds its ground for only 2 days, by which time it has lost body hair and its wings are tattered. Later the pressure lessens and territories are held for longer (median 16 days). It is clear that bees remember the location of their territories, because at night they often retire temporarily from their territory, and shelter together in cavities or old nests, returning to reclaim their territory the following day.

Similarly, *Polistes* wasps have been observed to maintain individual territories from which intruders are chased away (Polak 1993). Again, guarding a territory is a consuming activity, with an average of 13 chases a minute. In these species, a territory consists of a single tree or bush on the crest of a ridge. But individual species vary in preferring different parts of the ridge. *P. canadensis* aggregates at saddle points and *P. carnifex* congregates at peaks, even in the absence of the other species. Thus, general features of the preferred territory are species-specific and unlearnt. But as individuals return to their own tree each morning, the details of individual territories must be acquired.

In some cases, male meeting or aggregation sites are associated with large-scale geographical features and involve no learning at all. Drone aggregation sites are a famous example. Sites can persist over centuries. One site still in use was described by Gilbert White in Selbourne, England in 1768, although he did not know its function (Free 1987):

> There is a natural occurrence to be met with upon the highest part of our down in hot summer days, which always amuses me much...and that is the loud audible humming of bees in the air, though not one insect is to be seen. This sound is to be heard distinctly the whole common through from the Money Dells to Mr. White's avenue gate.

Drone congregation sites tend to occur in hilly terrain but their defining visual characteristics, if they have them, have been hard to establish. The sites are 15–25 m above the ground, are about 30–200 m across and have distinct boundaries. Drones are attracted to a site from hives in all directions from as far as 7 km, and they have been observed to fly over 1000 m mountains to reach it (Ruttner 1966). Once at the site, drones fly around and they are visited there by unmated queens, who may also come from several kilometres away. Ruttner (1966) has found that drones at a site will follow a tethered queen that is moved away from the centre of the aggregation area as far as its borders. But they then abandon her, as though tied to the area by an attractive force. It might be worth exploring whether magnetic anomalies are involved.

In the same way that some species learn multiple foraging or nesting sites, there are cases of insects remembering several potential mating sites. Male halictine bees, for example, patrol for females among food plants and return repeatedly to particular plants. Barrows (1976) has shown that bees relate the position of individual plants to local landmarks. Bees were recorded flying among bouquets of flowers in a flight room. The most frequently visited bouquet was removed and bees made looping and circling flights in the exact area of the missing bouquet (Fig. 2.4). Some individuals continued to inspect this site for an hour after the bouquet had disappeared.

Defining places

For us as street-map-wise humans, the obvious way of specifying a position on the ground is cartographically, as a position on a grid in x–y coordinates. How fine the grid needs to be and what it means to an animal to have a coarsely or a finely specified place is an interesting question to which we will return later. A place can also be labelled in relative coordinates as a distance and direction from a known reference location, for example, the animal's nest. Another possibility is to label it in a coordinate free way. Imagine a map cut into a jigsaw puzzle with every puzzle piece different, then a place could be defined as the unique hole into which a particular puzzle piece fits.

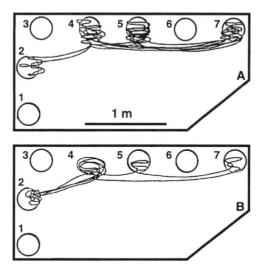

Fig. 2.4 Searching for mates. (a) The patrolling flight-path of a male halictine bee (*Augochlora pura*) among seven flower bouquets in a bee room. The male visited the bouquets in the order 4–7–5–7–4–2–4–5–7–5–4. (b) The flight-path of the same male 1 min after bouquet number 4 was removed. The order of visits was 4–2–4–2–4–5–7–4–2–7. Modified from Barrows (1976).

Using either of the first two methods, it is easy to formulate efficient instructions for reaching one place from another. Given a bicoordinate map, you can say how many x and y steps are needed to reach a particular destination. With knowledge of the distances and directions of both starting point and goal from a reference point, the animal could be told to go first to the reference point and then to the goal. Alternatively, this detour could be avoided by vector addition of the two instructions. The resultant vector will specify the direct path between start and goal. The jigsaw method is more problematical because no metric is given to define the location of the hole. At worst, the match between puzzle piece and hole could be found through random search until the puzzle piece slots into place. This highly inefficient process could be speeded up by always keeping the piece in the correct orientation while searching. What is really needed is for the hole to be labelled in some way so that it can be detected at a distance. For instance, an odour could be released from it or a visual landmark suspended above it. An agent equipped with the right sensory and navigational mechanisms could then approach this beacon and so locate the hole directly, without explicit knowledge of the distance it must travel.

Insects define places in two major ways. One is in terms of its distance and direction from another place. This information is initially acquired through a process known as path integration. Secondly, as shown in Figs 2.3 and 2.4, insects use visual landmarks to label a place in ways which are a little analogous to the jigsaw model.

Path integration

An animal leaves a place to which it wants to return and keeps a record during its journey of the net distance and direction it has travelled from its starting point. Ants and bees monitor direction primarily by means of a celestial compass that measures the horizontal position of the sun or of the polarised pattern in the sky caused by Raleigh scattering of the sun's rays (for review see Wehner and Rossel 1985). This compass is sophisticated enough to compensate for the daily movement of the sun through the sky (for review see Dyer and Dickinson 1996). Distance is measured by monitoring the optic flow generated by the insect's movements (bees: Esch and Burns 1996; Srinivasan *et al.* 1996) or by a combination of signals derived from optic flow and some other indicator of the insect's movements (ants: Ronacher and Wehner 1995). Although there have been a number of theoretical accounts (Mittelstaedt and Mittelstaedt 1973; Hartmann and Wehner 1995; Maurer and Séguinot 1995; Wittman and Schwegler 1995), the exact way in which the nervous system performs path integration remains an intriguing mystery. In whatever way it is accomplished, an animal that is equipped with this knowledge of distance and direction can always return directly to its departure point.

Path integration was first observed in ants early in the twentieth century by Pieron (1904) and by Santschi. However, it occurs very widely in invertebrates (Wehner 1992) and vertebrates (Etienne *et al.* 1996; see also Etienne *et al.*, Chapter 3). Its importance as a navigational tool can hardly be overemphasised. Figure 2.5a illustrates the remarkable nature of this feat in a remarkable insect, the desert ant. An ant runs from its nest foraging for insects that have been killed by the heat. It wanders in a tortuous way over the hot desert. Eventually some 140 m from the nest, after travelling a total distance of about 600 m, it finds a dead insect and runs straight home carrying it. Evidence that the foraging ant has really kept an accurate record of its net distance and direction from the nest comes from displacing the ant once it has found the prey. The ant seems oblivious to the insult and on release walks the same distance and direction that it would have done without displacement, guiding its path by external compass cues, seemingly ignoring local landmarks (Fig. 2.5b).

Similarly, a fiddler crab that has made a short excursion from its burrow uses information about its outward path to guide its return journey. The crab leaves its burrow on a feeding trip, walking sideways and turning so that its opposite side always points back towards the burrow, even when it has travelled too far for the burrow to be visible. Should the crab be startled, it reverses direction and scuttles straight home (Land and Layne 1995). To show that this escape run relies on the results of path integration, a piece of sandpaper is positioned on the sand near the burrow (Fig. 2.6). When the crab walks on to the paper, the paper is slowly and carefully pulled so that the crab's orientation does not change as it is moved over the ground. If the crab is now alarmed, it runs to a virtual burrow as though it had not been shifted. Unlike the desert ant, the crab's updating of the home direction is expressed visibly throughout the outward trip in the way that it points continuously towards the (invisible) burrow (J. Zeil, in preparation).

During path integration, the origin of the coordinate system is anchored at the animal's starting position, usually the nest, and the only use to which the result of path integration can be put is to attract the animal back there. Movement vectors can, however, be employed to

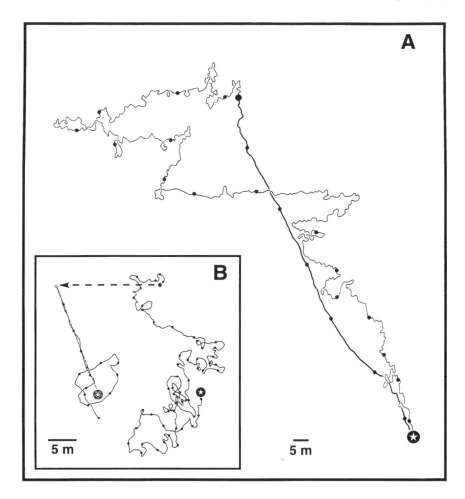

Fig. 2.5 Path integration in desert ants. (a) the twisty foraging path (thin line) and straight return path (thick line) of a desert ant, *Cataglyphis fortis*. Small dots are 60 s time marks. Large dot marks the site of prey capture. Star marks nest. After Wehner and Wehner (1990). (b) Ant is displaced after its foraging trip and walks as though it had not been moved towards a virtual nest situated 21 m SSE of the release site, which is the usual distance and direction of the nest from the feeding site. After Wehner (1982).

label the distance and direction of other places from the nest. An insect that has travelled several times to a foraging spot from its nest will learn the direction and the distance of its journey to that spot. It can remember this movement vector for a long time and will recall the vector as needed. The nest can thus act as a hub for movement vectors specifying several different places. For example, a solitary wasp needing nest material or water will recall different vectors as its motivational state demands.

However, it is risky to rely just on path integration to specify a place. Errors in estimating distance and direction accumulate with distance travelled (Wehner and Srinivasan 1981; Müller and Wehner 1988) and make the process insufficiently accurate for it to be the sole means of labelling a place. It is in fact often supplemented by the use of landmarks.

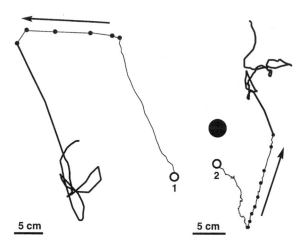

Fig. 2.6 Vector navigation in fiddler crabs. The trace on the left shows the path of a fiddler crab male feeding while moving away from its burrow (open circle). The crab's path is shown by the thin line. At some stage, the crab walks on to a piece of sandpaper which is pulled leftwards, as shown by the arrow. The crab's position during translation is marked every 200 ms by dots. After the sandpaper was stationary again, the crab was scared by a sudden movement of the experimenter and made a dash for its burrow (thick line). The crab runs to a virtual burrow, searching for the hole as though it had not been passively displaced. The path of a second crab on the right demonstrates that the direction and distance of the escape run are not influenced by a prominent and familiar landmark close to the burrow (black circle). J. Zeil (in preparation).

Landmarks

Displacement experiments that are in a way analogous to those used to demonstrate path integration show that places can be defined in terms of familiar visual scenes. Tinbergen (1932), in a classic study, proved that digger wasps memorise visual properties of landmarks near their nesthole, and that they use these landmarks to specify the nest site. He placed a circle of pine cones around the nesthole of a digger wasp that had been nest-bound during several days of rain. The wasp, on emerging from the nest, performed a specialised flight. Tinbergen was able to show that during this one flight the wasp acquired information about the scene immediately surrounding the nest. While she was foraging, he displaced the ring of pine cones a short distance from the nest. On her return, the wasp searched for the nest in the centre of the circle of cones showing that she had learnt the arrangement of pine cones and normally uses such knowledge to find the nest site.

Why should shifting the animal at the beginning of a journey and shifting landmarks at the end of the journey pick out such different guidance strategies? In both cases there has been a relative shift of insect and scene. However, the manipulation that reveals path integration displaces the animal at the beginning of the journey, when the performance of a home vector is high on the animal's priority list so that it tends to ignore small details of the surrounding scene. Whereas the manipulation that reveals the role of landmarks is a shift towards the end of the journey, when the vector has been payed out (like a length of rope), so allowing other navigational strategies to surface.

Landmarks as 2-D patterns

How do insects recognise such landmarks and how are they guided by them? A familiar landmark to an insect is not necessarily an object seen from a certain distance away in a particular direction, but rather the 2-D pattern that is imaged on its retina when it views the landmark from a particular vantage point. Landmarks in this pattern may appear as patches that differ from the background in intensity, in colour or in texture, and the patches will vary in retinal size according to the landmark's size and distance. A familiar place can thus be defined as the vantage point from which the insect memorises the 2-D pattern formed by the surrounding scene (Collett and Land 1975; Wehner and Räber 1979; Cartwright and Collett 1983). The size of the 'place', or the precision with which it is specified, will thus depend on how rapidly the view transforms as the insect moves away from the vantage point, and on the insect's ability to detect the transformation.

These statements stretch the truth somewhat, but there is a solid core to them. Evidence for a 2-D representation of this kind can be seen when insects search for a goal within an array that has been distorted from its usual arrangement. The insects spend most time looking where the distorted array generates the same 2-D pattern on the retina that the normal array does when the insect is at the goal. In the experiment illustrated in Fig. 2.7, bees were trained to collect sucrose from a small bottle top on the floor of a room. The position of this feeder in the room was marked by three black cylinders on the floor. When the feeder was removed, bees spent most time searching for it at the location defined by the position of the three cylinders. If the cylinders were moved either together or apart, bees searched where the positions of the cylinders on their eye would match those seen from the feeder during training. They continued to match retinal positions even though the consequence of doing so was that the bees' distances from the cylinders were grossly abnormal. These search patterns suggest that finding a place is in part a process of moving so that the image that an insect currently views comes to match the image which it had stored earlier when close to the goal.

More recently, it has been found that individual bees and wasps tend to face in a constant direction when they are close to their goal. On most flights, an insect will adopt roughly the same orientation when it is near to the feeder. The approaches illustrated in Fig. 2.8 are of the same wasp flying towards a feeder. The implication of this finding is that the 2-D pattern made by the landmarks is imaged in a constant way on the insects' retina. Patterns of landmarks seem to be learnt in retinotopic coordinates from a vantage point close to the goal.

These conclusions are in accord with the findings from earlier visual pattern learning experiments by Wehner (1972, review 1981) which suggested that pattern recognition in bees can be considered, in part at least, to be a process of retinotopically organised image matching. In one study, bees were trained to enter a horizontal tube behind which was a large, vertical disk divided alternately into black and white equiangular sectors, with different bees trained to radial gratings of different spatial frequencies. After training, bees were given a choice between two tubes with a similar sectored disk behind each. One disk was an exact match of the training pattern, the other was a similar disk rotated through half a period so that, viewed from the tube, the positions of the black and white sectors on the bee's retina were reversed. Bees hovered just in front of each tube before entering one. They had a strong preference for the tube attached to the disk that was in the training orientation. The

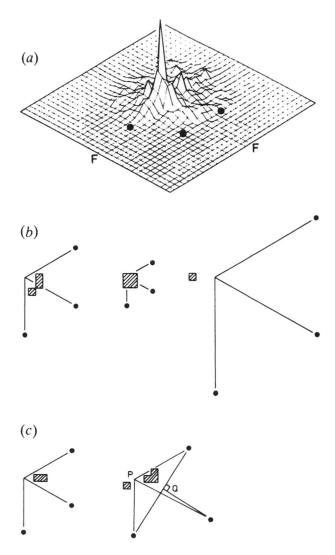

Fig. 2.7 Places as views of surrounding landmarks. Honey-bees searching for a missing source of sucrose at a site defined by three black, upright cylinders. (a) Relative time spent by one bee in each cell of an imaginary grid. Position of sucrose during training is marked by Fs on axes. Grid-lines are 8.7 cm apart. (b) Single bee's search when distance between landmarks is changed from the training situation. (c) Bee has choice of searching where bearings 'P' or distances 'Q' are correct. Leftmost column: training situation. Right columns: distorted arrays. Bee searches where landmarks have same bearings (shown by lines) as those experienced at the feeder during training. Hatched areas show where search density is at least 80% of the maximum. Adapted from Cartwright and Collett (1983).

preference broke down when bees were trained to fine radial gratings with individual sectors smaller than about 10° (Fig. 2.9).

The ability to distinguish between such patterns suggests that the pattern has been stored retinotopically, with the pattern only recognised when its elements fall on the same region of retina that viewed it during learning. Dill *et al.* (1993) have measured the amount of vertical translational shift that *Drosophila* will tolerate before the fly fails to recognise a pattern.

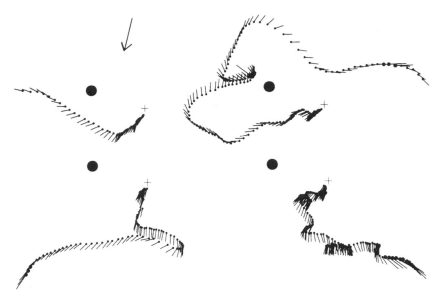

Fig. 2.8 A wasp approaches a feeder facing consistently in the same direction. Four approach flights of a single *Vespula vulgaris* to a feeder (+) on the ground with an upright cylinder (●) placed nearby. The arrow points north, and its length represents 10 cm on the ground. The wasp's position and orientation are plotted every 20 ms. The wasp generally aims at the cylinder before approaching the feeder. Once close to the feeder, she tends to adopt a preferred orientation that is constant over many flights. From Collett (1995).

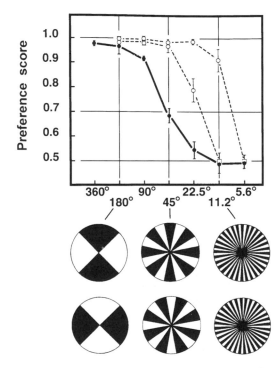

Fig. 2.9 Retinotopic memories. Honey-bees were trained to enter a horizontal perspex tube in order to collect sugar water. The tube was placed in front of and at the centre of a large vertical disk which displayed a radial pattern of alternating black and white sectors. Individual bees were trained to one of several such radial gratings each of which had a different spatial period. In tests, bees were given a choice between the training pattern (top row of radial patterns below the graph) and the same pattern rotated by half a period (bottom row of radial patterns). The *heavy solid line and dots* show the preference score (n+/Σn) of bees plotted against the period of the gratings that were used during both training and tests. *Dashed lines and open symbols* show data from control experiments in which bees were trained on the patterns with 11.2° and 5.6° wavelength and then asked to discriminate them from the radial gratings of lower spatial frequency. In these tests the centre of a black sector always pointed downwards. After Wehner (1981).

Recognition breaks down once the pattern has been displaced by more than about $3°$, which is the angular distance between the optic axes of adjacent *Drosophila* ommatidia.

Distance and context

The description of landmarks as items in a 2-D scene is only part of the story. As we will see in more detail later on, bees and wasps are not entirely ignorant of the distances of landmarks. There is good reason to segment the scene into regions corresponding to near and to far objects. If the insect must pin-point a nesthole, it should pay particular attention to and be guided by objects that are close to that site. Insects perform this kind of distance filtering and selection. For example, bees can be trained to find a small feeder with its location specified by an array of landmarks, some of which are small and much closer to the feeder than others. If, during tests, the near and far landmarks are separated so that the two subarrays signal separate sites, the bees' search is concentrated in the place specified by the close landmarks (Cheng *et al.* 1987).

However, knowledge of local landmarks is not enough. Insects working just with local landmarks would, like a puzzle piece searching for its hole, have problems in finding places. Local landmarks such as small stones and plants are not very different from each other and need to be embedded in a context. If memories of local scenes are retrieved just by observing the local landmarks, the insect may be trapped in the wrong place by the wrong set of local landmarks. Mistakes in retrieval can also happen if an insect approaches the correct landmarks at the end of a movement vector, but accidentally faces in an unusual viewing direction. The view on its retina may then fit best the memory for a different site so causing the insect to search inappropriately with respect to those landmarks. Interestingly, ants will ignore landmarks which usually indicate their nest when they are exposed prematurely to the landmarks on their way home. This has been shown both by displacing ants as in Fig. 2.5 and by displacing landmarks to various positions along the homeward route (Burkhalter 1972; Wehner *et al.* 1996). Ants continue along their home vector as though the unexpected landmarks were not there.

The role of local landmarks in specifying places thus needs support from additional navigational mechanisms which bring the animal to the approximate area and from contextual signals which prime the correct local memory (or memories). Evidence of priming by the surrounding panorama can be seen in the behaviour of individual bees that were trained outdoors to search for sugar water in two different sites 40 m apart. The location of the sugar water was defined by nearby landmarks which had different colours and shapes in the two places. When these local landmarks were swapped between places, bees looked for the sucrose in a position relative to the local landmarks that was determined by the surrounding context rather than by the appearance of the landmark array (Collett and Kelber 1988). This behaviour tells us that the context provided by a distant panorama primes the memory of local landmarks so strongly that objects which bear little resemblance to the originals can be substituted for them and bees will none the less search in roughly the correct location relative to the substitutes. This latitude means that under normal circumstances insects can respond to local landmarks when an unusual vantage point makes their appearance differ markedly from that which has been stored.

Learning places

Bees and wasps offer a rare opportunity to study elaborately structured behaviour that is designed specifically for learning about places. Bees, for instance, when they first leave their hive as inexperienced foragers must know enough about its immediate surroundings that they can return there. Path integration can inform them of the hive's general location, but, because they are flying and not in contact with the ground, dead-reckoning is insufficiently precise to be relied upon to bring them all the way home. To ensure their safe return, honey-bees, before embarking upon a foraging career, perform stereotyped learning flights around the hive. A bee keeper shifting a hive to a new location, has various stratagems to ensure that experienced foragers will also perform learning flights, for those bees that leave without doing so are unlikely to return. One trick is to leave the hive closed for a couple of days; another is to stuff grass into the entrance so bees have to remove the grass and are forcibly told that something has changed.

There is abundant experimental evidence that bees do acquire information about land-marks during the learning flights that they perform on their departure. For example, Wolf (1926) transported groups of 20–50 bees in a small box to a place beyond the bees' normal flight range from the hive. He placed the open box on the ground. Bees left the box, performed a learning flight and flew off. They all returned to the box in a short while. The box itself is not an essential landmark: when it was displaced by more than 2 m while the bees were away, they returned to where the box had been stationed during their departure flight.

Bees and wasps first encountering a rich foraging patch also need to learn its location and do so during learning flights performed when they leave the site (Lehrer 1993). Before sampling the patch they cannot know whether the site is worth learning, and delaying acquisition until departure seems a safer and more economical strategy than the speculative learning of all potential foraging sites that are approached. Moreover, learning flights are centred upon the exact position to which the insect will return. It would only be possible to pattern approach flights in this way if the site was obvious from a distance, and frequently it is not.

Pivoting and distance learning

The most striking feature of learning flights, in both wasps and bees, is that the insect pivots about the site to which it will return. This design feature is found whether the insect is learning a nest (Zeil and Kelber 1991; Zeil 1993a) or a foraging site (Collett and Lehrer 1993; Collett 1995). Take *Cerceris* a solitary wasp that digs a nest in the sand in which to rear larvae. It makes hunting trips from its nest and returns with provisions. Finding the tiny and inconspicuous entrance hole is tricky, and every morning, on leaving its nest, the wasp refreshes its memory of the site by performing a learning flight. It emerges from the nesthole, turns to face it and then backs away in a series of sideways zigzags or arcs that are roughly centred on the hole (Fig. 2.10, top). As the insect flies, its body axis (θ in Fig. 2.10B) rotates at an angular velocity that matches the velocity at which the arc (β in Fig. 2.10B) is described. Consequently, the target is viewed by roughly the same area of retina (ϕ_n in Fig. 2.10B) throughout each arc. The target falls on an area about 45° left of the mid-line during arcs to the left and 45° to the right of the mid-line during arcs to the right. Essentially, the insect pivots about the target, adjusting its translational velocity so that the angular pivoting speed is constant and independent of the wasp's distance from the target.

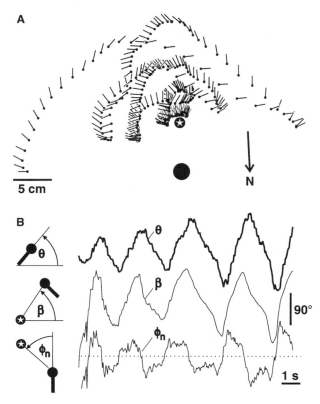

Fig. 2.10 Learning flight of a solitary wasp (*Cerceris rybyensis*) on leaving her nest. (a) The flight is shown from above. Circles with tails denote the wasp's position and the orientation of her longitudinal body axis every 40 ms. The star shows the nest entrance, and the filled black circle indicates a small cylinder placed upright on the ground. (b) The time course of various parameters of the same flight. θ is the direction in which the wasp faces, β is the wasp's bearing relative to the nest, and ϕ_n the horizontal position of the nest on the wasp's retina. Replotted from Zeil (1993a).

This pattern of movement makes learning flights ideal for picking out landmarks that are close to the goal. As the wasp pivots about the goal, the image of objects near to it will move slowly over the retina, whereas the image speed of objects beyond the goal will grow with increasing separation between object and goal to a maximum that equals the insect's turning speed (θ in Fig. 2.10). Consequently, objects close to the goal will be especially salient. On the one hand their image is blurred by image motion, and, on the other hand, they contrast strongly with the moving background. In addition, image speed during pivoting can provide a quantitative measure of the distance of an object from the pivoting centre (reviewed by Zeil *et al.* 1996).

This interpretation of pivoting is supported by the results of recent studies which explored what information is acquired specifically during learning flights. Some properties of landmarks, such as their colour and their position to the left or to the right of a feeder, can be learnt either on approach or on departure during learning flights (Lehrer 1993). The only characteristic that is learnt preferentially on departure is the absolute distance of a landmark from a feeder (Lehrer and Collett 1994). In experiments to investigate this possibility, some bees were allowed to see the cylinder only on arrival. It was removed while they fed and replaced after their departure. Other bees were allowed to see the cylinder only on departure during learning flights. It was put in position while they fed and removed when they had left. After this training, the two groups of bees were guided by different properties of the cylinder. Bees that had viewed the cylinder only on arrival were guided to a position defined by the apparent size of the cylinder as seen from the feeder, even if the cylinder was of a different physical size, so that the absolute distance was wrong. Bees that had viewed the cylinder only on departure behaved in the opposite way. They were guided to a position specified by the absolute distance between feeder and cylinder, even if the apparent size of the cylinder was wrong (Fig. 2.11).

That distance information obtained during pivoting may guide later approach flights is indicated by the form of the flight path taken by *Cerceris* when it searches for its nest on its return (Zeil 1993*b*). Although these wasps do not reproduce the whole learning flight, they fly through

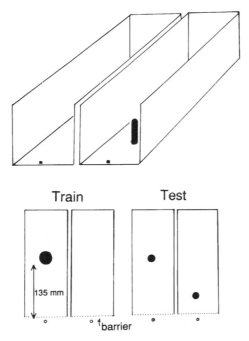

Fig. 2.11 Procedure used to train and test bees when learning the distance of a cylinder from a feeder. Top panel shows sketch of apparatus and bottom panel shows plan view of arrangement of cylinders and feeders during training and tests. A single, foraging honey-bee is placed on a small sucrose feeder (open circle) at the front of the channel containing a cylinder. Vertical strands of cotton ('barrier') prevent the bee from reaching the cylinder. The bee feeds and on departure performs a learning flight. It returns a few minutes later to find the feeder and cylinder switched to the other channel. Its learning flight on departure is shorter. Some bees only see the cylinder when they arrive. Other bees only see the cylinder when they leave. This training procedure continues for about six visits, until learning flights are very brief. The bee then arrives to find two cylinders of different sizes placed at different distances and two empty feeders. Bees which in training view the cylinder on arrival choose the cylinder of the correct apparent size. Bees which view the cylinder on departure choose the cylinder at the correct distance. After Lehrer and Collett (1994).

brief segments of arcs, which are similar to those of learning flights. This means that they can recreate the image motion that they experienced when pivoting round the nest during learning and thereby find it once more.

Initially, the insect must know the distance of landmarks so it can pick out those which are close to the goal. But, once it has learnt the appearance of close landmarks and can recognise them by their shape or colour, it can dispense with absolute distance information. It can then take a simpler approach path that does not generate the pivoting pattern of motion parallax. The resulting loss of motion contrast will not lead to problems in segmenting the scene, because bees are able to detect edges by luminance contrast or by colour contrast, as well as by motion contrast. Indeed, bees that are accustomed to recognise a pattern through edges defined by motion can recognise the same pattern through static edges arising from luminance or colour contrast (Zhang et al. 1995).

The sequence of approach flights in Fig. 2.12 shows how paths become straighter as a wasp becomes more experienced in reaching a site. This change is reflected in the information that bees use for guidance. Immediately after the learning phase, bees that have been exposed to landmarks both on arrival and on departure search for a feeder at the correct distance from a landmark, irrespective of its apparent size. After many more visits, bees search where the landmark has the expected apparent size, even though the absolute distance is incorrect (Lehrer and Collett 1994). The same phenomenon is seen in *Cerceris*. Search flights made by a wasp early in the day, soon after it has performed its daily learning flight, are governed by the absolute distance of the cylinder and its search pattern is unaffected by changes to the landmark's size. But later in the day after several returns to the nest, its search is guided by the landmark's apparent size (Zeil 1993b).

However, not all species make this switch with increasing experience. *Lasioglossum malachurum*, a solitary bee, searches consistently at the point defined by the distance of its nest from a nearby landmark and, even after many visits, it ignores changes to the landmark's size (Brünnert et al. 1994).

Retinotopic learning

A second important feature of learning flights is the direction in which the insect faces as it backs away. Its viewing direction tends to match its approach direction on later returns (Collett 1995; Vollbehr 1975; Zeil 1993b). Consistent viewing directions are needed if insects are to acquire retinotopically organised views and then use them to control their return flights. Viewpoint consistency seems to be achieved differently in different insects. The orientation of *Cerceris* during learning flights is determined by the position of a landmark close to the nest. When the wasp emerges from the nest, it looks back towards the nest, facing in the direction of the landmark, and it continues to back away in roughly the same direction, so that the nesthole lies between it and the landmark, as in Fig. 2.10. On its return, it approaches facing in the same direction, so that it can be guided by the landmark all the way back to the nest (Zeil 1993a,b). *Vespula's* learning flights on leaving a feeder are a little different. The wasp looks back at the feeder towards the end of the arcs. An individual wasp tends to face the feeder from one or two fairly constant viewing direction(s) over several learning flights and it adopts the same viewing direction on its later return flights, when it is

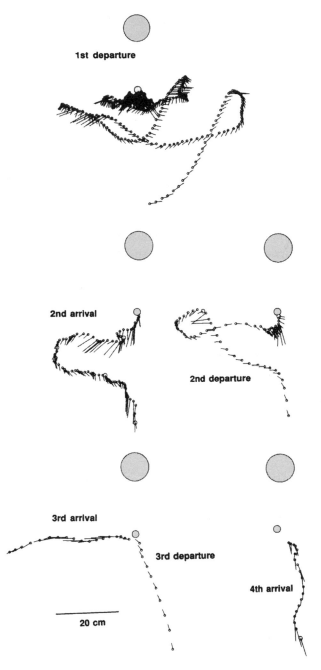

Fig. 2.12 The geometry of approach and departure flights becomes simpler with experience. A sequence of approach and departure flights of the wasp, *Vespula vulgaris*, towards and away from a feeder. Small circle shows feeder, large circle a nearby, black cylinder. Position and orientation of wasp is shown every 20 ms in the first departure and at 40 ms intervals in all subsequent flights. Tails are elongated when the wasp faces within ± 10° of the feeder. From Collett and Lehrer (1993).

close to the feeder (Fig. 2.8). This correlation makes it likely that the wasp learns view(s) of landmarks at the ends of arcs when rotational velocity is low (Collett 1995).

Wasps and bees tend to maintain a constant orientation on their return. They also have the useful ability to move sideways. This allows them to uncouple their direction of flight from their viewing direction. Consequently, an insect, which is returning to a goal and moving so that its current image comes to match its stored view, 'knows' that any mismatch can be corrected by translational movements. Its landmark guidance system need not be concerned with rotational errors.

Keeping station

An animal perched on a solid substrate has no problem in staying still. But, for an animal in a fluid medium, keeping in one place is an active process. Hoverflies will hang almost motionless in mid-air, now and then leaving their hovering station briefly to pursue a passing object that comes into visual range in case it might be a mate. The advantages of energetically expensive hovering over restful perching are speed of reaction and a better view. Guard bees of *Tetragonisca (Trigona) angustula*, a stingless bee from South America, hover for hours just in front of the nest entrance, chasing away intruders in order to protect the flight corridor leading to the nest entrance. Water striders hold their position on the surface of fast flowing regions of streams where insects trapped in the surface layer are most likely to be caught. All these insects employ a mix of two complementary mechanisms for holding their preferred position in space.

The first is to compensate for image motion. A hoverfly in still air, close to the branch of a tree, jitters no more than a few millimetres in any direction. When the branch waves in a gust of wind, the fly will follow the movements, stabilising the image motion on its retina. Similarly, if the nest box of a guard bee is moved back and forth through a few centimetres, the hovering guards copy the movements, flying forwards, backwards or sideways to keep their position relative to the hive constant (Zeil and Wittmann 1989). The responses caused by movements of the nest in 3-D can be evoked by 2-D patterns which move only in the plane of the nest entrance. Stripes which move sideways or up and down cause the hovering guard to follow suit and rotating spirals induce the bee to approach or to retreat as the spirals appear to contract or expand whether this occurs on frontal or lateral retina (Fig. 2.13). The insects are able to extract the separate components of optic flow anywhere on their retina and then move correctly to reduce them (Kelber and Zeil 1990, 1997).

Minimising image motion can only be a partial solution to keeping station because compensation cannot be complete. For reasons of stability, the effective gain of the control system will be less than 1 and consequently there will always be some residual image motion. For a water strider facing upstream and trying to keep in the same spot, the residual image motion on its retina would be consistently in the same direction. If the bug relied wholly upon minimising image motion, it would gradually drift downstream. Maintaining station is surer if there are mechanisms to keep the image of the surroundings in a constant retinal position. Junger (1991a) has provided a beautiful demonstration of positional control in water striders swimming on an artificial stream. The insects will keep station when the only visual cue is a single small light bulb seen in its frontal, dorsal visual field in an otherwise darkened room

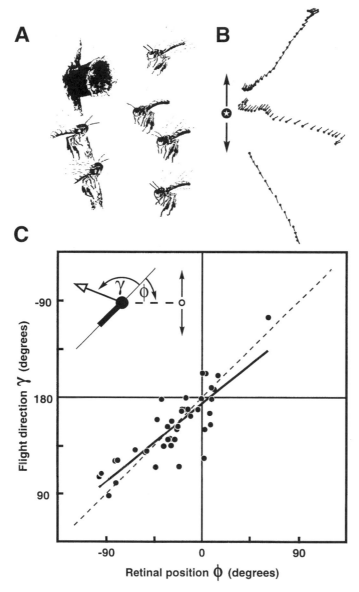

Fig. 2.13 Stationkeeping by the stingless bee, *Tetragonisca angustula*. (a) Artist's view of a group of hovering guard bees protecting the flight corridor to their nest. Drawing from Wittmann (1985). (b) Three guardbees reacting to expanding pattern motion generated by a rotating spiral in the plane of the front of their nest box. The bees are viewed from above and their positions are drawn every 20 ms as they move away from the nest entrance (star). Modified from Kelber and Zeil (1997). (c) Scatterplot shows the relationship between the flight direction (γ) in response to pattern expansion and the retinal position of the centre of expansion (ϕ) at the beginning of pattern motion. The dashed line shows what would happen if bees flew directly away from the retinal position of the centre of expansion. Solid line is the regression line through the data points. From Kelber and Zeil (1997).

(Junger 1991*b*). The bug compensates for its drift by discrete jumps against the direction of water flow, so that it holds the light bulb at a constant retinal elevation. If the bulb is suddenly raised, the bug allows itself to drift with the stream until the bulb is returned to its original position on the retina (Fig. 2.14). If the bulb is lowered, the bug jumps forward. The water strider remembers the bulb's desired retinal position, and it moves in the appropriate direction to restore the bulb to that position.

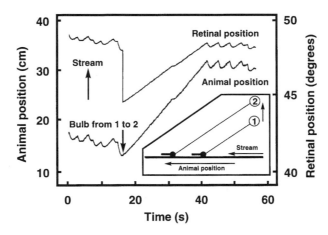

Fig. 2.14 A water strider keeping station on an artificial stream flowing at 0.75 cm/s. A small bulb located 115 cm from the bug was moved from position 1 to position 2. The insect compensated for the change in the bulb's height by moving backwards so that the bulb returns to its initial retinal position. Graph plots time course of the insect's position on the stream and the retinal elevation of the bulb. Modified from Junger (1991*b*).

With a slightly more elaborate visual stimulus, it becomes possible to watch the water strider as it adopts a new stored template. Instead of a single bulb, five bulbs were arranged symmetrically along a horizontal arc. The water strider soon stabilised itself with respect to this array (Fig. 2.15a). The leftmost lamp was then switched off and an additional lamp at the right end of the row was turned on. The bug turned to its right as though the change on its retina were caused by its own unwanted rotation (Fig. 2.15b). The consequence of the turn was that the stored template of the array was again occupied by five bulbs. However, when the bug jumped forward it no longer moved exactly up stream. In some way the bug detected this mismatch and after about 30 s, it had turned so that it again faced upstream (Fig. 2.15c). The visual consequence of this manoeuvre is that the bug now has a bulb missing from the left-hand end of its putative template and an extra one added to the right. At some point, the bug is induced to adapt its template to match this new retinal situation. To prove that the stored template has really been updated, the leftmost bulb was relit and the rightmost bulb extinguished. The bug now turned to the left keeping the bulbs in the position demanded by the revised template (Fig. 2.15d).

Minimising image motion cannot help hoverflies and guard bees regain their hovering station when they return after chasing other insects; a positional control system has to be engaged. If the most prominent nearby landmark is slowly moved away from a fly while it hovers, the fly does not immediately compensate for this displacement. It allows the

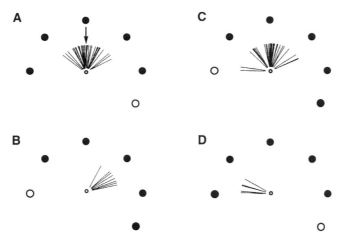

Fig. 2.15 Amending a stored image. Water strider uses a semicircular array of small light bulbs to keep its position on an artificial river in an otherwise completely darkened room. (a) Five bulbs are illuminated and bug tends to jump upstream as shown by the fan of straight lines pointing away from the centre. Each line represents the direction of one jump and the arrow shows the direction of water flow. (b) Directions of initial jumps after the leftmost lamp is switched off and an additional light is switched on at the right side of the array. (c) Stable distribution of jump directions, which is reached 30 s after the constellation of bulbs has been switched. (d) Initial direction of jumps immediately after the bulbs are switched back to the original arrangement. Modified from Junger (1991a).

landmark to shift away from its stored retinal position. Other stabilising reflexes hold the fly in place. However, the balance shifts to positional control when the fly returns after a brief excursion. It comes back and stations itself so that it is at the same distance from the landmark that it was before the landmark's displacement (Collett and Land 1975) (Fig. 2.16). The fly must have guided its return using positional information that it had acquired before the landmark was moved.

Returning to a place

Fixed routes

During their short excursions, guard bees and hoverflies may retain continuous visual contact with the objects that define their hovering station. But journeys are generally much longer. Bees, for instance, will fly as much as 8–10 km from their hive to collect nectar (Visscher and Seeley 1982) and are then guided by familiar landscape features along the route. Experienced foragers that have been tracked over part (Janzen 1971) or all of their path in their natural environment are usually observed to follow a fixed route. When paths are recorded they look stereotyped over a variety of scales, not only over relatively long distances, but also when recorded in more detail over much shorter distances close to a feeder (Collett and Rees 1997). Figure 2.17 illustrates the stereotyped homeward paths of two desert ants walking among small shrubs. Individual ants that are familiar with a foraging site have idiosyncratic paths that they follow, both when they home normally after feeding, and when they are carried back to the foraging site after they have reached their nest (Wehner et al. 1996).

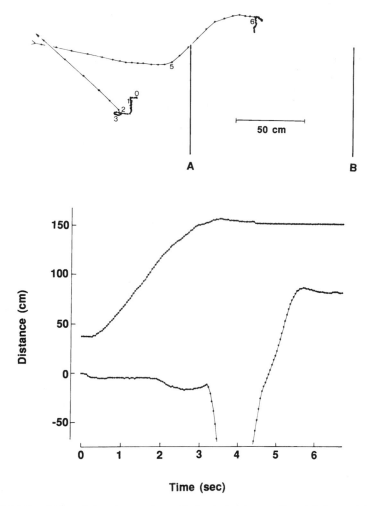

Fig. 2.16 The behaviour of a hoverfly hovering near to a vertically oriented chequered board. Fly hovers stably, unaffected by the movement of the board as the latter is shifted from A to B. At about 3.3s the fly starts chasing another insect. It returns to a position at roughly the same distance from the board as it was at the beginning of the sequence. Top: position of the fly viewed from the side is shown every 40 ms and labelled every second. Bottom: plots of distance along the horizontal axis against time. The upper trace shows the position of the board, the lower trace shows that of the fly.

Routes of this kind indicate that ants learn landmarks distributed along it. Direct evidence that desert ants learn route landmarks has been obtained by training ants to go to a feeder along a path with two visually distinct artificial landmarks. One landmark was placed so that it was on the left side of the ant's homeward route and another on the right side. Ants just about to set off home were carried from the feeding site to a separate test area and a replica of one or other landmark was placed directly in the path of their home vector. The ants began walking along their home vector, as in Fig. 2.5. They then adjusted their path to detour consistently to the right around the landmark that was normally viewed on their left and detoured to the left around the landmark normally on their right. The ants thus recognised each landmark and corrected their course relative to it (Collett *et al.* 1992).

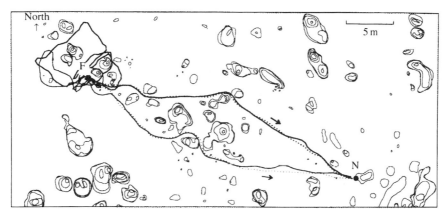

Fig. 2.17 Routes followed by two desert ants returning from a feeding site (F) through desert scrub to their nest (N). Shrubs are marked by contour lines at 15 cm height intervals. Dotted lines show the normal idiosyncratic path of each ant. Solid lines show the paths followed by the same ants when they were carried back to the feeding site after reaching the nest. The ant's path after displacement and release is the same as it is on normal return journeys. From Wehner *et al.* (1996).

A number of studies suggests that insects are not acquainted with the topography of a wide area, but that their knowledge is restricted to scenes that they view from a corridor along their fixed routes (for review see Wehner and Menzel 1990). Baerends (1941) study of the hunting wasp, *Ammophila* gives a classic example. These wasps often catch prey that is so heavy that they have to drag the prey back to the nest over the ground. A wasp so encumbered can easily be followed and its path recorded. Once the wasp had reached the nest, Baerends caught it and carried it, still grasping its prey, to a new location where it was released. Wasps returned straight home along habitual routes from some areas which they obviously knew from previous trips, but they were lost when released at positions close by. After a search they may come across a section of familiar terrain and then take a habitual path home. Such paths are often not straight and may skirt around large objects like trees. A wasp deposited at sites quite close together may follow very different paths. The wasp whose behaviour is illustrated in Fig. 2.18 seemed to know the direct way home along the gravel road when released at positions 3, 5 and 9, but from positions 4, 6, 7 and 8 it searched for some time and then always took the longer route around the bushes. When walking along the ground the wasp's vision is often obscured by vegetation, and periodically it climbs up a bush for a better vantage point so that it can redirect its path.

Homing from and learning about unfamiliar terrain

Exploration and learning remain part of an experienced forager's life as old patches become exhausted and new ones are found. The history of shifting resources may be read from the complex paths that develop between nest and foraging sites (Fig. 2.2). New spatial knowledge accretes in a haphazard way and routes may for this reason be far from optimal.

New foragers that have not had the opportunity to store landscape information about their route have a variety of techniques to ensure a safe return after a long journey. The problem is less severe for newly recruited ants than it is for bees, for most ants follow chemical trails or a nest mate, both on the outward trip and back home again. Many ant species lay trunk trails which persist for long periods. These trails may be cleared of debris and form wide visible

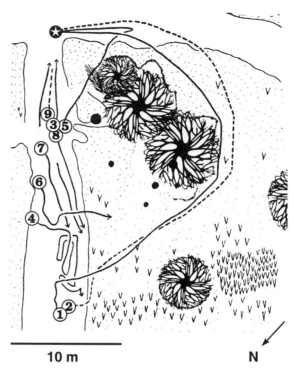

10 m

N

Fig. 2.18 Homing routes of a digger wasp, *Ammophila campestris*. The same wasp was caught repeatedly as it approached its nest (star) carrying prey. It was carried to a release point within its hunting area and then let free. The release points are numbered sequentially. The wasp takes the direct way home from release sites 3, 5 and 9, from sites 1 and 2 it detours around bushes rather than homing directly and from sites 4, 6, 7 and 8 it walks away from the most direct way home. Eventually, it finds the longer route around the bushes, sometimes after some searching. After Baerends (1941).

paths which allow the rapid deployment of a foraging force. Trunk trails lead into a tree like structure of dividing paths carrying ants over a wide area around the nest. Scouts that leave marked trails may then lay their own orientation trails on their outward trip in order to guide their later return to a well-used path.

Ants, such as *Cataglyphis*, that forage individually over long distances and lay no trails rely heavily on path integration. It is usually supposed that on its outward trip an ant will initiate just a single integrator when it is at the nest. This may, however, be an oversimplification. In species with extensive trail systems there are signs that path integration has multiple origins. An ant leaving a familiar path far from the nest may use that point of departure as an additional reference point from which to initiate path integration. Consequently, the vector that it follows after finding food leads a short way back to the familiar trail rather than to the nest (Wehner 1992). In principle, operating several integrators at the same time allows the ant to follow a complex and well-marked route home, but to retain the possibility of going directly to the nest if mistakes are made on individual segments and the ant loses its way.

Following chemical trails is slow, as ants go back and forth across the trail sampling it with their antennae. Experienced ants can speed up their journey twofold by shifting from reliance on chemical trails to the use of visual cues, as Harrison *et al.* (1989) have demonstrated in *Paraponera*. Figure 2.19 is taken from Wehner's (1992) description of this work. Ants are trained along a Y-shaped platform to take the left branch. On their way home after feeding, they deposit a pheromone trail. In tests with the feeder removed, ants take predominantly the left branch to reach the foraging site (Fig. 2.19b). In this case, pheromone and visual cues both direct ants to the left. Their preference for visual cues can be shown by swapping the arms so that the pheromone trail is on the right. Experienced ants then continue to take the left fork, but naive ants take the right fork (Fig. 2.19c). However, if the landmarks on both sides of the platform are screened (Fig. 2.19d), experienced ants resort to following the pheromone trail and take the right branch.

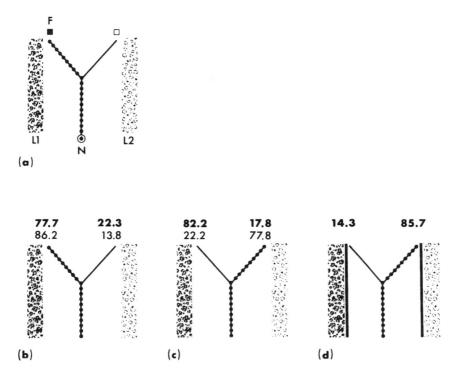

Fig. 2.19 The ponerine ant, *Paraponera clavata*, prefers visual over chemical cues. (a) Sucrose (F) is available at the end of the left branch of a Y-shaped platform. L1 and L2 are natural landmarks either side of the platform. Dotted lines shows pheromone trail left by ants when returning to their nest (N). (b) Feeder removed. (c) Pheromone trail is switched to right fork. (d) Pheromone trail is switched to right fork and the visual landmarks are screened. Percentage choice for each fork are of experienced ants (bold figures in upper row) and naive ants (lower row). From Wehner (1992), plotted from data of Harrison *et al.* (1989).

Flying bees and wasps cannot use chemical trails and are subject to winds that reduce the accuracy of path integration. They must therefore depend more on locale-specific landmark information. The results of displacement experiments show that honey-bees become acquainted very rapidly with the countryside immediately around their hive. Becker (1958) studied young honey-bees when they left the hive for the first time. Bees, before becoming regular foragers, take short orientation flights lasting between 4 and 12 min. Becker caught bees at the hive when they returned from their first exploratory flight. She fed them and released them from sites at different directions and distances from the hive. The homing success of these bees decreases with the distance of the release site from the hive (Fig. 2.20). In

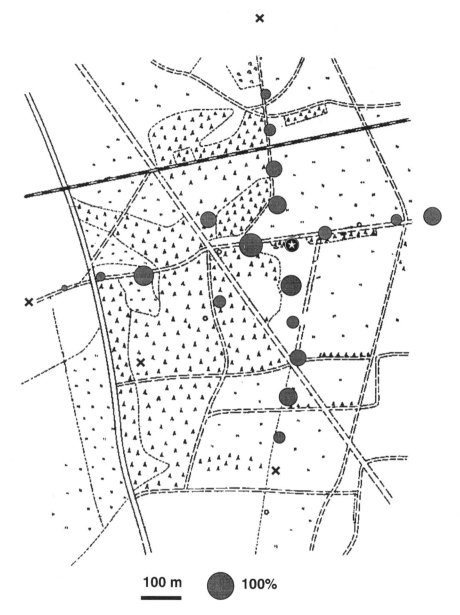

100 m ⬤ **100%**

Fig. 2.20 The homing success of honey-bees after their first learning flight. Young bees were caught immediately on returning to the hive (marked by a star) from the first orientation flight of their life. They were then released at different distances and directions from the hive. The percentage of returning bees from each site is shown by the size of the shaded circle. Bees released at the sites marked by a cross did not return to the hive. After Becker (1958).

a second experiment, Becker (1958) looked at the ability of experienced foragers to home after their hive had been moved to an unfamiliar area and they had been allowed a single orientation flight in the new location. A large proportion of these bees reached the hive from as far away as 500 m (Fig. 2.21). However, with displacement of more than 250 m, most

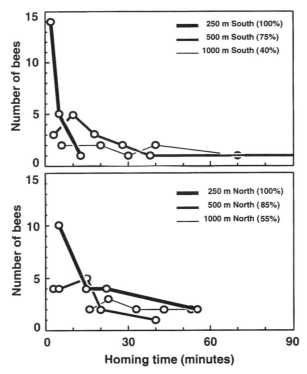

Fig. 2.21 Homing times of experienced honey-bee foragers in unknown terrain. A hive was transported to an unfamiliar area and experienced foragers were allowed to perform one orientation flight in the new terrain. Bees on returning to the hive were caught and released at different distances south (top graph) and north of the hive (bottom graph). Twenty bees were released at each site and the homing time of each bee was noted. The percentages of returning bees are given in brackets. Data from Becker (1958).

bees were rather slow in returning. The long delay suggests that they had to search around extensively before they encountered a place or saw a beacon which they recognised from their earlier orientation flight.

Landmark guidance along familiar routes

How then do experienced foragers employ landmarks to guide themselves along familiar routes? Our understanding is rudimentary, but part of the process is the use of local views that have been acquired periodically along the route. Guidance mechanisms must then ensure that the insect is brought from one acquired view to the next. One way in which insects do this is to follow a sequence of beacons. Another is to associate movement vectors or trajectories with local views.

Beacon aiming

Flying and walking insects learn the appearance of prominent objects that lie along the route and aim straight at them. These objects need not be directly on the route. Bees have often been observed to depart from the most direct path between two places and to make for isolated trees or objects that are some way off to the side (von Frisch 1967; Chittka *et al.* 1995). Such markers are especially helpful for maintaining course in strong winds.

It is difficult to discover what bees learn about beacons in natural landscapes because manipulating the countryside is hard. Wolf (1927) attempted this in an unused airship field. His experiments were made difficult as the bees deprived of other objects followed him around as a beacon. Progress has been made by Chittka and Geiger (1995), who in heroic experiments, erected 3.46 m high artificial landmarks in bare areas of heathland. They erected three sets of large, differently coloured tetrahedral tents (X, Y, Z) along a 270 m route between hive and feeding site. The last set of landmarks 'Z', which consisted of two blue tents, were placed together just beyond the feeder. The first two sets, 'X' (three yellow tents) and 'Y' (one green tent), were placed at 90 m and 180 m, respectively, from the hive (Fig. 2.22a). Once bees were accustomed to the tents, the positions and order of the tents were changed during tests. When bees were tested with just two sets of 'Z' tents, one at 180 m and one at 270 m, some bees landed prematurely at 180 m (Fig. 2.22b). Premature landings increased a little, but not significantly, when 'X' was put back in its normal place 90 m from the hive (Fig. 2.22c). However, premature landings at the first 'Z' increased greatly when 'X' was replaced by 'Y' so that bees encountered the sequence 'Y, Z, Z' (Fig. 2.22d). Bees seem to 'know' that they have passed 'Y' and become primed to land at the first 'Z' that they encounter, even though it appears 90 m too soon. These results show that individual landmarks are recognised and can be labelled by colour and/or shape. They also show that bees are sensitive to sequence. Actions are not driven solely by the last visual stimulus that is encountered. The sequence of tents 'Y then Z' elicits a different action from the sequence 'X then Z'.

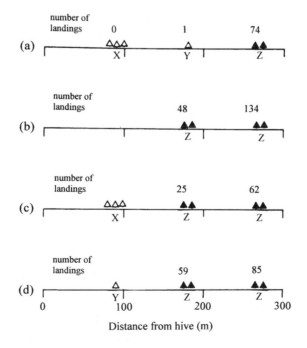

Fig. 2.22 Honey-bees using tents for navigation on a bare heath. Different coloured tents are distributed along a 270 m path between hive and feeding station(s). Top: tents in training arrangement and numbers of bees landing at the training feeder at 270m and at a test feeder at 90 and 180m. Below: different test situations and numbers of bees landing at the two feeders. Details in text. After Chittka *et al.* (1995).

Transitions between beacons

An insect that flies from beacon to beacon along its route has to have some means of switching between beacons in a controlled manner. It needs to relinquish fixation of the first beacon and place itself in an appropriate position to gain a standard view of the next one. One way to engineer a controlled transition is to link a particular flight trajectory to a close-up view of a beacon. Beacon switching can be analysed most easily when the insect is near to its goal and flying low over the ground. At this stage of the approach, small objects just a few centimetres high come to serve as beacons.

In one attempt to analyse beacon switching, bees were trained to forage at a site midway between two objects: a black cone 15 cm west of the feeder and a blue cylinder 15 cm to the east (Collett and Rees 1997). Over some hours, a bee approached the array from a constant direction, in this case roughly from the north. It aimed sometimes at the cone, sometimes at the cylinder and sometimes at both objects in turn. In the approach illustrated in Fig. 2.23a, the bee initially fixated the cylinder, secondly the cone and thirdly the cylinder once more. It then moved towards the feeder so that both landmarks travelled peripherally over the retina. Because the bee arrived from the north, the cone moved over the right eye and the cylinder over the left. Occasional tests were introduced in which the feeder and one of the flanking objects was removed. When just the cone was present, the bee approached it and moved to place the cone to its west and when the cylinder was present the bee moved to place the cylinder to its east. Superimposed trajectories of the path of the object over the bee's retina accumulated over several tests show that the object travelled from the front towards the periphery of the retina. Movement was across the right eye in tests with the cone and across the left eye in tests with the cylinder (Fig. 2.23b). Bees seem to have learnt distinguishing features of the two objects and to have associated a different trajectory with each object. This association can help provide for an orderly transition between different segments of a route.

Trajectories linked to scenes

Consider again the orchid bee's foraging route in Fig. 2.2. The bee must fly long distances between different plants and it seems likely that when the bee leaves each plant, it recalls a dead-reckoning command which specifies the distance and direction of the next plant to be visited, for there is no guarantee of a distinctive beacon to guide the way. One cue that may trigger such a movement is the scene viewed on departure. Displacement and release experiments provide some evidence for this hypothesis. Menzel et al. (1996) have performed an interesting experiment of this kind in a landscape that was carefully chosen to be bare of large beacons which could guide the bees' homeward path. Bees were trained to forage at one site in the morning and at another in the afternoon, so that the two sites were equally familiar. When bees caught at the hive were released at the morning site in the afternoon, or at the afternoon site in the morning, their homeward vanishing bearings were appropriate to the release site rather than to the time of day. This behaviour suggests that the appropriate trajectory was evoked by a view of the surrounding scene. Support for this conclusion came from the direction of the bees' trajectories when they were released from an intermediate site. The trajectory direction was then also intermediate averaging those from

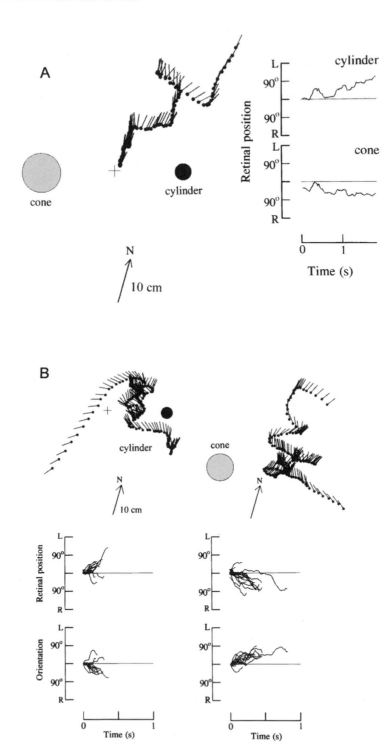

the morning and afternoon sites. Bees at the intermediate site seem to have recalled both trajectories and elaborated a mean trajectory. On the assumption that bees were not familiar with the intermediate site and that there were no beacons to guide them, such a trajectory requires bees to have recognised features of the two training sites from the intermediate site. Furthermore, these recognised features must be large objects that are visible at a distance.

Maze learning

Mazes provide a useful test-bed for performing more controlled experiments on route following. Bees and ants are very good at learning even very complex mazes to reach a food reward (e.g. Schneirla 1929; Zhang *et al*. 1996). So far, the findings from such studies transfer nicely to longer routes. Particularly striking is the readiness with which bees and ants learn sequences of different kinds.

Bees will learn sequences of motor commands (turn left, turn right) and of movement vectors of different directions and distances (Collett *et al*. 1993; Zhang *et al*. 1996). Motor commands and movement vectors can be linked to specific visual stimuli such as colours or stripes oriented in a specific direction, so that the bee follows a particular trajectory on seeing a particular visual pattern (Collett *et al*. 1993, 1996; Zhang *et al*. 1996). Lastly, bees and ants have been shown to learn sequences of visual patterns. Bees and ants have been trained through mazes which are composed of several identical compartments, each of which has an exit-hole that is marked by a different pattern. When insects are given the choice in one compartment between the positive patterns from that compartment and that from a different compartment, they prefer the pattern appropriate to their current compartment (Collett *et al*. 1993; Pastergue-Ruiz and Beugnon 1994). In the experimental apparatus shown in Fig. 2.24, ants (*Cataglyphis cursor*) were trained to find their way to and from their nest through four boxes. The way home was labelled by a disk in box A, by a star in box B, by a rectangle in box C and a diamond in box D. Ants preferred the disk over the star in box A and the star over the disk in box B. Their memory must have been primed by some internal contextual cue, because, as far as we can know, the two boxes looked and smelt very much the same. The insects acquired knowledge of the sequence of visual patterns, even though in principle it would have been enough to recognise each pattern individually without knowing the order. The incidental learning of sequences is likely to confer some benefits. Low spatial resolution (4° at best in these ants) and a small learning network may make it hard to learn many patterns without risk of confusing them. Insects may use the contextual signals provided by the learnt sequence to help to disambiguate and retrieve stored patterns.

Fig. 2.23 From aiming at beacons to image matching. A single bee is trained to forage at a feeder (+) with a cone 15 cm to the east and a cylinder 15 cm to the west. (a) Approach flight videotaped from above. Circles and tails show the position of the bee's head and the orientation of its body axis every 20 ms. Graphs show the retinal position of the cylinder and cone during the course of the flight. Bee first fixates cylinder and then the cone. Finally, both objects travel towards the lateral visual fields of the left and right eyes, as the bee moves towards the feeder. Arrows point north and their length represents 10 cm on the ground. (b) Tests with one object and no feeder. Bee fixates the object and then flies so that the object moves laterally over the retina. In tests with the cylinder, the bee moves so that the cylinder usually travels across the left eye, whereas in tests with the cone the bee moves so that the cone travels across the right eye. Bees thus link a different movement to each object. Bottom panels show the retinal trajectories of cylinder and cone obtained from several tests together with the accompanying change in body orientation. From Collett and Rees (1997).

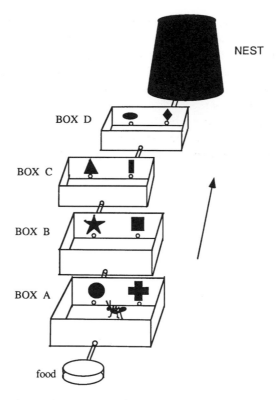

Fig. 2.24 Maze used to show that ants learn sequences of visual patterns. Boxes are 9 × 6 × 4.5 cm. The position of the exit tube and its associated positive pattern and the position of negative pattern within each compartment are exchanged from trial to trial. Ants readily discriminate patterns within each compartment and learn the sequence of positive patterns. Figure courtesy of G. Beugnon.

Conclusions

We began with evidence that arthropods have good reason to be familiar with several places within their environment and that one important way in which they specify a site is in terms of the landscape viewed from that site. Places are best defined on several scales. Views of landmarks close to a site will allow a location to be pin-pointed, while more distant landmarks can help an insect to reach or to recognise an area.

We have stressed that landmarks are learnt retinotopically from particular viewpoints and that they are used as beacons or in image matching or as visual patterns to which specific motor responses can be linked. This all fits well with insects learning and following fixed routes. Both displacement experiments and the observation of insects' normal foraging paths provide ample evidence that an insect's typical mode of operation is to keep to familiar routes. However, within this framework there is still room for flexible navigation and the performance of novel routes.

Large-scale image matching or the use of large beacons allow insects to approach a location from anywhere within a wide area. For instance, colonies of *Cataglyphis* which happen to nest in an open area of sand which is surrounded by shrubs will, if displaced from their nest, return there from different positions at the periphery of the area. They will do the same if displaced to the border of an equivalent empty area of sand surrounded by vegetation. They seem to move until the skyline matches that seen at their nest (Wehner *et al.* 1996).

One perplexing example of flexible navigation is the lobster's ability to perform straight escape runs towards a nearby burrow that is not its own and is not directly visible (Karnofsky *et al.* 1989). It is by no means clear that this performance can be explained by our current thinking. The many question marks in this account expose our collective ignorance, or in more upbeat vein, tell us that there are many exciting problems for future research.

3   Role of dead reckoning in navigation

Ariane S. Etienne, Joëlle Berlie, Joséphine Georgakopoulos and Roland Maurer

In the late fifteenth century, early transoceanic navigators, such as Vasco da Gama and Christopher Columbus for the first time lost sight of land for a long period. They then had to make their way through a no man's land or rather through a no man's sea. Possibly, they had to overcome greater navigational and psychological barriers than our first present day space travellers, who could always see the globe from where they started their mission and maintained constant contact with their base. To avoid getting lost, there was only one thing our early explorers could do: keep track of their own position relative to their point of departure.

To achieve this, the navigators had to measure two components of the ship's course throughout their journey: first, the direction in which they were sailing relative to some known permanent features they could see, such as the sun or certain star configurations; and secondly, the distance they travelled in this direction during a particular time span. To assess directed distances, the sailors had to estimate the ship's velocity with the help of a log (i.e. of a floating piece of wood attached to a line) at regular intervals and to multiply velocity by time. The continuous transcription of the directed distances the ship had covered into a log book allowed the seamen to add up these vectors and thus to estimate their current position with respect to their point of departure.

Dead reckoning (i.e. 'deduced reckoning'), also called path integration, is precisely the process that allows a navigator to deduce their position (in relation to a particular point of departure) from their own movement.

In our present example, the sailors venture to explore the unknown sea. They therefore transcribe their successive positions onto an empty map, which is linked to the filled map of familiar space through the point of departure of their current excursion. Newly discovered land can then be entered onto the empty sea map by reference to the sailors' own position.

As illustrated on a different scale by the foraging behaviour of golden hamsters, updating position with respect to a given point of reference also helps a subject to determine his or her position within a familiar environment (Georgakopoulos and Etienne 1994). The hamsters were trained under infra-red light to proceed from their nest to two or three food sites. The food sites were located in two or three identical, interlinked boxes, at different relative locations within each box. External spatial cues were provided by the articulated structure of the apparatus. Furthermore, three dim light sources were located at the same relative position within each box. These weak lights were the only visual cues the hamsters could see.

Test trials also occurred under infra-red light and involved the removal or displacement of the light cues. Olfactory cues on the floor were always neutralised and in a number of trials the food sources were removed or shifted in parallel with the light cues. Irrespective of these changes, the hamsters returned to the same feeding sites as during training. In the majority of test trials, the subjects followed fixed routes from the nest to the two or three feeding places and seemed to rely on rote motor learning. On the other hand, the animals also performed much more flexible trajectories. Sometimes they visited the three food sources in a reversed order, starting with the most remote box. In other cases, they detoured through the centre of a box or corrected initially wrong orientations. Yet, the animals nearly always ended up by aiming precisely at each particular food location.

On the whole, these results suggest that even when external cues were absent or irrelevant, the hamsters always knew in which box and where in the box they were located. In our test conditions, the subjects' 'position sense' (Gallistel 1994) depended on dead reckoning: The animals derived their location and heading in the familiar test space from their preceding locomotion, i.e. from the sequence of rotations and translations they had realised from the moment they had left the nest exit until they had reached their current position.

Our two introductory examples illustrate extreme cases, in which the navigator deduces his position mainly or only from his own locomotion. Under more common circumstances, external references set the general frame in which the subject moves and determines his location. However, it is through the interaction between these stable references and the short-term registration of his own locomotion that the subject remains best and most continuously informed on his current position with respect to one (or several) points of reference.

This chapter starts by illustrating dead reckoning by homing behaviour from various species tested without the availability of location-based cues. The input variables and information processing that are required to compute a position vector independently of known landmark-place associations will be described briefly. Considerations on the functional value of dead reckoning, most likely an innate strategy, will be followed by data on its interplay with known stable references from the environment. Current experiments examine to what extent mammals optimise navigation by resorting to both classes of spatial information when they remain mutually correlated.

Estimating the return vector in the homing situation

Phenomena

In our two introductory examples, humans and rodents updated their position with respect to a well-determined point in space where they initiated their large-scale sea voyage or small-scale foraging excursion. To this purpose the subjects use self-generated information, i.e. information deriving from the choice and performance of changes in orientation (due to rotations) and/or location (due to translations). The continuous 'integration' of these changes yields a vector that points from the point of departure to the subject's current position. By inverting this vector, the subjects can therefore return 'home' along a direct path at any time or from any point of their trip.

The ability to 'home' irrespective of familiar references from the environment remains the hallmark and safest operational criterion for dead reckoning. Figure 3.1 illustrates homing through path integration in arthropods and mammals, which were tested according to the same paradigm. After a guided L-shaped outward journey to a feeding site, spiders (*Agelena labyrinthica*), bees (*Apis mellifera*), ants (*Cataglyphis fortis*) and hamsters (*Mesocricetus auratus*), laden with food, returned spontaneously to their retreat or nest along the shortest path. Dogs and humans were trained or instructed to return to the arbitrary point of departure of the guided outbound trip. Both bees and ants walked to the food source and back to their colony in view of the sun or correlated skylight patterns. The other species were deprived of any external reference.

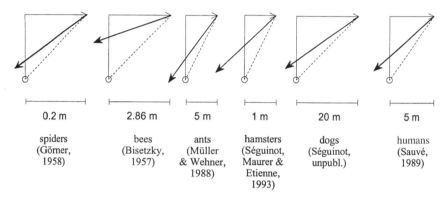

Fig. 3.1 Dead reckoning in arthropods and mammals. All subjects followed an L-shaped detour (thin line) starting at their retreat or some arbitrary point of departure (small circle). The hatched lines indicate the correct return to the point of departure, and the heavy arrows the observed return directions. For (walking) bees, the return direction was deduced from their dance axis. Bees and ants could use the sun as a directional reference. Hamsters and dogs were deprived of visual, auditory, olfactory and tactile information. Humans were tested blindfolded and wearing earphones and had to execute a mental task that interfered with the mental representation of the outward journey. The return directions were assessed in terms of the subjects' position after they had moved over a given (bee-line) distance away from the endpoint of the outward journey.

All species showed similar return behaviour. First, the subjects always attempted to return directly to the point of departure. Furthermore, besides random errors, the mean return directions from all experimental groups showed systematic biases. In the examples shown here, the subjects made an 'inward error' by overcompensating the outward rotation. This suggest that unrelated species may process the return vector according to similar computations (see below). (For further data see Wehner 1992 and Maurer and Séguinot 1995).

To choose an (approximately) correct return direction after a detour outward journey, the subjects had to measure and combine the angular and linear components of their locomotion in a continuous manner. In a similar manner, the estimated return distance, which is not shown here, depends on the evaluation of translations as well as rotations.

Figure 3.2a reproduces the complete homing performance in a desert ant, both direction and distance of the return to the colony being taken into account. From her camouflaged nest exit, the ant explores the fairly homogeneous environment of her colony in search for food,

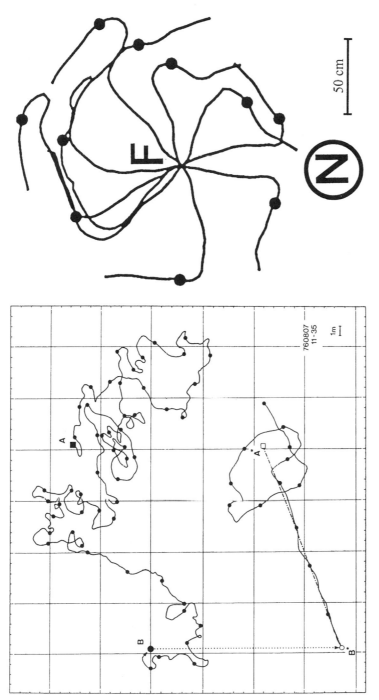

Fig. 3.2 Homing in desert ants and golden hamsters. Left: Starting from her underground nest at A, the ant (*Cataglyphis albicans*) follows a circonvoluted foraging path to B, where she is caught in a glass tube that contains food. Being shifted over 18 m to point B (dotted line), she proceeds from there towards the expected nest location at A*. Fixes (●) are taken every 10 s. From Wehner (1982). Right: The hamster (*Mesocricetus auratus*) follows a bait from its nest N to a food source F on a platform, along a direct path. While the subject fills its cheek pouches, it is slowly rotated and therefore returns in the wrong direction. The lines which radiate from F represent 10 return journeys. The black dots indicate the first point of the return journey where the bee-line distance from F ceases to increase. The experiment takes place under infra-red light, after stirring the substrate on the arena floor and during the diffusion of pink noise. The nest is removed from the arena before the animal starts its return to the presumed nest location (from Séguinot et al. 1993).

mainly dead arthropods which succumbed to the heat on the desert floor. After having been provided with a food item and at the same time been displaced over a distance of 18 m, the ant proceeds along a direct path towards the point where she expects the nest to be. In the vicinity of the supposed nest site, the ant shifts from a direct return path to systematic search loops to locate the virtual nest entrance (Wehner and Srinivasan 1981; Müller and Wehner 1994).

This remarkable behaviour illustrates the fundamental principles of dead reckoning and may be conceptualised in the following manner. At the end of the active outward journey, the ant has computed a 'vector' representing her current position with respect to the nest (exocentric representation of position) or the position of the nest in relation to her head (egocentric or head-referred representation of position). (For a discussion of an exocentric or egocentric conception and formalisation of dead reckoning see Etienne *et al.* in press.) During her displacement, she carries this vector with her. Loaded with food, she walks parallel to the vector path she would have followed had she not been displaced. The ant maintains the same direction until she has covered the whole length of her homing vector, and then switches over to search loops to find the goal.

Golden hamsters showed comparable homing behaviour in the restricted frame of an experimental arena, as shown by Fig. 3.2b. The experiment (Séguinot *et al.* 1993) took place during the simultaneous elimination of visual, olfactory and acoustical cues. From its cone-shaped nest located in the open space of a square arena (3.55 × 3.55 m), the subject was led by a bait to a platform covered with food items. The nest was removed from the arena. While the animal filled its cheek pouches on the platform, the latter was slowly rotated to induce the animal to home in the wrong direction, passive rotations leading to a rapid accumulation of errors (Etienne *et al.* 1988). Thus, during its homing attempts in successive trials, the animal proceeded in various directions, unrelated to the former nest location, and in most trials did not re-enter the original nest zone which may still have contained olfactory cues. However, the observed homing behaviour still expressed that the animal was taking into account the homing distance: Upon having covered the approximate distance along a fairly straight path, the animal changed over to a curved progression, which followed the perimeter of a circle with a radius close to the distance between the feeding place and the former nest site. In the majority of trials, the curved search path followed a direction opposite to the direction in which the subject had been rotated on the platform, before the initiation of the return. These results therefore bring to light that hamsters, like desert ants, measure, compute and store the direction and length of the homing vector through separate processes.

Input variables

As already mentioned, dead reckoning requires the continuous assessment of the angular and linear components of locomotion. Direction and distance can be measured according to two basically different modalities, depending on whether the subject uses external references or relies exclusively on cues from within the organism. This distinction is particularly important with respect to the measure of direction.

Direction

In our example of homing after a controlled L-shaped outward journey or a long exploratory excursion in the desert, ants and bees measure the current direction of their locomotion in terms of the angle between the axis of their progression and the position of the sun with respect to the horizontal plane (sun azimuth). The availability of an external compass allows the subjects to measure the direction in which they are heading in a continuous manner. Furthermore, the insects do not need to assess their movements at the food source. At the end of the outward trip, they memorise the vector they have travelled in terms of its length and of its direction with respect to the sun. To return home, they can reactualise this vector by orientating it with respect to the sun.

In contrast, spiders and mammals, when tested in darkness, estimate direction through purely 'internal' cues, without the help of an external reference system. To measure rotations, spiders rely mainly on proprioceptive input (Seyfarth and Barth 1972; Seyfarth et al. 1982), while mammals use vestibular information and efference copies ('copies' of locomotor commands) as well as somatosensory feedback (for a review see Etienne et al. 1996). Analytical data on humans show that vestibular signals predominate over other types of internal directional information in the estimation of rotations (Bles et al. 1984). This can be explained through the fact that the vestibular system is equipped with particular sensors for measuring rotations: the semicircular canals are stimulated by inertial forces resulting from angular acceleration only (Mayne 1974).

However, estimating direction and changes of direction through purely internal signals imposes severe limitations on the precision and use of dead reckoning. First, the variables that are measured by the nervous system consist of changes in the stimulation of particular sensors, which can only be evaluated at the very moment of their occurrence. Second, for storing and recalling the outbound vector at the feeding site, a stable external compass is needed. Without such a reference, the subject has to continue to update its positional vector while moving around the food source. This greatly increases the accumulation of errors that affect the estimation of each particular rotation.

Distance

The question of how distance is estimated has not yet been answered in an exhaustive manner, either for invertebrates or for vertebrates. Recent findings on *Apis* (Esch and Burns 1995; Srinivasan et al. 1996) and on *Cataglyphis* (Ronacher and Wehner 1995) seem to contradict the assumption of von Frisch (1965) and his colleagues that distance is measured through energy expenditure. The current literature reports that these insects use the translatory components of optical flow to measure the distance travelled. As shown for *Cataglyphis*, kinaesthetic information also plays a part, possibly through a step-counting mechanism, the ants walking at a constant speed and with a constant step length during particular foraging trips (Wehner et al. 1996). On the other hand, the energy consumption hypothesis has been reformulated in the following terms. Changes in the tension of the honey-sac wall act on stretch receptors and can be instantaneously transmitted to the central nervous system. The longer the distance flown, the more the crop content diminishes and the less the tension of the crop wall and corresponding stimulation of the stretch receptors (Neese 1988). Let us mention, however, that any measure related to energy expenditure can, at best, represent the total length of the performed path and not the length of each unidirectional path segment, as required for path integration.

In mammals tested without external references, translations are, like rotations, measured through the combination of vestibular signals, somatosensory information and efference copies. Recent experiments (Berthoz *et al*. 1995) showed that humans are capable of assessing precisely the distance, duration and velocity profile of a single passive forward shift. Translations can therefore be measured through the stimulation of the vestibular otoliths through linear acceleration only, independently of additional information from non-inertial sensor systems. However, unlike the semi-circular canals, the otoliths function as general accelerometers and therefore respond both to inertial forces resulting from linear acceleration and to changes in the direction of gravity; thus, the complete pattern of vestibular stimulation during a horizontal translation has to be treated at a higher level of the central nervous system to yield unambiguous information (Mayne 1974). We may therefore understand that in contrast to the assessment of rotations, somatosensory information and motor commands play a greater part than vestibular signals in the estimation of translation. Labyrinthine-defective patients, for instance, estimate the distance over which they walk blindfolded to a previously presented visual target as well as normal control subjects (Glasauer *et al*. 1994).

Experiments in which various species of rodents (see Etienne *et al*. 1996) had to return to a given point in space after a passive outward shift and without the help of external cues gave heterogeneous results. Depending on the species as well as on the shape of the outward journey, the animals compensated for the outbound shift to various degrees, and sometimes not at all. These data confirm that in the estimation of distance inertial signals are strongly complemented by cues which derive from active locomotion (see Etienne *et al*. 1988).

On the whole, the question of how mammals assess distance without external feedback remains unanswered. Recent literature on humans suggests that part of the coding process of distance depends on the anticipation of the effort necessary to accomplish the upcoming locomotion along a (unidirectional) path (Corlett 1992). This brings us back to the energy expenditure hypothesis, the anticipation of effort amounting to anticipating energy consumption. Let us mention here that the concepts of effort and energy expenditure are related to a number of different variables. Thus the anticipation of effort induces locomotor commands, while energy expenditure is linked to efference copies and to proprioceptive feedback as well as to metabolic variables.

Returning to insects, let us emphasise that different species show different responses to particular experimental manipulations, such as loading the animals during locomotion (Schifferer 1952; Etienne 1978; Schäfer and Wehner 1993); conversely, particular species may respond differentially to different experimental variables (such as carrying a load or overcoming an increased resistance by pulling an object) that have in common the effect of inducing a change in energy expenditure during a constant time span of locomotion (Etienne 1978). More experiments are needed to decouple the effect of a number of different but tightly correlated inputs that are subsumed under the term of effort, energy expenditure or metabolic cost. (For further references concerning the estimation of rotations and translations in mammals see Etienne *et al*. 1996.)

Computations

Homing by dead reckoning is very different from the process of path reversal (*Wegumkehr*), i.e. the inversion of each outbound segment memorised during the outward trip. To return to the point of departure of a sinuous excursion along a direct path, the subject continuously computes a positional vector which may be compared with an extensible rubber thread that links him to the point of departure. This means that position is updated instantaneously and automatically, rotations and translations being taken into account simultaneously.

In our introductory example, the navigators deduce their position on the open sea by vector addition, i.e. by adding up the distances which they had covered in particular directions. Modern vessels are equipped with inertial navigation systems that perform the basic processes of vector addition with great precision: Inertial forces resulting from angular and linear accelerations are measured by angular and linear accelerometers. The integration over time of the components of the acceleration in some fixed orthogonal reference system (plus the vessel's velocity at some initial time t_0) yields the velocity at later times t ($t > t_0$). Proceeding in a similar fashion, a second integration over time yields the vessel's position. Note that an error in the determination of velocity leads to a positional error that accumulates as time progresses, requiring additional independent checks or 'fixes' at 'anchor' points. By definition, accumulation of errors is intrinsic to all route-based orientation strategies, in which changes in orientation and/or location at a given time t_n are assessed on the basis of orientation and/or location at the time t_{n-1}.

Biological and technical dead reckoning systems (see Kayton 1990) share some basic aspects in the uptake and processing of information, such as the separate measurement but combined treatment of rotations and translations, the step-by-step or incremental estimation of position and the necessity of resetting the integrator through additional location-based information. On the other hand, all species tested so far commit not only random but also systematic errors while returning to the point of departure of an outward path with two or several segments (see Fig. 3.1). These errors show in a convincing manner that neither higher vertebrates nor arthropods update position by relying on a mathematically correct, trigonometric algorithm which implies the twofold time integration of changes in the x and y components of the subject's progression, as proposed by Mittelstaedt and Mittelstaedt (1982)

This viewpoint has been illustrated for the first time with respect to homing by *Cataglyphis*. Setting out from an extensive analysis of the errors which affect the homing direction of these ants after a two-segmented outward journey, Müller and Wehner (1988, 1994) arrived at an iterative arithmetic algorithm that matches the ants' homing behaviour to a large extent. According to this formalism, the insect performs something like a distance-weighted mean direction computation, which may be considered as an approximate version of path integration: 'While proceeding from one step of unit length to the next, the ant adds some measure of the angular distance between its nth step and the direction of the mean vector pertaining to its $(n-1)$th step, and does so by scaling down all successive angular contributions in proportion to the distance it has moved away from the nest' (Wehner and Wehner 1990). Interestingly, within certain limits this algorithm describes systematic biases in the homing directions shown not only by other arthropods, but also by mammals (see references in fig. 3.1).

By now, dead reckoning has become a privileged field for modelling, in a mathematical as well as in a neurophysiological (McNaughton *et al*. 1991, 1996; Hartmann and Wehner 1995) and a connectionist perspective (Maurer 1993 and in press). It is indeed of great interest to try to understand and to simulate how path integration is implemented in animals ranging from invertebrates to higher vertebrates (for a critical review on modelling path integration see Benhamou and Séguinot 1995; Maurer and Séguinot 1995).

The functional significance of dead reckoning

Throughout the behavioural and neurophysiological literature on dead reckoning one finds the implicit assumption that this navigational strategy is hardwired and therefore functional from an early age onwards, irrespective of any experience. To our knowledge, this has been confirmed by one study only, namely the development of the return to a shelter in cockroach larvae. In test conditions where 'kinaesthetic path integration' only could be used, first-instar larvae were able to orient towards their shelter from hatching. With age, the accuracy of the kinaesthetically controlled return direction did not change. By contrast, visually guided return to the shelter appeared only on day 2 and became better oriented through landmark learning between days 2 and 3 (Dabouineau and Rivault 1995).

Developmental data on path integration in mammals are missing. In adults, however, pilot experiments have shown that hamsters, tested under infra-red light, are capable of homing precisely in a completely unknown environment (see Fig. 3.3). From its nest cage, the subject entered an unfamiliar arena through a tunnel, and was lured away from the periphery, towards more central regions of the arena. At a given moment, the animal was frightened by a strong noise. Of 12 subjects, 11 animals headed directly back in the direction of the tunnel exit, where they had initiated their first excursion into the arena. Direct homing behaviour occurred independently of the subjects' orientation and location at the instant they were frightened.

As already stated, hamsters home exclusively on the basis of self-generated signals from within the organism when they are tested under infra-red light (Etienne *et al*. 1986). Thus, our animals' capacity to show immediately well-oriented escape behaviour confirms a complementary fact we observed throughout our study on homing in hamsters: During repeated testing in constant conditions, the accuracy of dead reckoning does not change, at least not in adult animals.

Evidently, a navigational strategy that is adapted to all terrains and works without specific prerequisites offers significant advantages. Dead reckoning allows a sedentary subject to return home during his first excursions, and, at a later stage, to home independently of learned landmarks, which may not always be available. Species like bees and ants, which update their positional vector with the help of the sun compass, explore their environment over considerable distances without resorting to any means of navigation other than dead reckoning. For species like dusk and night-active mammals, which measure rotations without an external compass, dead reckoning is open to rapid drift (see above). Without the additional help of learned landmarks or other references, these species can therefore rely on dead reckoning over limited excursions only, and by no means perform homing behaviour over longer distances (see Bovet 1992). However, dead reckoning may be used in combination

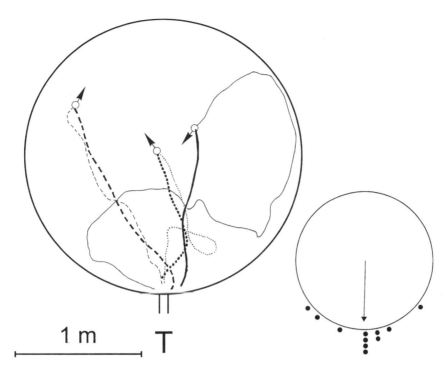

Fig. 3.3 First return to nest in a new environment by hamsters. Each hamster was kept for 24 h in a shielded home cage, in the unfamiliar test room. In the single test trial, the hamster entered the experimental arena from its cage through a tunnel (T), was guided by a bait away from the periphery and then frightened by a sudden noise. The experiment took place under infra-red light. Left: outward (thin line) and return (heavy line) journeys of three subjects. The small circle with an arrow indicates the location and orientation of the subject at the moment it heard the noise. Right: orientation of return to periphery. Twelve subjects were tested; one subject walked for 2 min along the arena wall before daring to move away from it and was discarded from the analysis. The vector represents the mean return direction of the remaining 11 subjects (direction of vector 1.7°; length 0.90; *P*<0.001, Rayleigh test); the points around the arena indicate the position of each subject at a distance of 15 cm from the arena periphery. On average, the hamsters took 26.3 s (range: 10.5–60 s) to follow the bait during the outward journey, and 1.5 s (range: 1.0–3.0 s). to return to the arena periphery (Etienne and Berlie unpublished results).

with other strategies: Within their home range, rodents, for instance, travel on familiar trails (Jamon 1994). While progressing along these fixed routes, they may at any moment start a short round trip into unexplored parts of their home range and find their way back to the trail through dead reckoning.

Comprehensive theories of navigation (Gallistel 1990) emphasise that dead reckoning is closely interwoven with the so-called cognitive map, i.e. the representation of the familiar environment as a system of interconnected locations. According to this view, path integration provides the subject with positional information that is instantaneously translated on to the map system. Through the map, dead-reckoning can therefore cooperate with location-based information, i.e. particular landmark-place associations. As a pre-wired and automatically functioning mechanism, path integration may also play an essential part in the construction of the map of a given environment; in this perspective, path integration may be compared with a metric frame on to which the subject grafts a set of (learned) landmarks.

This viewpoint emerged from the neurophysiological literature as soon as place cells, which embody the representation of familiar places, were discovered in the hippocampus of mammals (O'Keefe 1976; O'Keefe and Nadel 1978). At the present time, it lies at the core of recent models that describe the hippocampus primarily as a path integration system to which 'view-specific visual information (i.e. landmark panoramas seen under a certain angle) become bound secondarily by associative learning' (McNaughton *et al.* 1996). Further research along these lines will show whether path integration really plays this fundamental role for spatial navigation in mammals and other vertebrates, and how this process considered in itself and in relation to landmark learning is implemented by neural networks.

The interrelation between dead reckoning and landmarks

To optimise navigation, dead reckoning and landmark-map information should interact as closely as possible, as stressed by the above-mentioned functional considerations. In insects and mammals, the interrelation between dead reckoning and location-based navigation has been approached so far in two complementary experimental conditions, implying either a conflict or the possibility of a mutual confirmation between the two categories of spatial information.

Insects

In conflict situations, ants and bees rely much more on compass-assisted dead reckoning than on learned landmarks according to recent data (Wehner 1992; Wehner *et al.* 1996; see also Collett and Zeil, Chapter 2). Thus, the insects tend to ignore landmarks if they are not in tune with route-based vector information. On the other hand, the animals revert to landmark guidance if they cannot use vector information. This has been shown to be the case when sun compass cues are not available (Dyer and Gould 1981), or when the subjects are tested in a zero-vector state, i.e. just after their return to the colony from a foraging excursion (Wehner *et al.* 1996).

In test situations where dead reckoning and landmarks remain correlated, bees rely predominantly on dead reckoning while in flight, but switch to the use of landmarks to pin-point the goal station before landing. In certain conditions, however, bees and ants follow a particular landmark or a sequence of landmarks to reach a goal and therefore deviate from the straight path, which is imposed by vector information (Menzel *et al.* 1996; Wehner *et al.* 1996). In desert ants, landmark guidance is linked to the adjustment of the path to obstacles, which the animals bypass consistently to the right or left. In spite of this apparent coordination between dead reckoning and landmark guidance, the ants establish no consistent link between the two strategies: In experiments where the training situation involved two identical landmark objects placed along the animal's homing vector, at different distances from the nest site, the ants did not identify each landmark through its position in subsequent test conditions, but responded to each landmark as if it were the one closer to the nest (Collett *et al.* 1992).

There is, however, one functionally important situation in which route-based vector information leads to the use of landmarks: When the insects approach a zero vector state upon entering the nest region, they start to search for landmarks that match the precise snapshot memory of nearby landmark-objects they have previously associated with the nest entrance (Collett *et al.* 1992; Collett 1996; Wehner *et al.* 1996).

Rodents

As suggested by homing experiments in mice (Alyan and Jander 1994) and golden hamsters (Teroni *et al.* 1987; Etienne *et al.* 1990), rodents differ significantly from hymenopteran insects with respect to the relative weight they give to dead reckoning and landmarks when tested in an open environment, such as a large arena. In minor conflict situations, when dead reckoning and distal landmarks diverge up to 90°, these rodents return to the nest along compromise directions, with visual cues playing a much greater part than dead reckoning. For hamsters, if the conflict is increased, either by a stronger angular divergence between the two categories of spatial information or by repeated shifts of the visual references, the subjects resort to dead reckoning or no longer show a preferential homing direction. It seems therefore that in an open test space, hamsters rely on stable references from the distant visual environment much more than on the evanescent outcome of dead reckoning based on internal signals only. On the other hand, the animals seem no longer to trust learned visual references if the latter are unstable or too divergent from dead reckoning.

Single cell recordings in the hippocampus and related structures of rats confirm these results on the neurophysiological level: For small discrepancies between visual and inertial cues, the place field of place cells and the directional preference of head direction cells follow the shift of visual cues; for larger discrepancies, the activity of the cells tends to remain aligned with the inertial frame of reference (McNaughton *et al.* 1996).

The question arises whether animals can be trained to invert their spontaneous preference for dead reckoning and visual landmarks in conflict situations. Whereas this is very unlikely to be the case for bees and ants because of their hardwired behavioural predispositions, mammals may well be flexible enough to recalibrate the role of different strategies through learning. That this is indeed the case was illustrated by homing experiments during minor conflict situations with golden hamsters (Etienne *et al.* 1993).

Each subject lived in a large arena with a nest box at a constant peripheral location. On test and training trials, the arena, with the hamster in its nest, was rotated by 90°, putting dead reckoning at variance with the distal visual environment. The animals, which had to return from a food source at the arena centre to their peripheral nest, were rewarded for using dead reckoning (i.e. for returning to the actual, rotated position of the nest, in relation to which they had updated their position). At first, they favoured the distal room cues (i.e. returned to the standard nest location), but after a training period ranging from 44 to 108 trials, four of six subjects switched to using dead reckoning. Thus, hamsters are capable of changing the relative weight that they normally attribute to dead reckoning and spatially relevant visual cues, albeit with considerable difficulties. In further experiments, the reliance on dead reckoning was greatly enhanced when a cue card at the nest entrance (or elsewhere along the arena wall) was rotated along with the arena, pitting one proximal cue plus dead reckoning against distal cues: All subjects rapidly learned to return to the rotated nest.

The last result illustrates an important point. Normally, inertial dead reckoning occurs in inertial or absolute space. In laboratory conditions, it therefore remains correlated with general, stable features of the test environment, such as the shape of the experimental room and the outlay of objects within this frame (Cheng 1986; Gallistel 1990). During locomotion, the subject may expect to view learned, spatially meaningful references under a new perspective by means of positional information derived from dead reckoning. In our experiments, this expectation was only confirmed with respect to the proximal cue card, which therefore gained the status of an exclusive visual reference.

This leads us to the interplay between dead reckoning and the use of landmarks in conditions where the two categories of spatial information are correlated and therefore may complement each other. The co-operation between dead reckoning and landmark information can be assessed through the following criteria: (1) both categories of information should reinforce each other, so that navigation becomes more precise when they are available simultaneously; (2) landmarks that are ambiguous and therefore yield no positional information by themselves should be identified through dead reckoning; in this condition, they may, in turn, help the subject to specify the goal location; and (3) through episodic fixes (Gallistel 1990) on familiar external references the subject can clear the path integrator of the accumulated errors. We are currently investigating whether these criteria are fulfilled by homing behaviour in golden hamsters.

Figure 3.4a illustrates experimental procedures conceived to examine criterion (2). Each subject lived in its own arena with a peripheral nest. The arena was completely surrounded by an optical enclosure and contained a symmetrical landmark array with four identical cylinders, one of which was baited. During a preliminary training phase, the hamsters followed a bait from the nest exit to the peripheral locations a or c, in darkness. From these two points, the subjects learned to proceed by themselves to the baited goal cylinder G. By training the subjects to follow two different paths to the same goal we expected that the animals would not resort to rote motor learning to reach the goal, but memorise the goal location in terms of a nest-to-goal vector. During the test phase, each subject was led along six new peripheral routes to point a, b, c or d, from where it had to set off to reach the presumed goal cylinder. Intramaze cues were neutralised before each test.

Each subject underwent two successive experiments that differed with respect to the optical conditions during the training and test trials. In a first experiment L (for 'light'), the hamsters were briefly exposed to the illuminated arena upon leaving the nest. Then they were led along the arena periphery in darkness. The lights were turned on again at the end of the guided outward journey, so that the animals could proceed to the presumed goal cylinder across the fully lit arena. In a second experiment D (for 'darkness'), the same subjects were retrained and re-tested according to the same procedures as in experiment L, except that the lights were never turned on. Thus, the animals had to proceed in darkness from the arena periphery to the goal.

In experiment L, our six subjects proceeded to and explored a particular cylinder in almost all test trials. In 89% of the performed trials, they chose the correct goal cylinder. The success rate decreased in proportion to the length of the guided outward journey along the arena periphery. In experiment D, the subjects refused to cross the arena in darkness and instead returned home at the end of the guided outward journey in one-third of the trials. The animals' rate of refusal was related to the distance they had to walk across the arena to reach the goal cylinder. However, in all but one trial where the animals reached and explored a cylinder in search for food, they chose the cylinder at the correct goal location. Their success rate was therefore almost 100%.

These results suggest that our subjects planned their goal-directed itinerary through vector addition, irrespective of the sight of the landmark array. One explanation may be that the

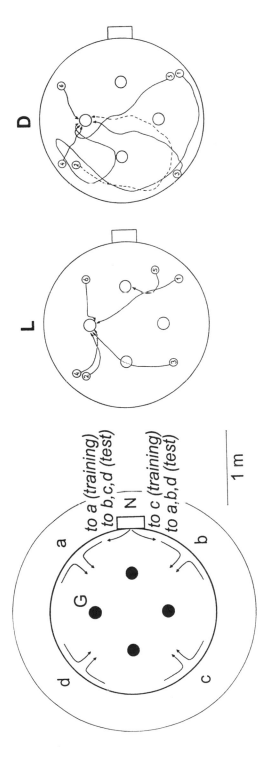

Fig. 3.4 Locating a feeding source through vector information and ambiguous landmarks. Left: experimental set-up. The arena (inner circle) was surrounded by a symmetrical optical enclosure (outer circle); around its centre, it contained a symmetrical landmark array consisting of four identical cylinders (black spots). Only the cylinder at location G contained a hidden food source. During training and control trials, the subject was led in darkness from the nest exit along the periphery to point a or c, from where it had to learn to proceed alone to the goal cylinder at G. In test trials, the subject was led from its nest along six new routes to point a, b, c or d; from the current peripheral endpoint, it had again to proceed alone to the presumed goal cylinder. Before each test trial, the four cylinders were exchanged against each other, the thick sawdust substrate on the arena floor was thoroughly stirred and flattened out again, and the arena walls were covered with a plastic sheet. Preliminary tests had shown that the animals could not smell out the food in the cylinder at the goal location. Right: the paths one subject followed from the periphery to the goal cylinder in each test trial. L, under light; D, in darkness (unpublished results).

animals compute the final path from the arena periphery to the goal location at the endpoint of the guided outward journey, by combining their own current position vector with the memorised goal-position vector. A second, simpler hypothesis (Collett pers. comm.) would be that the animals carry out a similar computation throughout their journey from the nest to the goal. This amounts to saying that once the animals have stored the nest to goal vector in long-term memory, they are able to reach the endpoint of this vector, i.e. the goal location, through any path at all, directly or along detours, by continuously subtracting the performed path from the fixed goal-position vector.

Figure 3.4b reproduces the itineraries from the periphery to the presumed goal cylinder for one subject which passed all trials in both experiments. In experiment L, the subject proceeds fairly directly to the presumed, visible goal cylinder and commits one error. In experiment D, the animal reaches the goal in all trials, four times directly and twice by following a convoluted path. Whatever the shape of its itinerary, the animal never seemed to be lost or to search for additional cues (as observed in former situations where the subject was disoriented through rotations and at the same time deprived of familiar landmarks).

Returning to our initial question, namely the co-operation between dead reckoning and visual landmarks, our results suggest the following interpretation. In experiment L, the sight of a beacon at the expected goal location may have confirmed the trajectory the animal had planned in advance through vector subtraction; at the same time, this process led to the identification of the goal landmark through its location. This allowed the subjects to proceed unhesitatingly to the presumed goal. In experiment D, the planned trajectory was not confirmed by any perceptual feedback information and therefore the animals were less confident walking through the arena, particularly when the anticipated distance to the goal was long. On the other hand, in experiment L the sight of four identical cylinders may have confused the subjects, as they chose a cylinder at the wrong location more often in light than in darkness. This was particularly the case after relatively long guided detours around the periphery, when vector information should be more affected by accumulated errors than after short preliminary detours.

These results open up further perspectives in the study of vector navigation by mammals, not only with respect to our current question on the co-operation between dead reckoning and landmark information, but also with regard to the extension of vector navigation through vector addition. In our actual experiments, hamsters seem able to operate on two vectors, their short-term current position vector and the long-term goal-position vector. Further experiments will show how many vectors hamsters and other mammals may store and combine with each other to navigate between several places in the most economic and adapted manner. Let us mention, however, that real vector navigation, which involves the combination of an indefinite number of vectors, has, as far as we know, only been realised by man-made technical systems.

Acknowledgements

This research is supported by the Swiss NSF grant 31–39311.93. The authors wish to thank A. Kfouri for critical remarks on the manuscript.

4 Spatial representations and homing pigeon navigation

Verner P. Bingman

For many years racing pigeon hobbyists from Toledo, Ohio would gather together for a summer weekend and send their birds to Houston, Texas for the big 1300 mile race. What would occur on that weekend in Toledo and Houston would be repeated in a similar fashion in many different places, at different times of year and attests to the remarkable navigational ability of the racing pigeon, *Columba livia*. The winning pigeon would return home in about 2 days, and even a middle of the pack bird would return in 3–4 days. It is this remarkable navigational ability that motivated European ethologists of the 1950s to ask the question: How do they do it? However, as simple a question as this is, it is remarkable how different scientific cultures have interpreted the same question in very different ways. For ethologists beginning in the 1950s, answering this question has focused on the nature of the environmental stimuli that permit a pigeon to locate its position in space and/or direction of displacement relative to home; in other words, the sensory basis of the pigeon's navigational map. In contrast, for the comparative cognitive psychologist who only recently has considered the homing ability of pigeons, the question would be interpreted more in terms of the structure of the spatial representation (e.g. a cognitive map) rather than its sensory basis. It is the intent of this chapter to explore these different perspectives and attempt to reveal how insights from one perspective can lead to better understanding of the other.

The homing pigeon navigational map

Sensory mechanisms

A homing pigeon differs from a racing pigeon by its superior ability to navigate home from a variety of different directions at a cost of being somewhat slower. The difference is probably more a consequence of training than selective breeding. In any event, it is the homing pigeon that has served as the primary research animal for studies on pigeon navigation. The experiments of the German ethologist Gustav Kramer and his colleagues (Kramer 1959) mark a watershed moment in the conceptual development of understanding the navigational mechanisms that allow homing pigeons to return home from distant, unfamiliar locations well beyond the range of their spatial experience. Kramer's principal empirical contribution was demonstrating that homing pigeons primarily rely on the sun to orient or determine directions in space (compass) while some other mechanism was responsible for allowing pigeons to determine their position in space relative to home (navigational map). Conceptually, after being displaced to some distant, unfamiliar release site, a homing pigeon would first determine its location relative to home by relying on its navigational map. For example, the navigational map would indicate that the pigeon was north of home. At this point in the navigational process, the pigeon would rely on the sun as a compass to determine south and fly towards home. Thus, navigation was modelled to be based on a two-step map and compass process.

In support of this two-step process was the finding that clock- or phase-shifting birds produced predictable deflections in their orientation after release. As a consequence of the earth's rotation, the azimuth position (compass direction with respect to the horizon) of the sun varies during the course of the day. Therefore, if a pigeon, or any animal, is to use the sun as a directional reference for orientation, e.g. find north, it must compensate for the sun's apparent movement by relying on some circadian timing mechanism. Hoffmann (1954) trained starlings (*Sturnus vulgaris*) to orient in a specific direction in an experimental arena. He found that changing the light–dark cycle of the captive birds, and thereby altering the endogenous circadian rhythm(s) normally entrained to the light–dark cycle, led to predictable changes in directional preferences. For example, by advancing the light–dark cycle by 6 h such that a bird's subjective day would begin at real midnight and end at real noon, a starling trained to use the sun compass to go north would actually go west. Why? A bird phase-shifted in this way and tested during real morning (subjective noon) would interpret the sun in the east to be in the south. Based on the bird's experience, at noon, the subjective time according to the bird's internal clock, north would be 180° away from the sun. Therefore the bird would go west, 180° away from the actual eastern azimuth of the sun.

Later, Schmidt-Koenig (1958, 1961) performed similar 6 h phase-shift manipulations on homing pigeons allowed to fly from locations distant from home, and he observed similar 90° deflections in orientation. These results indicated that the sun serves as an independent compass employed once a bird has determined the direction of displacement with respect to home. But in the case of the homing experiments, why was the sun not considered part of the navigational map? Primarily, there was nothing about interpreting the use of the sun as a possible map that would have predicted the observed 90° deflections following 6 h phase-shifts, and the training arena experiments already indicated that the sun could be used as a compass. Other experiments (e.g. Keeton 1970) showed that the sun's zenith elevation was not used to determine latitudinal displacement with respect to home. Together, these findings clearly showed that the sun is used exclusively as a compass and not used to determine position with respect to goal locations (map).

The role of the sun as compass is an established finding in the ethological analysis of spatial orientation. However, identifying the sensory basis of the navigational map has certainly been more of a challenge. Numerous environmental stimuli have been suggested as possible cues used in the operation of the navigational map. Surprisingly, what has emerged is the realisation that atmospheric odours are the primary, and possibly exclusive, environmental stimuli used by pigeons to determine their relative position with respect to home from distant, unfamiliar locations. (As described below, from familiar locations or from locations where familiar stimuli are in sensory contact, other, landmark-based information can be used in addition to atmospheric odours.) The first indication that some atmospheric quality may be critical for the navigational map was the finding that birds held in cages that blocked their exposure to winds invariably failed to learn a navigational map (Kramer 1959; Wallraff 1966). Subsequent experiments unequivocally identifying atmospheric odours as critical stimuli for proper functioning of the pigeon navigational map fall into three basic categories: (1) deprivation experiments in which birds are made either permanently or temporarily anosmic; (2) developmental studies in which young birds are given manipulated exposure to winds, thereby altering navigational map development; and (3) so-called false-release site experiments in which birds are given exposure to air from one location but actually released from another. A number of review articles summarise nicely the large number of research papers supporting the olfactory hypothesis, and the reader is referred to those for a more extensive discussion (Papi 1991; Wallraff 1991, 1996).

I would like to offer as an example one particularly elegant experiment identifying atmospheric odours as critical elements of the homing pigeon navigational map. Ioalé *et al.* (1990) held young pigeons in an outdoor aviary during their first summer. The aviary was artificially exposed to odours of benzaldehyde carried by fan-generated winds blowing from the north-northwest allowing the birds to learn a specific odour/direction association. At the end of the summer, the birds were exposed to benzaldehyde just prior to release from a number of distant, unfamiliar locations situated in a variety of directions with respect to the home loft. Regardless of where they were released, the birds primarily flew south. In contrast, a group of control birds raised in a similar aviary without exposure to benzaldehyde, but also exposed to benzaldehyde prior to release, oriented toward home. The straightforward interpretation of this result is that during the summer, the experimental birds associated north-northwest winds with the odour of benzaldehyde. When they were later taken to some distant location, exposed to benzaldehyde and released, the experimental pigeons determined their location as north-northwest of home (the origin of benzaldehyde–wind experience during the summer) and flew south even though south was an inappropriate direction.

As convincing as the evidence supporting the olfactory hypothesis is, several prominent researchers none the less continue to question the generality of atmospheric odours as cues for the navigational map (see Able 1996; Wiltschko 1996; Wallraff 1996 for an insightful discussion). For example, R. Wiltschko (1996), among others, has questioned the usefulness of olfactory deprivation experiments. Briefly, she argues that olfactory deprivation may result in some general information processing deficit that is non-specific to homing, and that it is this general deficit that explains the homing deficits following such manipulations. However, this criticism certainly does not apply to at least one kind of deprivation manipulation. Currently, the most popular olfactory deprivation technique involves intra-nasal injection of zinc sulphate ($ZnSO_4$; Benvenuti *et al.* 1992; Schlund 1992). Cheri Budzynski recently completed an experiment in which homing pigeons were trained on a spatial non-match-to-sample task in a T-maze. The task requires a pigeon to move down the stem of a T-shaped maze and then turn left or right at the top of the stem into one of the two arms of the T. The task is non-match-to-sample because within a trial a pigeon is first forced down one arm of the T (sample). After a brief delay, the pigeon is then given a free choice between the two arms and it must choose the other arm (non-match) to receive a food reward. The task challenges an animal's spatial working memory ability because it must remember which arm it went down during the sample phase if it is to choose the correct arm during the free choice phase of a trial. It is a challenging working memory task, and performance on this task is disrupted by brain lesions to the hippocampal formation (Reilly and Good 1987), lesions that also disrupt various aspects of homing pigeon navigation (Bingman et al. 1995). After being trained on the task, the birds were given intra-nasal injections of $ZnSO_4$ identical to those that disrupt homing and tested for their working memory ability on this task. Working memory performance was unimpaired following $ZnSO_4$ treatment, demonstrating that general information processing (in this case spatial working memory) is unaffected by this anosmic procedure. Also, it should be noted that even if one ignores the olfactory deprivation experiments, there are still a large number of experiments based on manipulating exposure to atmospheric odours (developmental and false-release site studies) that stand in support of the olfactory hypothesis.

A more important point is the possibility that atmospheric odours may not be the only environmental stimulus used in constructing a navigational map. Indeed, research in the field of avian orientation/navigation has consistently taught us that we should be open to any and all surprises. Support for some non-atmospheric odour contribution to the navigational map emerges from research indicating that birds from different locations (Wiltschko et al. 1987a; but see Benvenuti and Brown 1989) and those having different early experience (Wiltschko et al. 1987b; but see Benvenuti et al. 1990) do not always respond to olfactory manipulations in the same way. What alternative environmental stimulus might be used? Certainly the most discussed alternative would be information from the earth's magnetic field (see Walcott 1991 for a review; but see Papi 1995 for an interesting perspective on magnetic field effects). It should be emphasised here that it is well established the earth's magnetic field can serve as a compass, like the sun compass, for orientation (Wiltschko and Wiltschko 1988). However, the possible contribution of the earth's magnetic field to the navigational map would be independent of the earth's magnetic field as an orientation mechanism, and is considerably more speculative. Another environmental stimulus could be low frequency infrasounds (Kreithen and Quine 1979; Schöps and Wiltschko 1994). However, neither of these alternatives has convincing experimental support, and until experimental support warrants a change, it is probably best to operate under the assumption of Wallraff (1991) that homing from unfamiliar, distant locations is based primarily on the use of atmospheric odours.

Before ending this section, I would like to make the reader aware that in discussing the navigational map, I am specifically discussing how pigeons might use information gained at a release site to approximate their relative position with respect to home. It is clear that information at a distant release site is sufficient to permit navigation home (Wallraff 1980). Additionally, it is likely that pigeons can also use information en route to a release site, so-called outward journey information, to supplement information gathered at the release site to determine the direction home (Tögel and Wiltschko 1992; Benvenuti et al. 1994). However, although interesting, outward journey information will not be explored further.

Representational structure

Increasing interest in animal cognition among psychologists (O'Keefe and Nadel 1978; Gallistel 1990) has created an intellectual atmosphere that has or should persuade ethologists to consider the homing pigeon navigational map not only from a sensory perspective but also how environmental information is organised and used. As a departure point for discussing this issue, it might be useful to compare the features of the navigational map with so-called cognitive maps discussed in the psychological literature (O'Keefe and Nadel 1978; Gallistel 1990). What is a cognitive map? Both O'Keefe and Nadel and Gallistel view a cognitive map roughly in terms of a representation in which the spatial, possibly geometric, relationships among places is coded with respect to distance and direction. Empirically, the critical feature of a cognitive map is that it allows an organism to move freely among goal locations and permits the computation of novel routes to goal locations without any previous experience with those routes. It is the flexible nature of a cognitive map representation that distinguishes it from so-called route learning. Route learning is simply navigation between goal locations using a route that has been learned either by path integration (see below) over short distances or repeated association of stimuli along a specific route during movement between goal locations that potentially could operate over longer distances. Route learning is inflexible, permitting navigation only between specific goals that lie along a previously experienced route.

The first question is whether the pigeon navigational map can be considered a cognitive map? To answer this question, we need to know a how navigational map representation is structured. Two hypotheses have dominated discussion of this topic, and unfortunately, there is, as yet, little evidence that would help distinguish between the alternatives.

The gradient map

Wallraff (1974, 1991) proposed that the navigational map of homing pigeons is based on a spatial representation in which at least two stimulus gradients exist in the environment, with the two gradients changing in space along different directional axes. For example (Fig. 4.1a), one could hypothesise a gradient made up of some atmospheric quality that increased in strength to the northwest of the loft and decreased to the southeast of the loft. Additionally, some magnetic field parameter, such as intensity would increase to the northeast of the loft and decrease to the southwest (the gradients need not be orthogonal). A displaced pigeon at an unfamiliar location would assess the relevant atmospheric quality and magnetic field intensity. The pigeon could then compute its northwest/southeast displacement with respect to home based on the difference in intensity of the atmospheric quality between the home loft and its current position, and northeast/southwest displacement based on the difference in magnetic field intensity between the home loft and its current position. With this information, the pigeon could compute a homeward vector, the directional component of which would be identified with the sun compass. It needs to be emphasised that if the navigational map is represented as a gradient map, the gradient is not followed to return home. The gradient is used only to determine relative position to the home loft. The sun compass would be used to actually take up an approximate homeward bearing as demonstrated by deviations in the directions taken by birds following phase-shift manipulations.

What is attractive about the gradient hypothesis is that it reduces the navigational map to a relatively simple computational process (if the inputs can be accurately assessed!), it explains why birds can orient homeward from places they have never been before, it explains why the

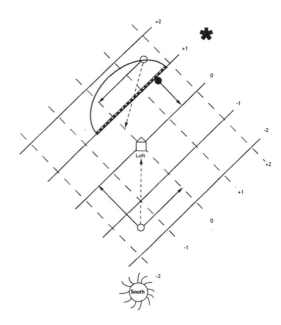

A. Gradient Map

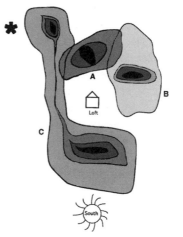

B. Mosaic Map (atmospheric odours)

range of the map has been suggested to be almost 1000 km (Wallraff 1981; Ioalé *et al.* 1983), and it explains why from very large distances reversals in orientation can be observed (gradient reversals, Wallraff 1993). Would such a gradient map be an example of a cognitive map? It would meet the empirical criterion of allowing a bird to determine a goal-oriented response (homeward orientation) from places it has never been before. However, the map structure would be based on a coordinate system relying on intersecting stimulus gradients; a type of mapping system that is generally not discussed by researchers interested in cognitive maps. The structure of this kind of gradient map would certainly be different from the kind of map a rat generates in a room to navigate to an escape platform in a water maze (Morris *et al.* 1982). Can both be called cognitive maps? If not, what are the consequences of different map structures on neural aspects of the map?

The olfactory mosaic map

Papi *et al.* (1972; Wallraff 1991) proposed that the homing pigeon navigational map relied on the heterogeneous distribution of atmospheric odours or a mosaic patchwork of irregularly changing odours (Fig. 4.1b). Through a relatively simple associative mechanism, pigeons would associate different atmospheric qualities with different directions from the loft, thereby learning the directional distribution of odours around the loft, i.e. an olfactory map. Learning could occur at the loft by relying on wind-borne odours (which could explain why pigeons standing on a roof will invariably face into the wind) and/or by spontaneously flying in the area of the loft. When displaced to a distant, unfamiliar location, a pigeon would sample the atmospheric quality of the location, and based on its acquired mosaic map that represents the directional distribution of odours with respect to the loft, it could determine its direction of displacement and then determine the direction home by use of the sun compass. As a quick example, at the loft a pigeon associates winds from the north with odour quality A (Fig. 4.1b). After displacement, the pigeon finds itself at a location where the intensity of quality A is very strong. By strong I do not want to imply that a pigeon would make the type

Fig. 4.1 Possible navigational map representational structures. (a) A hypothetical gradient map. Two environmental gradients are shown: one increasing in intensity to the northwest, the other to the northeast. When taken to a location to the south of the loft (open circle), a pigeon would measure the difference in stimulus intensity between that at the loft and its current location. Based on this difference, a pigeon could compute a northwest-southeast displacement vector and a northeast-southwest displacement vector (solid arrows) and then sum the vectors to compute the path home (dashed arrow). Of particular interest is when non-linearities occur in an environmental gradient. Looking near the thick asterisk, note that +1 values of the northwest-southeast gradient bow out to the northwest. However, the map representation of the pigeon retains the linear properties that generally characterise the gradient (thick alternating black and white triangles). When a pigeon is released from the open circle to the north, it would actually interpret its displacement as if it was at the dark circle because its representation would not take into account the physical irregularity. As such, the computed homeward vector (dashed arrow) would be somewhat away from home because of the difference between the actual and represented northwest displacement offering an explanation for why pigeons don't always fly directly toward home. (b) A hypothetical mosaic map based on atmospheric odours. Three atmospheric qualities, A, B and C, are distributed around the loft with intensity varying from high (darker areas) to low (lighter areas). A pigeon east of home would experience relatively high 'B' intensity and know it was east of home. However, such a map can be highly irregular, leading to errors. For example, 'C' is strong to the south and the spatial representation of 'C' would be dominated by this southern high intensity zone. Based on this representation, exposure to high intensity 'C' would lead to a northerly orientation. However, near the thick asterisk to the northwest, there is a pocket of high intensity 'C' that might not be captured in the representation because of its size, distance from the main 'C' zone and closeness to 'A'. Therefore, a pigeon released from there might also orient to the north and not be homeward oriented.

of quantitative assessment that would occur if the map was structured like a gradient map. For the mosaic map, a pigeon would only need to determine qualitative, coarse measures of intensity. In any event, knowing that odour A occurs at the loft with northerly winds, the pigeon would determine that it is roughly north of home and use the sun to fly south.

What is attractive about the mosaic hypothesis is that it can explain why birds held in an outdoor aviary and are never allowed to fly can still learn a navigational map if they are exposed to wind-borne atmospheric odours (Wallraff 1966). It is hard to imagine a gradient map being learned without any flight at least a few kilometres from the loft. However, it is also hard to imagine that a mosaic map could be used from as far as 500–1000 km from the loft. Interestingly, it has been recently reported that the range of the navigational map is only about 100 km, with good homeward orientation beyond 100 km being based on information picked up *en route* to a release site (Benvenuti *et al.* 1994). If true, a 100 km range map could certainly be represented as a mosaic map.

Could a mosaic map be considered a cognitive map? The answer would seem to be no. Although birds successfully identify the direction home from distant sites where the birds have never been before, if the odours are familiar, which they must be based on the principles of the mosaic map, can a bird really be said to be at an unfamiliar location? Now if a small set of odour/direction associations is acquired at the loft, and those associations can be combined in novel ways from intermediate areas between 'olfactory patches', then maybe a cognitive map designation can be saved. However, because such a mosaic map can be learned at the loft without flight experience, it is almost certain that although the birds could use such a map to determine the direction of displacement from the loft, distance from the loft would probably be difficult to determine. The mosaic map would allow a pigeon to approximate the direction home, and a bird would know when to stop, or start looking for the loft, only when encountering familiar landmarks. Because distance between locations is a critical feature of a cognitive map, the suspected lack of distance information in a mosaic map would seem to disqualify it as a cognitive map. However, it should be kept in mind that if a mosaic map exists, its properties remain a mystery and it is premature to apply any permanent labels.

The navigational map: some final comments

It needs to be emphasised that it is unknown whether homing pigeons acquire either a gradient-like map, a mosaic-like map or something entirely different. Experiments like those of Ioalé *et al.* (1990) certainly suggest that a mosaic-like map can be learned under restricted experimental conditions, but whether pigeons allowed to fly freely acquire a similar map has yet to be determined.

Homing pigeons rarely fly off exactly in the direction of home, and although many factors may influence the direction taken by a bird (e.g. Kiepenheuer *et al.* 1993), one factor that certainly contributes to errors in initial orientation is a navigational map that is a less than perfect representational reconstruction of the environment. A gradient-like map may rely on environmental gradients that are not necessarily linear in space and therefore errors in determining the homeward direction should be common when non-linearities occur (Fig. 4.1a). Certainly the boundaries among atmospheric qualities that would determine a mosaic-like map would not be expected to be very sharp and such a map would probably permit only a rough approximation of the direction of displacement with respect to home (Fig. 4.1b; Wallraff 1989).

Finally, one last comment on the navigational map as a possible example of a cognitive map. Cognitive maps are thought to be independent of any particular environmental feature: there is no fixed origin from which space extends and features are found within a neutral spatial framework. If the navigational map of homing pigeons is a cognitive map, then the home loft is simply one of many objects found within the boundaries of the map. With respect to the map, the loft is no more important than anything else (although it is certainly very important to other neurobehavioural systems of pigeons, such as those that regulate emotions and reproductive behaviour). However, research on homing only examines whether a pigeon returns to the home loft and nowhere else. Indeed, the navigational map can be conceptualised as home loft centric, with the loft at the origin and space extending out from the loft to form a possible coordinate system. If true, it would be difficult to argue that a loft-centric navigational map would be an example of a cognitive map. Therefore, an interesting question to answer would be whether the navigational map can be used to navigate to more than one goal location. I am familiar with one relevant experiment. H.-P. Lipp at the University of Zurich (Lipp 1992) trained homing pigeons housed in one loft to fly to a feeding loft. In other words, his birds could navigate to their home loft where they essentially lived, and a separate feeding loft where they ate. He then released pigeons from locations more or less equidistant from the two lofts. Food-deprived, hungry birds flew to the feeding loft while non-deprived pigeons flew to the home loft. It is tempting to speculate that the pigeons used the same navigational map to navigate to both locations indicating that the navigational map is not necessarily loft centric and therefore perhaps more like a cognitive map. Alternatively, it may be that the pigeons learned two independent navigational maps; one home loft centric, the other food loft centric with the map representation being activated dependent on the motivational state of a pigeon.

Non-route-based familiar landmark navigation

Sensory basis

Pigeons taken to a distant location where they have never been before must use their navigational map to determine the direction home. However, it has been well established that when birds are released from a familiar location, a location where they are in sensory contact with familiar environmental stimuli, they can rely on those familiar stimuli to determine the direction home (see Wallraff 1991; Wallraff et al. 1993). I prefer to call this navigational mechanism familiar landmark navigation, but most researchers use the term pilotage. Before continuing, the distinction between route-based and non-route-based familiar landmark navigation needs to be made. An example of route-based familiar landmark navigation is that of Bingman and Ioalé (1989). Homing pigeons used as part of a larger experiment were released about five times from the same location. Subsequent to this training, the birds were rendered anosmic and released again from the same training location. Anosmic pigeons that had never been to this location before would not orient toward home because of an impaired navigational map. However, the experimental pigeons that had been trained there previously oriented home! The successful homeward orientation of the trained pigeons that experienced the release location previously is readily explained by assuming that during training they associated features (landmarks) at the release site with the homeward direction determined by their navigational map, which was functional during training. When they were returned to the training location anosmic, they simply relied on the previously acquired association between non-olfactory features of the release site and the direction flown during training. I refer to this type of familiar landmark navigation as route-based because the learned association is specific to a previously experienced route where a repeated flight path would be used. It would be considered an example of taxon navigation as described by O'Keefe and Nadel (1978) and clearly would not be an example of a cognitive map.

Route-based familiar landmark navigation, however, does not mean that pigeons are simply following a chain of familiar landmarks home. Data from Bingman and Ioalé (1989) suggested that from a familiar training site anosmic homing pigeons relied on both local landmarks and the sun to guide their flight home. In other words, they behaved in a manner consistent with the possibility that they might be able to follow a series of landmarks home. However, in a similar study, Luschi and Dall'Antonio (1993) found normal shifts in orientation following a clock-shift manipulation when anosmic homing pigeons were released from a familiar training site. Their findings, in contrast, suggest that when anosmic homing pigeons are released from a familiar training site, when route-based familiar landmark navigation would occur, landmarks only allow the recall of the direction home, to be identified by the sun compass, and do not participate in directly guiding the birds home. The somewhat contradictory results from these two studies leaves open the question of whether familiar landmarks perceived from a familiar training site can be used to help guide birds home or simply allow the recall of a compass direction.

Of more interest for the present discussion, however, is what I refer to as non-route-based familiar landmark navigation. In this case, familiar landmarks would be used, but they would be used even from places a pigeon has never been before. A hypothetical example could be a bird returning home. At a certain point during the flight home, a pigeon would begin to perceive familiar landmarks (for example landscape features). Using spatial information extracted from the familiar landmarks, the pigeon could direct a course home, and it could do so even if it was perceiving the familiar landmarks from a location where it has never been before. Possible documented examples of this flexible use of familiar landmarks to generate novel routes toward home can be found in Lednor and Walcott (1988), Bingman et al. (1989), Grüter and Wiltschko (1990) and Wallraff et al. (1993). Even with this kind of non-route-based familiar landmark navigation, it is unclear if landmarks would only allow a pigeon to approximate its position relative to home with actual orientation being guided by the sun (or magnetic) compass, or whether and to what extent the landmarks themselves could directly guide the flight orientation of the birds. However, because of the prominent part compass mechanisms play in spatial behaviour, it seems reasonable to assume that familiar landmarks are used together with the sun compass in a map and compass fashion.

Because only non-route-based familiar landmark navigation can be considered a possible example of a cognitive map, the following discussion will explore it exclusively. The intuitive answer to the question of the sensory basis of familiar landmark navigation is that familiar landmarks are visual. But does the empirical evidence support such an obvious assumption? The answer is probably yes. Downhower and Windsor (1971) working with bank swallows (*Riparia riparia*) provided good evidence that these birds use the visual topography of the finger lakes area of New York to navigate to their nesting colonies. Working with homing pigeons, Schmidt-Koenig and Walcott (1978) released birds wearing frosted lenses from distant, unfamiliar locations. Although the pigeons could still locate the disk of the sun as shown by their use of the sun compass (Schmidt-Koenig and Keeton 1977), the frosted lenses precluded form vision and therefore the use of familiar visual landmarks. Perhaps surprisingly, the pigeons oriented home like controls demonstrating that their non-visual navigational map and sun compass operated close to normal. However, few of the birds returned home, with most birds returning close to the loft but unable to localise it. These data are probably the most compelling data suggesting that as a bird approaches its loft and begins to rely on familiar landmarks for navigation, and that the familiar landmarks are at least in part visual. Streng and Wallraff (1992) also relied on frosted lenses to explore more fully the importance of visual familiar landmarks for navigation, and their results also support the use of visual navigational cues.

Using another approach, Braithwaite and Guilford (1991) and Braithwaite and Newman (1994) performed experiments in which pigeons were released from a chamber that either permitted or did not permit viewing familiar landscape features. They observed that viewing familiar landscape features significantly improved the time taken to return home by the pigeons, suggesting that the birds recognised and used visual information from the familiar landscape features to help navigate home. However, positive results were found only from locations where pigeons had previously been released and not from locations where the pigeons had never been before but where familiar landscape features were likely visible (Braithwaite 1993). Although not conclusive (see Braithwaite 1993), the data suggest that the type of visual landmark use examined in these studies may be specific to route-based familiar landmark navigation and not generalised to non-route-based familiar landmark navigation.

The existing experimental evidence supports the intuitively appealing proposition that homing pigeons use familiar, visual landmarks to navigate home. However, progress in this area is limited by the fact that one can only realistically manipulate the visual ability of a bird and not the visual environment other than by limited deprivation. As is the case for research into the sensory basis of the navigational map, the most compelling evidence supporting the use of some environmental stimulus for navigation is to manipulate that stimulus in a way that predicts a specific change in orientation rather than impaired orientation (e.g. the Ioalé *et al.* 1990 olfactory experiment described earlier). The practical impossibility of manipulating environmental landscape features will make progress in this area difficult. However, some insight could be gained by studying landmarks under semi-natural laboratory conditions. For example, Rosemary Strasser has been examining how homing pigeons may use stimuli in a room, 'landmarks', to locate hidden food. Probably the most important result that has come out of her work so far is that when using room landmarks to build a representation of space, homing pigeons seem to combine multiple stimuli into a single representation in preference to learning separate associations between each of the room stimuli and the goal.

Of course there is no reason to assume familiar landmarks must be visual. Indeed, Benvenuti and Fiaschi (1983) have shown that anosmic pigeons forced to rely on familiar landmarks to orient homeward could do so even when wearing frosted lenses that precluded form vision. This result certainly suggests that familiar landmark information can be something other than visual. However, the pigeons in this study were released from a repeated training site and therefore were engaging in route-based familiar landmark navigation. Whether familiar landmarks other than visual ones can be used for non-route-based familiar landmark navigation remains uncertain.

Representational structure

How are familiar landmarks organised representationally to permit goal directed responses from locations a pigeon has never been before? The answer to this question is unknown. Notable is that in contrast to the navigational map, flying in the area of the loft is likely to be important for learning the use of familiar landmarks (Wallraff 1966), although perhaps not necessary (Bingman *et al.* 1990). The likely importance of flight is interesting because familiar landmarks would be perceived from different perspectives, and the different perspectives might facilitate the encoding of distance information among the landmarks. It is also at least worth speculating that non-route-based familiar landmark navigation probably shares more features with the cognitive maps of rats in a laboratory setting than any other aspect of homing pigeon navigation: they both are based on visual cues, they both operate within a restricted spatial domain and the hippocampal formation of the brain seems to play a similar part (see below).

Because of the difficulty in trying to understand the representational properties of non-route-based familiar landmark navigation, Michael A. Jones carried out a neural network analysis to generate some working hypotheses on how familiar landmarks may be learned and used (Jones and Bingman 1996). Briefly, the learning success of the various networks examined was based on how well the network used angular position to a number of landmarks to identify the direction of home from places the network (pigeon) had never been before; a non-route-based test of learning! Two interesting results emerged from the network analysis. First, the distribution of landmarks in space correlated with how well a network learned. If two landmarks were used, learning was better if they were located in different spatial hemispheres, i.e. opposite sides of the loft (polarised), than if they were located in the same hemisphere, i.e. on the same side of the loft (non-polarised). Second, learning was better if four landmarks were used in the network compared with a network that used six landmarks. If these results generalise to real pigeons in the real world, the network analysis suggests that how landmarks are distributed could influence how precise a familiar landmark representation can be. Perhaps more important, pigeons may use only a subset of the available landmark information in constructing a familiar landmark representation because too much information interferes with accurate use. One thing that is attractive about the network analysis is that it is testable under controlled laboratory conditions. One could train pigeons to locate a goal in a room based on landmarks with the expectation that landmark distribution would influence performance and that in an experiment where many landmarks would be available, only a subset would be used (see Cheng and Spetch, Chapter 1). However, the possibility that birds would use only a subset of the available landmarks creates a potential problem for field studies where one might hope to manipulate one or two landmarks or landscape features but not know if the landmarks were part of the familiar landmark representation used for navigation.

The avian hippocampal formation: insights into the representational structure of homing pigeon navigation

It should be clear from the previous discussion that considerable progress has been made understanding the sensory basis of the homing pigeon navigational map and, to a lesser extent, familiar landmark navigation. How that sensory information is represented, however, remains pretty much a mystery. Research examining the role of hippocampal formation in homing pigeon navigation can be used to suggest some similarities and differences between the navigational map and familiar landmark navigation. A summary of the critical role of the amniote hippocampal formation in spatial cognition can be found in Bingman *et al.* (1995; see Sherry and Healy, Chapter 8). What will be highlighted here is how research on the hippocampal formation can foster insight into representational structure.

The hippocampal formation and navigational learning

If a 4–6-week old pigeon is given a lesion of the hippocampal formation, it will show a striking deficit in learning to navigate by familiar landmarks (Bingman *et al.* 1994, 1995) and learning an olfactory navigational map (Bingman *et al.* 1990). This is an interesting finding because despite the obvious sensory and likely representational differences between these two mechanisms, they seem to share a common hippocampal-mediated learning mechanism. What might that learning mechanism be? An experiment carried out by Bingman and Jones (1994) revealed the striking result that homing pigeons could not use the sun compass to learn the location of a goal in an experimental arena. They still could use the sun compass for orientation during homing (Bingman *et al.* 1996), but they could not use it for spatial learning. Although speculative, Bingman and Jones argued that when a young bird learns the spatial distribution of atmospheric odours while learning a navigational map or the spatial distribution of landmarks while learning to navigate by familiar landmarks, they use the sun compass to establish a directional reference or framework to learn the spatial location of the relevant stimuli (Fig. 4.2). Specifically, they argued that: (1) the sun compass is not only used for orientation during homing, but also in the learning of navigational mechanisms; (2) for navigational learning , the sun compass basically establishes a spatial reference framework in which the location of environmental stimuli are located or represented; and (3) the importance of the hippocampal formation for navigational learning is specifically related to its participation in this process of sun-compass-mediated navigational learning.

From a representational perspective, the most important consequence of this model is that during learning, the spatial distribution of atmospheric odours and familiar landmarks would be coded within the same representational framework established by the sun compass, even though they are generally based on different sensory modalities and contribute to distinct navigational mechanisms that are not equally dependent of the hippocampal formation.

Based on this model, the hippocampal formation is viewed as setting up a directional framework that permits map learning. Is there anything special about the relationship

Hippocampus

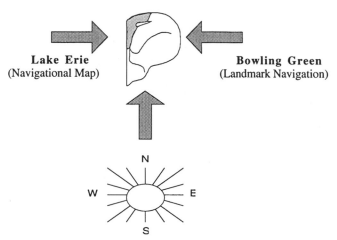

Lake Erie
(Navigational Map)

Bowling Green
(Landmark Navigation)

Learning a Navigational Map

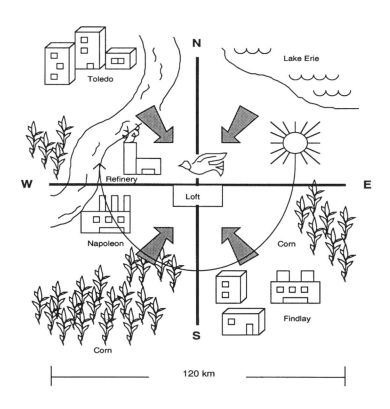

Learning Landmark Navigation

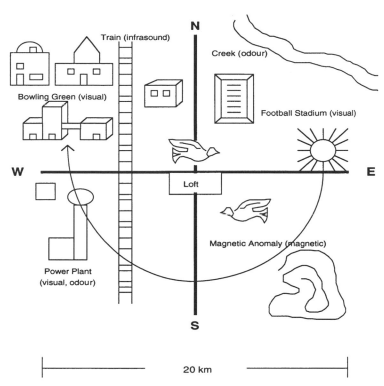

Fig. 4.2 Learning a navigational map and familiar landmark navigation. The figure attempts to capture what might be the critical common feature shared by navigational map and familiar landmark navigational learning. In both cases, environmental stimuli are represented within a directional framework established by the sun compass. The hippocampal formation of the brain is critical in allowing information from the directional reference to be integrated with features of the available environmental stimuli, to allow for the acquisition of the two types of navigational mechanisms.

between the sun compass and hippocampal formation? Probably not. McNaughton *et al.* (1996) have suggested that when rats learn a cognitive map of their environment, they rely on a spatial reference established by path integration. In other words, a rat's ability to return to a starting point relying on information it remembers during an outward journey, i.e. path integration (see Etienne *et al.*, Chapter 3), a relatively simple spatial navigation system, is also hypothesised to be the basis for more complex map learning. Further, just as the hippocampal formation is hypothesised to be important for sun-compass-based navigational learning in homing pigeons, McNaughton *et al.* suggest that the hippocampal formation is equally critical for path integration-based cognitive map learning in rats. From relatively simple spatial mechanisms, sun compass orientation and path integration, emerge more complex navigational mechanisms through mediation of the hippocampal formation.

It is also worth noting that even within a species more than one reference may be used to guide map-like learning. Although the sun compass is the primary directional reference used by birds for orientation, and presumably navigational learning, recall that they can also rely on the earth's magnetic field. Indeed, birds prevented from seeing the sun can learn a navigational map (Wiltschko *et al.* 1987c). If the model for navigational learning described above is correct, one might expect that homing pigeons can also use the earth's magnetic field to establish a directional framework for navigational learning and the hippocampal formation would be important for magnetic-field-based learning as well.

The hippocampal formation and the operation of navigational mechanisms

Although the hippocampal formation is critical for the learning of an olfactory navigational map and for non-route-based familiar landmark navigation, its role in these mechanisms varies once learning has taken place. The hippocampal formation continues to be important for the operation of landmark navigation (Bingman *et al.* 1984, 1988, 1995). Experienced homing pigeons given hippocampal lesions continue to navigate poorly close to the loft where non-route-based familiar landmark navigation would be used. However, the hippocampal formation does not play any necessary role in the operation of the navigational map (Bingman *et al.* 1984, 1988). Experienced homing pigeons given hippocampal lesions orient homeward from distant, unfamiliar release sites, where the navigational map would be used, in a manner indistinguishable from intact animals.

What might be the origin of this difference? Clearly, the navigational map engram can be accessed without a hippocampal formation (Bingman *et al.* 1995). However, saying that whatever spatial engram is used to navigate by familiar landmarks cannot be accessed without a hippocampal formation does not say a lot. Although purely speculative, I would like to suggest that for the navigational map, the sun compass is used during learning as a spatial reference, but when learning is complete, perhaps after a limited developmental time period, the navigational map based on olfactory cues no longer requires any input from the spatial reference exploited for learning. During homing, the sun compass operates as an independent compass for orientation only, and only after the direction of displacement with respect to home is determined by the independent navigational map. Non-route-based familiar landmark navigation may differ. The sun compass, or magnetic compass, may be also necessary to interpret the distribution of familiar landmarks to establish the direction home once navigation by familiar landmarks has been learned. In other words, the sun compass is used for learning but also for reading the distribution of familiar landmarks. As such, the essential difference between the navigational map and non-route-based familiar landmark navigation is that, once learned, the information from the navigational map is accessible without using the sun compass as a directional reference, whereas navigation by familiar landmarks continues to use the sun compass as a directional reference to interpret the distribution of familiar landmarks. If we assume the hippocampal formation is critical whenever a directional reference is used to learn and/or some map-like spatial representation is to be used, then we have a working hypothesis as to why hippocampal lesions impair the operation of familiar landmark navigation but not navigational map operation. With respect to representational structure, a navigational map may simply be a number of odour/direction associations that requires a hippocampal formation for the initial associations. Navigation by familiar landmarks, in contrast, may be viewed as more dynamic, with a sun compass directional reference used for continued learning and interpretation of landmark distribution with respect to goal locations, which necessitates continued participation of the hippocampal formation.

Conclusions

I have tried to convey to the reader a feel for the considerable complexity associated with a navigational system that manifests itself in a stimulus-rich environment and an animal species capable of using most of the available information to navigate home and perhaps to other goal locations. I am sure the reader is surprised about how much we still need to learn about spatial representations in homing pigeons; however, it is the challenge and interest of this problem that makes the exploration so enjoyable.

5   Spatial memory, landmark use and orientation in fish

Victoria A. Braithwaite

Introduction and background

Fish are a large and very successful taxonomic group. There are over 22 000 living species of teleosts (Pitcher 1993) and the cartilaginous fish, such as sharks and rays, swell the numbers even more. Being such a large group, fish are found in a wide range of aquatic habitats. For example, some fish live in, and swim around, highly, colourful and visually rich coral reefs while others explore and live in underwater caves, or at extreme depths where little, or no, light penetrates. This diverse array of habitats has led to fish facing many different types of spatial problems.

Spatial orientation and memory are fundamental for all fish, from those that remain on a very restricted area of a reef, or coast, to long-distance migrants. An ability to track current location relative to the position of important features in the environment, such as shelter, will increase a fish's chances of escaping from predators. Generally, efficient movement is aided by a map and an animal that knows the location of different resources with respect to one another can construct a map for a familiar area. Although somewhat scant, there is evidence that fish can form and use simple maps (Reese 1989; Teyke 1989; Rodriguez et al. 1994). Many animals, including fish, can also use compass information from a variety of sources (e.g. the sun or the magnetic field) to provide a reference for unidirectional movement, and there is little doubt that some of the long-distance journeys made by fish rely on compass information (Carey and Scharold 1990). Furthermore, fish orientation mechanisms have the added complexity of the three dimensionality of the aquatic environment. As well as moving from site A to site B along a substrate, fish may also make vertical movements within the water column which in some instances, such as daily vertical migrations, may consist of hundreds of metres (Clarke and Wagner 1976).

There is plenty of evidence that fish have the capacity for general learning and memory (Kieffer and Colgan 1992), and the many documented fish migrations, such as salmon (*Onchryhnchus*, Quinn 1984), plaice (*Pleuronecles platessa*, Arnold and Metcalfe 1989) and various reef fish (e.g. surgeon fish, *Acanthuridae*, Myrberg et al. 1988) suggest that fish also have the capacity for spatial learning and memory. Migratory movements are perhaps the most striking example of fish requiring and using spatial memory. There are, however, many simpler situations where fish rely on spatial memory; for example, learning and remembering the relative profitabilities of different food patches, or remembering the location of an attractive mate.

Compared with most other vertebrates the orientation strategies and mechanisms employed by fish are poorly understood. Making direct observations on fish behaviour is comparatively more difficult than for birds and mammals. One way around this problem is to transfer the fish into laboratory tanks or artificial streams and reefs with specially built glass observation walls. Controlled laboratory observations have been extremely useful for revealing just what spatial feats fish are capable of, and which senses fish use to help them orientate and navigate. Laboratory work, however, can never fully replace studies of fish in the natural, but difficult to sample, real world. Fortunately, recent improvements in telemetry have begun to make tracking fish in the wild considerably easier and are beginning to allow us to determine far more accurately how fish move in their natural aquatic systems when left undisturbed.

This chapter reviews fish spatial and orientation behaviour. I have divided the chapter into four different sections that consider distinct aspects of spatial behaviour. The first examines spatial memory and the importance of memory for recognition of home sites and good foraging locations. In the second section the role of landmarks is addressed, how these are used by fish to label resources and the sorts of landmark fish use. The third section surveys the types of compass cues fish appear to use and finally in the last section I present a brief overview of fish homing and migration. There are a few excellent reviews that deal in depth with salmonid migrations so it is not my intention to cover much of that material here (Dodson 1988; Quinn 1992; Dittman and Quinn 1996). Instead, I wish to draw attention to studies involving less familiar fish species to emphasise just how diverse fish are and how much we still have to discover about their orientation behaviour.

Do fish have spatial memory?

Many species of fish live within home ranges or territories. For these fish spatial memory could provide them the means of remembering the distribution of profitable feeding sites or crevices and spaces that provide shelter from potential predators. Furthermore, spatial memory could be used to develop systematic search strategies allowing fish to forage efficiently on patchily distributed food patches so that recently depleted areas are not returned to before food has been replenished. The following examples are chosen to illustrate the wide range of situations in which a fish may require spatial memory.

Maze learning

Spatial memory has classically been studied by testing animals such as rats and pigeons in maze tasks (e.g. Suzuki *et al.* 1980; Chappell and Guilford 1995). Maze-type tasks are versatile in that they can be used to ask very precise questions about what information is attended to and learned. For example, does the animal learn to use landmarks within the maze, or those around the room housing the maze? Alternatively, does the animal use an algorithm (a list of instructions such as 'keep turning left') to solve the problem? Mazes have been used to test fish spatial memory; Roitblat *et al.* (1982) tested Siamese fighting fish (*Betta splendens*) in an eight-arm radial maze. The fish were trained to swim down the different arms to search for food. In this experiment, the optimal strategy was simply to visit each arm once without repetition. After training the fish visited about seven of the eight different arms, and showed a strong tendency to choose sequences of adjacent arms. Thus, as a fish came out of an arm it usually turned in a consistent direction, either clockwise or anti-clockwise, to swim down the next. Roitblat and his colleagues developed simple statistical models to determine whether such a high performance could be produced if an algorithm was used on its own or whether the fish appeared to use a combination of an algorithm and memory. The results from the models suggested that the fish could not be relying on an algorithm alone and that they must have used additional knowledge about which arms had been depleted.

In a more recent investigation Girvan and Braithwaite (1997) have examined maze learning in three spined sticklebacks (*Gasterosteus aculeatus*) taken from two different populations, one from a river, the other from a pond. Fish from both populations were trained to solve a simple maze under one of two situations (see Fig. 5.1). In the first, small plants were placed next to the open door at each decision point, in the second, there were no added cues. Thus some fish were able to solve the maze by learning an association with a plant landmark and an open door, while the remaining fish had to learn a form of algorithm based on the sequence of open doors (e.g. left door, right door, left door). Interestingly, fish from the pond population learned to solve the maze faster when the plant landmarks were available than when there were no added cues. The sticklebacks from the river population, however, were equally fast at solving the maze with or without the plants. This suggests that fish from the different populations were remembering different types of information to solve the maze. The pond fish preferred to use the learned association between the plant landmarks and open doors, while the river fish appeared to perform equally well using a simple algorithm. Current work is addressing whether this observed difference is due to genetic differences between the two populations, or to the effects of development in the different types of habitat.

Learning the spatial distribution of feeding sites

There is some evidence that fish can remember the location of profitable food patches in non-maze tasks. Three spined sticklebacks can remember for at least 6 days which of two potential patches were baited during training (Milinkski 1994). On test days, where both food patches were equally profitable, the fish showed clear preferences for the patch they had previously fed at. Similarly, juvenile Atlantic salmon, *Salmo salar* (Gotceitas and Godin 1992) tested in an artificial stream with two food inlets were able to learn and remember the positions of these different feeding sites. During trials only one food inlet at a time was operated but if the food input point was switched part way through a trial the fish were able to move to the alternative site to continue feeding. This experimental design may resemble the natural situation, where salmon parr often have more than one feeding station within their home range and will move between these different feeding stations during the day (Stradmeyer and Thorpe 1987).

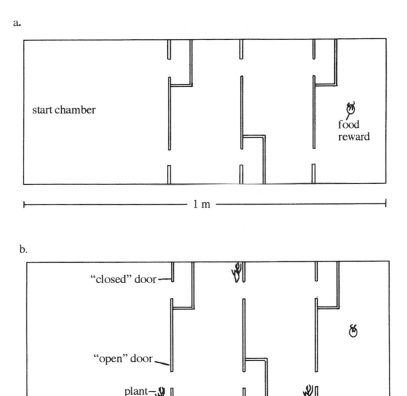

Fig. 5.1 Two maze conditions used to test maze learning in three spined sticklebacks. (a) First condition, no added cues. (b) Second condition, small plastic plants were positioned next to the 'open' doors. Dividing walls (22 × 30 cm) were made of white water-proofed card. Each divider had two doors (2 × 3 cm), only one of these was 'open' and led through to the next section. The 'closed' door led into a small blocked off chamber. Fish had to swim through the door to see if it was 'open' or 'closed'. On completing the maze the fish were rewarded with two bloodworms in a small dish in the last section.

Search strategies

Noda *et al.* (1994) found that the planktivorous reef fish, stout-body chromis (*Chromis chrysurus*) also use spatial memory to aid their foraging. These fish use a local search strategy combining spatial memory and temporal knowledge about water currents to predict locations of their zooplankton food source. The observed population exhibit local search strategies at three foraging areas. Having selected a specific foraging region, individuals swim in a circuitous pattern over the coral and boulders hunting for food. The fish always completed their search pattern before moving off to the next food patch. This organised movement over the food patch meant that a depleted area was not revisited. Such search strategies are also useful for exploring and mapping unfamiliar areas. As the animal moves in a particular pattern it can learn about the topography of the area it is exploring. A suggestion that fish may be capable of using such exploratory search strategies comes from work on goldfish (*Carassius auratus*). When placed in a large unfamiliar tank the fish systematically explore one area before moving on to the next (Kleerekoper *et al.* 1974).

Systematic searching behaviour has also been studied in the blind Mexican cave fish (*Anoptichthys jordani*). As their name suggests, these fish cannot use vision to learn the spatial features of their environment. Instead they have developed a technique that uses their lateral line system. When placed in an unfamiliar tank, or when a novel object is placed in a previously familiar environment, the fish exhibit distinct exploratory swimming behaviour; their swim speed increases and they concentrate their activity around the edges of the tank, or the newly inserted object. Once they have explored the environment their swim speed decreases again. The increased swim velocity optimises the lateral line organ stimulation, which is then used to detect obstacles, walls or objects close to the fish. In a series of experiments with blind cave fish Teyke (1989) revealed that these fish can learn and remember the spatial layout of an area they have been allowed to explore. Groups of fish were allowed to spend approximately 30 h in a test tank before being returned to holding tanks. Teyke then re-introduced different fish into the test tank after delays of 1, 2, 3 or 14 days. The fish returned to the test tank within 2 days of their initial experience showed greatly reduced exploratory behaviour, but those returned after a delay of 3 days or more explored the tank as much as they had when they were first exposed to it. Thus the blind cave fish appear to remember the spatial details of the test tank for about 2 days.

Learning positions of shelter or escape routes

For many species of fish, access to shelter or knowing an escape route may be the only form of defence against predation. Fish will find considerable advantage in being able to locate quickly this means of escape. Perhaps the most famous example of fish spatial memory comes from the work by Aronson (1951, 1971) on the escape response of gobiid fish (*Bathygobius soporator*). When these tide pool fish are threatened and alarmed they will jump, with considerable accuracy, into neighbouring pools. Aronson (1971) hypothesised that the fish were able to do this because at high tide, when the pools were covered by the sea, the fish can swim over the general area and learn the local topography around their home pool. When threatened at low tide the fish use their spatial memory to locate accurately a pool to escape into. Aronson used a series of artificial pools to show that naive gobies, which had been prevented from exploring the topography and spatial relationships of the pools were highly inaccurate in locating pools to jump into as they tried to escape. Fish with only one high tide experience, however, were remarkably precise at locating an escape pool.

Blackeye gobies (*Coryphopterus nicholsi*) seek shelter in burrows and have been used to demonstrate experimentally that locating the burrow is dependent on the fish being familiar with its environment. Using an experimental tank Merkel (1994) trained blackeye gobies to locate and use a burrow in response to a simulated predator attack. Once trained half the fish were allowed to spend an additional 5 h in the experimental tank. When all the groups were tested with a further simulated attack the more experienced group of fish were quicker to relocate the burrow. It seemed likely that their extensive experience in the test tank allowed them to learn the location of the escape burrow more accurately. However, it might also be that the extra experience may have enhanced their ability to recognise suitable escape burrows. To distinguish between these two possibilities Merkel tested the fish a second time with the burrow position shifted to a new location. Now, the more experienced group took longer than the comparatively inexperienced fish to find the shifted burrow. Thus, it was not the extra training with the burrow itself that had improved the experienced fish's ability to locate the escape burrow in the first test, but the fact that they had presumably learned and remembered its spatial location.

Structured space use in a home range

The final example to illustrate the importance of being able to use spatial memory comes from a study on pike (*Esox lucius*). Fat head minnows (*Pimephales promelas*) are able to detect alarm pheromone in pike faeces if the pike have been fed previously on minnows (Brown *et al.* 1995). When fathead minnows detect alarm pheromone they respond with a stereotypic fright response: they increase their use of cover, swim more rapidly in exposed areas and are more likely to school (Smith 1992). These behavioural changes make minnows more difficult for pike to catch. Thus pike face a dilemma: if they eat minnows they advertise that they are a predator by excreting minnow alarm pheromone in their faeces. The pike have solved this problem by using a latrine, a localised area where they defecate away from their hunting grounds. Pike held in aquarium tanks occupy a home area where they are fed and spend most of their time; however, the majority of the pike's faeces are deposited at the opposite end of the tank. Presumably in a natural river or pond use of such a site-specific latrine will greatly reduce the likelihood that the hunting grounds are contaminated with minnow alarm pheromone. The forgetful pike unable to relocate its latrine will go hungry.

Landmarks used for fish orientation

Landmarks can be used in a variety of ways to provide information about a goal or a destination (e.g. Suzuki *et al.* 1980; Collett *et al.* 1987; Biegler and Morris 1996). For example, they may serve as beacons marking a goal, or the geometrical relationships between several landmarks can be used to calculate a trajectory to a destination. An animal can also use its knowledge of the distribution of landmarks to construct a map to help it plan efficient routes from one area to another. Landmarks can be of several different forms or modalities, as long as the animal is equipped with the relevant sensory apparatus to detect them. Fish are no exception to this, for example, Myrberg *et al.* (1988) suggested that surgeon fish on coral reefs rely on their vision to follow a series or chain of landmarks to take them from their foraging grounds to spawning sites. Alternatively, mature salmon on their homeward migration relocate their natal stream based on its unique olfactory composition (Dittman and Quinn 1996). Other species of fish, however, have developed different ways of detecting landmarks. This idea was raised in the previous section with the example of blind Mexican cave fish detecting objects using their lateral line organ. Perhaps a better known alternative is the detection of electric fields to provide information about the positions of environmental cues, e.g. elephant nose fish, *Gnathonemus petersii* (Cain *et al.* 1994).

On the whole, work investigating the types of landmark used by fish have been carried out in laboratory tanks. Thus, although we have discovered what sorts of landmark various species of fish can use in artificial environments, relatively little attention has been given to whether these types of landmark are used by fish in their natural habitats.

Landmarks labelling food patches

Experiments have shown that fish can use landmarks to label the location of food patches. Warburton (1990) showed that goldfish (*Carassius auratus*) can learn to use simple objects, such as plastic blocks or rocks and plants, as beacons to locate food buried under the surface of the gravel in a test tank. Moreover, Warburton found in a second task that some of the fish could learn to use these landmarks indirectly. Although the fish found this a more difficult task to learn, when they had to choose between two patches the fish learned that the food was in the patch that did not contain a landmark.

More recently, juvenile Atlantic salmon or parr have been shown to use landmarks for locating food patches (Braithwaite *et al.* 1996). In the wild, salmon parr live within home ranges during most of their period in freshwater and within these home ranges their use of space is highly structured (Gibson 1993). The young fish hold station just above or resting on the substrate in one or more favoured feeding sites. As food items drift past the fish they move up into the water column to intercept their prey before quickly returning to their feeding station (Keenleyside 1962; Gibson 1993). The feeding stations held by these fish are often no more than a smooth topped rock or pebble, but something about that rock or pebble, among the many others in its home range, allows the fish to recognise it as one of its feeding stations. To determine whether salmon parr can use visual landmarks to recognise a feeding patch or site, Braithwaite *et al.* (1996) tested whether the fish could track a moveable food source, in the presence or absence of conspicuous visual landmarks (Fig. 5.2). The salmon parr had to determine which one of two potential feeding patches, each distinguishable by conspicuous coloured landmarks, was the rewarded site. The patch was rewarded with a stream of pelleted food for a limited period each morning. To lower the possibility of the fish using other cues, such as a particular side of the tank, the position of the rewarded patch and its accompanying landmark was interchanged in a random sequence between trials with the non-rewarded patch. Thus, to locate food the fish had to remember which landmark was associated with the rewarded patch and be waiting on that patch when the food was delivered. After training the majority of salmon parr tested were able to locate the rewarded feeding patch showing that these fish can use conspicuous visual landmarks to predict the position of food.

Results from the second phase of the experiment showed, however, that the situation was a little more complicated than first appeared. The fish were again presented with two feeding patches but now these were labelled with visually identical landmarks. The same procedure was used as before and the feeding patches were moved around the test tank between trials to prevent positional biases from forming. As expected, the fish were initially unable to discriminate between the two patches. Surprisingly, with experience, however, the juvenile salmon could locate the rewarded patch in spite of both patches having identical visual landmarks. This result could be interpreted in two ways. Either the fish learned to use tiny visual inconsistencies between the two patches, even though the materials used to create the landmarks and patches were carefully selected for their durable, difficult-to-scratch surfaces. Alternatively, the fish may have used non-visual information. One possibility is that the salmon parr may have deposited some form of olfactory cue on to the rewarded patch to mark it. This olfactory landmark could then be used to locate the patch as it was moved around the test tank. Previous work by Stabell (1987) has suggested that juvenile Atlantic

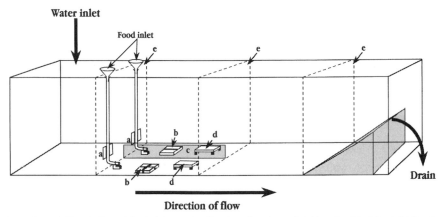

Fig. 5.2 Large through flow tank used for training and testing juvenile salmon (total length of tank 2 m). (a) Front screen landmarks; (b) base-plate; (c) central baffle; (d) shelters; (e) screens. The two base-plates and associated landmarks (on the front screen and the base-plate) were randomly switched between the two sides of the tank between trials. The central baffle prevented food particles from drifting between the patches. Fish could swim between patches over the central baffle. Tank filled to a depth of 25 cm.

salmon may use some form of scent marking: parr were able to discriminate odours extracted from gravel used to line their tank compared with odours extracted from a tank housing other fish. Additionally, juvenile salmon have been observed rubbing their flanks and ventral surfaces on rocks and pebbles used as feeding stations, possibly marking these in some way (pers. obs.). However, there is as yet no conclusive supporting evidence for scent marking in fish.

Using local and global landmarks

In studies of animal orientation landmarks are sometimes divided into two main types: local, which are close to the goal, and global, which are more distant. A few experiments with fish have addressed the use of these two landmark types. One particular experiment by Huntingford and Wright (1989) investigated how local and global landmarks were used by three spined sticklebacks to label a potentially dangerous feeding area. Fish were housed singly in tanks divided into three equal sized compartments by opaque partitions fitted with sliding doors. The central compartment was designated the home compartment and the side compartments as feeding patches. Each food patch contained a food hopper stocked with tubifex worms. When the sliding doors were open the food hoppers on both sides were visible to the fish in the central home compartment. Over each sliding door there were plastic landmarks, a blue cross above one door and a black square above the other. The positioning of these local landmarks, on the left or right partition, was randomised between the different test tanks.

The fish were trained to feed in both patches. Each fish soon developed a preference for one of the patches, which they would usually visit before feeding at the second. Once the fish were readily eating food in both patches a second period of training began. The fish were now encouraged to avoid their preferred food patch by the delivery of a simulated predator attack whenever they entered this patch. Once the sticklebacks had learned to avoid their preferred food patch they were given one test trial in which the local landmarks above the doors were switched, and no further simulated attacks were given. By switching the local landmarks Huntingford and Wright were able to determine whether the fish learned to label the 'dangerous' patch with these or with the global landmarks outside the tank, such as the walls, ceiling, pipes or light fittings. As the local and global landmarks now provided conflicting information, the food patch fish visited first revealed which type of landmark these fish were using.

Of the 13 fish tested, nine sticklebacks swam straight into the safe patch and stayed there, regardless of the fact that it now had a 'dangerous' local landmark above the door. The remaining four fish approached the safe door, then turned and entered the previously dangerous patch, which now had the 'safe' landmark over the door. Thus the sticklebacks exhibited individual variation in the type of landmark that they preferred to use. While the majority of the fish appeared to rely on global landmarks to label the food patches as 'dangerous' or 'safe', Huntingford and Wright's study shows that some sticklebacks preferred to use the local landmarks above the doors.

It is not clear from the previous experiment why individual fish used different types of landmark to label the two food patches. Other observations on spatial learning in sticklebacks, however, have revealed similar patterns of individual variation in the type of spatial cue used. Braithwaite and Hockings (unpublished data) designed an experiment to examine how much attention fish paid to local landmarks along the length of a maze. The maze used was similar to the one shown in Fig. 5.1 except that now the first section contained four green plants in each corner and the second section four brown plants. They found that approximately a third of the fish tested solved the maze by remembering the local landmarks (the different coloured plants) in the different sections of the maze, while the remainder ignored these and used either global landmarks, or an algorithm of the correct sequence of open and closed doors. Together with Huntingford and Wright's result this is quite intriguing as it suggests that individuals from the same population may use quite different spatial strategies to solve the same sorts of problem.

Investigating spatial memory and landmark use in three spined sticklebacks has raised some rather interesting problems. Results from Girvan and Braithwaite (1997), described earlier, revealed differences in spatial behaviour between populations. The results reported in this section have suggested that within populations there is also considerable variation in the types of spatial information fish prefer to learn. Work examining these within and between populations difference is currently underway.

Piloting with chains of landmarks

Although the evidence is rather limited, some field data also indicate that fish use sequences of environmental landmarks to guide movements. Coral reef fish, for example, follow very predictable paths as they swim between feeding patches within their home area and use these paths repeatedly throughout the day (Reese 1989). After displacing parts of the coral reef, Reese observed that butterfly fish (family *Chaetodontidae*) stopped swimming along a particular path and started to search for the missing coral head. It was suggested that the fish were using particular structures on the coral reef as landmarks to guide them along their route. Reese also discovered that fish deflected from their current swimming path only resumed their routine pattern of swimming once they were able to relocate a familiar area of the reef. In general, reef fish have a highly developed visual sense with olfaction playing a relatively minor part. Although the possibility they may have used olfactory landmarks cannot be ruled out, it seems likely that the landmarks used by the fish were visual.

Types of compass used by fish

Memory for the spatial features of an environment is most advantageous to fish which can use this information in conjunction with a compass. Such attributes frequently permit fish to travel considerable distances, both between feeding areas and more extensively while on migration. An ability to form and use a map will enable fish to plan the most direct route to destinations such as feeding sites. Compasses can then be employed to determine the direction fish should move in. The combination of a map and a compass may also be used together to guide fish through unfamiliar areas or to enable them to cover large distances more efficiently. Earlier examples showed that fish can remember the spatial relationships between landmarks and it seems very likely they will use these learned relationships to form maps of their familiar surroundings (e.g. Aronson 1971; Merkel 1994). This next section will build on this by considering the role of compasses. Tracking work has revealed that several species of fish can maintain highly directed swimming over long distances, for example, Pacific blue marlin (*Makaira nigricans*) and blue sharks (*Prionace glauca*) (Carey and Scharold 1990; Holland et al. 1990) and it seems likely that this directness is made possible through the use of compass information.

One source of compass information frequently used by terrestrial animals is the sun (see Bingman, Chapter 4). To use a sun compass the animal requires some form of timing mechanism, or 'internal clock' and the accuracy of this clock influences the accuracy of the compass. The ability of several fish species to time their daily spawning migrations very precisely gives some indication that fish may have a sufficiently accurate 'internal clock' for use with the sun compass (Helfman et al. 1982; Quinn and Ogden 1984).

Experiments exploring whether fish use a sun compass initially compared the homing performance of displaced fish on sunny and overcast days. Large mouth bass (*Micropterus salmoides*) were captured from the opposite sides of a large pond (1.56 ha) and their initial movements were observed as they were released in the centre of a circular test pool (Loyacano and Chappell 1977). On clear, sunny days the fish were able to orientate themselves in the correct 'homeward' direction. On overcast days, however, the fish were found to distribute themselves randomly around the edges of the pool. This result strongly suggests that the large mouth bass were using the sun as a compass. It seems slightly surprising that the fish were unable to orientate on overcast days. Other animal groups typically overcome this problem by using more than one type of compass and if directional information for their preferred compass is unavailable they will switch to using a back-up compass. Thus, for example, a bird such as a pigeon (*Columba livia*) may preferentially use a sun compass but when cloud obscures the sun the bird may revert to using a magnetic compass (Walcott 1996). Such a system of back-up compasses seems quite widespread, from bees to birds, so quite why this is not the case for large mouth bass is not clear.

Immature bluegills (*Lepomis macrochirus*) also use a sun compass. Goodyear and Bennett (1979) showed that it is possible to clock-shift these fish. This technique, frequently used when investigating the use of the sun compass in birds (for review see Schmidt-Koenig *et al.* 1991), is used to put the animal's perceived time of day out of phase with the real time of day. This can be achieved by placing the animal in an artificial light regime. When the animal tries to use the sun compass, its orientation is shifted or displaced, and the size of the displacement corresponds to the number of hours by which the animal is clock-shifted. In spite of Goodyear and Bennett's demonstration that clock-shifting can be used on fish, there has been little work using this extremely useful technique, and many questions about sun compass accuracy and the use of back-up compass systems remain to be answered.

More recently, Levin *et al.* (1992) used an outdoor four-armed chamber with a mirror to investigate sun compass orientation in the micro-characid (*Cheirodon pulcher*). Each of the four arms ended in a trap and the number of fish gathered in each arm were counted 15 min after fish were released into the chamber. When tested under normal sunlight, both in the morning and afternoon groups of fish showed a clear preference for the arm in the south. However, when a mirror was used to deflect the apparent position of the sun by 180° the fish were then found in the northern arm. These results demonstrate the use of a sun compass by these fish.

Another compass cue closely linked to the sun is the pattern of polarised light. Using polarised light to provide compass information can sometimes be more versatile than using the sun, as polarised light patterns may be available even when the sun is obscured by cloud. Evidence that fish do use polarised light is scant but work has now begun to address this compass type in salmonids (Hawryshyn *et al.* 1990). Rainbow trout were trained to swim to a refuge at one end of a training tank under specific polarised light conditions. The fish were then transferred to a circular test pool where their orientational responses were scored. Trout tested under the same conditions experienced during training were perfectly able to orientate in the direction of the refuge. However, when the spectral composition of the light was manipulated the accuracy of orientation varied considerably between trout. These results strongly suggest the trout can use polarised light to provide compass information. In an interesting twist, Hawryshn and his colleagues also discovered that as the fish developed they lost their ability to use the polarised light for orientation: fish weighing about 30 g exhibited accurate orientation with regular polarised light, while trout between 50 and 60 g were incapable of using it as a compass. This loss of polarised light sensitivity seems quite surprising as the fish still need to orientate out at sea. Perhaps in the open sea the fish swim at depths that do not allow the use of polarised light as an orientation cue. It would be interesting to know whether mature salmonids regenerate their ability to use polarised light for compass information as they begin their return journey back to freshwater.

Polarised light patterns are strongest around sunrise and sunset. Many nocturnal migrating birds using polarised light patterns for compass information rely on the cues at sunset (Able 1993). Those species of fish that perform their daily migrations at the beginning and the end of the day might also use polarised light to provide compass information, for example, juvenile grunts which undertake morning and evening migrations between their diurnal resting sites and their nocturnal feeding areas (Quinn and Ogden 1984). By capturing fish either during their inward or outward migration and displacing them 100 m or 5 km away

Quinn and Ogden found that the displaced grunts generally moved in the direction in which they had been swimming before they were caught, even if this took them away from their normal feeding or resting area. This suggests that these fish rely most heavily on directional information to orientate and do not use, to any great extent, the landmarks along the route. Exactly which sort of compass cue is used by the grunts is not clear. As the fish swim to the resting areas just before sunrise and return just after sunset, it is unlikely they use the sun as a compass. It is, however, the best time of day to gain compass information from polarised light patterns.

Alternatively, the grunts in Quinn and Ogden's study may have relied on other compasses; leading candidates for alternative systems are compasses based on detection of electric and magnetic fields. Kalmijn (1978) has suggested how fish might use electromagnetic orientation. He has proposed that elasmobranchs can determine compass directions both by using the electric fields induced by the ocean currents flowing through the earth's magnetic field, and by determining their magnetic compass headings from the electric fields they induce around themselves as they swim. The specialised electroreceptor system consisting of the ampullae of Lorenzini provide the method for transducing the information.

More recently, the use of magnetic compasses in teleost fish has also been proposed. Walker (1984) showed that yellowfin tuna (*Thunnus albacares*) can learn to discriminate between two earth strength magnetic fields. Subsequently, Walker and various colleagues have looked for the possible anatomical sites for magnetic detection (Kirschvink *et al.* 1985; Walker *et al.* 1988). In some salmonid fishes, single-domain particles of magnetite have been found in the anterior skull. In controlled experiments, single units (nerve axons), within an area presumed to be the trigeminal nerve near the snout of both brown and rainbow trout (*Salmo trutta, Oncorhynchus mykiss*) have shown robust responses to changes in magnetic field intensity. Interestingly, the units did not respond when the direction of the magnetic field was altered but the intensity remained constant (Walker 1993). This result, very reminiscent of research exploring the avian magnetic compass, suggests the magnetic information used by fish is based on a measure of inclination of the magnetic field rather than direction.

Compasses are likely to play an important part in fish for assisting both homing and long-distance travel. Yet our knowledge of how fish use their compasses is considerably inferior to what we know for other animal groups, such as birds and insects. Work on avian migrant compasses has been pioneered by Ken and Mary Able, and one of their many useful contributions have been the series of 'cue-conflict' experiments (for a review see Able 1993). Here two relevant compass cues are given to the test animal. One of these compass cues is manipulated so that it provides conflicting directional information to the other unmanipulated cue. The animal's orientation is then examined to determine which of the two cues it has used for compass information. Such cue-conflict techniques could be usefully applied to different fish species to determine whether fish, like birds, can use multiple forms of compass and to explore which compass systems are used in preference to others.

Homing and migration behaviour

In this final section I examine fish homing and migration behaviour and the important contribution that telemetry has made to this field. It is inevitable that salmonid migrations will appear in a review on fish orientation, but despite the relative wealth of work contributing to this area of fish orientation behaviour I have chosen only to highlight the main results and mention the most recent advances. For the interested reader I thoroughly recommend two recent reviews (Quinn 1992; Dittman and Quinn 1996).

Tracking fish movements

Investigating fish movements in streams is not easy and in the past there have been some incredibly brutal attempts to quantify fish homing behaviour. Perhaps one of the most shocking accounts involved the use of a poison called 'Fish Tox' poured into a half-mile study area of stream in an attempt to estimate homing ability of cutthroat trout (*Salmo clarki*) (Miller 1954). The study of fish homing has benefited enormously from technological advances in tracking techniques. Radio tracking has proved an effective technique for monitoring fish movements in rivers (Solomon 1982). Ultrasonic signals, from transmitters often carried in the stomachs of fish, can be detected by receivers on boats and have been used to follow fish in deeper water in lakes and at sea. The boat's satellite navigational system can be used to track the position of the boat as it follows the fish fitted with the ultrasonic transmitter. This technique was used by Ueda et al. (1995), to study the homing behaviour of land-locked sockeye salmon (kokanee salmon, *Oncorhynchus nerka*). These fish are ideal for homing studies because once they mature they return with considerable accuracy to their natal area within the lake. Mature fish can be tagged, displaced and their homing movements tracked.

Telemetry of movements made by small fish was initially hampered by the size of the tags or transmitters. This has recently been overcome by the application of miniature passive integrator transponder (PIT) tags. These tiny tags (11 mm in length) can be inserted harmlessly into the body cavity of fish as small as 80 mm. Each tag has a unique code that can be used to identify individual fish. Various types of antennae have been designed to read these tags but have typically required fish to swim through narrow tubes housing the antenna coils, which may affect the fish's natural behaviour. A recently developed system by Armstrong et al. (1996), however, has improved on these previous designs. They have used a flat-plate antenna (each plate measuring $100 \times 30 \times 2$ cm), which is placed on the bed of a stream. By setting up four plates in a 10 m section of stream, Armstrong and colleagues were able to monitor the fine-scale movements of 36 wild juvenile Atlantic salmon (8.7–10.5 cm in length) previously inserted with PIT tags. Each time a fish swam over an antenna plate the code from the tag was read and information about the time, place, fish identity and antenna on which the fish was recorded were sent to a computer co-ordinating the four antennae. The beauty of such a system is that continuous, detailed information can be collected continuously over many days without disturbing the fish subsequent to tag insertion. Such techniques are already allowing extremely detailed observations of fish exploration and homing (Armstrong et al. 1997).

Homing in fish

Homing is a component of migration but it can also be observed in non-migrating fish. For example, fish resident within a general area will sometimes set up a home range or a territory that they defend from intruders (e.g. long fin damsel fish, *Stegastes diencaeus*; Ludlow 1996). If a fish is displaced from this home range it may try to return through some form of homing. Various situations may lead to such displacements. Periods of highly increased water flow, such as a flood, may wash fish downstream. Alternatively, very dry periods can create droughts which may drive fish towards deeper, more permanent bodies of water. Predators may also be responsible for displacing fish by chasing their intended prey out of a home range and into unfamiliar areas. All of these scenarios involve the fish leaving a particular home area for alternative sites. Whether fish will attempt to return home will depend upon how strongly they were attached to the previous site, the level of competition in the new area and the quality of resources available compared with those at the home site. A fish's ability to home will depend partly on the distance to the original site and partly on the nature of the cues they use to detect 'home'. For example, if the fish relies on olfactory information to locate its home range, can it detect these olfactory cues at the displaced location?

Studies of homing in fish frequently involve capturing and displacing fish a variety of distances from where they were caught and observing subsequent movements. Experiments manipulating the fish's senses have attempted to investigate the mechanisms underlying their homing behaviour. In some studies fish have been blinded (LaBar 1971; Ueda 1995) and in others they have been made anosmic (LaBar 1971; Garcia de Leaniz 1989). Results from these types of manipulation suggest that fish do use both visual and olfactory information to help them home. Olfactory deprivation experiments, however, should be reconsidered in the light of recent evidence that suggests anosmia may potentially decrease the motivation of fish to swim (Essler and Kotrschal 1994). It is likely that, the effects of depriving fish of visual information will have similar effects. Thus, we are still some way off understanding the different roles of the separate senses during homing.

One elegant study of fish homing investigated the homing behaviour of *Ulvaria subbifurcata*, a small benthic fish found in shallow, rocky marine habitats off the coast of Newfoundland (Green and Fisher 1977). Using both scuba diving and an underwater observation chamber Green and Fisher were able to monitor the movements of tagged individual fish. They discovered that these fish live in fairly small, well defined home ranges of approximately $3\,m^2$. Displacements to various distances were carried out and fish were observed to home even after a displacement of 270 m. To examine the fish's initial orientation Green and Fisher designed a release chamber. This consisted of a 130 cm diameter PVC disc attached to a 15 cm diameter cylinder with eight evenly spaced holes cut into the sides. The apparatus was set up on the sea floor directly beneath the hatch of the observation chamber. Observers then placed individual fish into the central cylinder and monitored which cylinder hole the fish left through and the compass bearing of the fish as it moved off the edge of the PVC disc. Although there was some scattering, the fish were significantly oriented in the homeward direction, suggesting that they were able to determine their present location with respect to home. As these experiments were performed at night, and in some instances under a cover of ice, the use of visual and certainly celestial cues seemed most unlikely. In a later study at the same site Goff and Green (1978) examined the effects of rendering the *U. subbifurcata* anosmic or blind. Control (untreated), anosmic and blind fish were displaced and released either 19 or 20 m from their home range. After 24 h the home sites were searched to determine how many fish had returned. Goff and Green found that compared with a 94% return rate for the controls fewer than 30% of the blind or anosmic fish returned home. They suggested that both vision and olfaction may be necessary for *U. subbifurcata* to home as the blind fish that returned home had presumably used olfactory cues, while the anosmic fish had presumably recognised visual features associated with their home site. The decreased motivation for swimming observed in anosmic fish (Essler and Kotrschal 1994) may also have influenced the poor return rates of the treated fish.

A capacity to return to a home range after displacements of several hundred metres has been demonstrated in several species of freshwater fish, for example brown trout (Halvorsen and Stabell 1990), and Atlantic salmon (Saunders and Gee 1964; Garcia de Leaniz 1989). Although some of the displaced fish exhibit the capacity to home, only a relatively small proportion of fish were actually recaptured at their home site. Studies of smaller-scale displacements with minnows (*Phoxinus phoxinus*) have also revealed similar individual variation in homing response (Kennedy 1981). Such variations in homing could be produced by a number of factors, ranging from a lack of motivation for returning to a familiar area, to succumbing to a predatory attack.

Recent work by Huntingford *et al.* (unpublished data) has shown that the type of displacement fish experience can be an important influence on homing performance. Juvenile Atlantic salmon were left to settle for 6 days in an artificial stream (16.5 m long, 0.6 m wide and 0.6 m deep). The fish established home ranges and showed considerable site fidelity to these locations. Over a series of trials fish were displaced using one of two different techniques. First, fish were caught with hand nets and displaced downstream ([1]thought to be similar to the fish being chased out of a home range by a predator)[2]. After being held for 1 h the fish were released and any homing behaviour was monitored. In the second displacement the water level was dropped to force the fish to leave for deeper water. This was intended to simulate a drought situation. After 1 h the water level was restored and again, any homing behaviour was monitored. Huntingford and colleagues found that the fish were significantly less likely to home if they had left their home range in response to rapidly falling water levels compared with fish displaced by being chased and caught in a hand net. This study indicates that juvenile salmon appear able to assess the risk associated with returning home and homing behaviour is based on the relative risk of mortality.

Salmon homing and migration

Finally, no general review of fish orientation would be complete without some consideration of the study of adult salmon homing to natal streams. Salmon migration has been a focus of attention for many years. Typically, salmon spend between 0 and 3 years in freshwater before migrating downstream to the sea. We know remarkably little about the movements of salmon during their time at sea, which is largely due to the difficulty of following the fish once they leave freshwater. The salmon remain at sea until they begin to mature at which point they begin their homeward migration. First, they must locate the correct area of coastline and then they need to find the right estuary that will lead them back to their natal stream. Hasler and Wisby (1951) were among the first to propose that returning adult salmon probably used olfaction to guide them home. The results of subsequent work in which juvenile salmon were exposed to low concentrations of synthetic odorants, such as morpholine, supported this olfactory hypothesis, when returning Coho salmon (*O. Kisutch*) were successfully lured to alternative streams scented with the same concentrations of morpholine (Hasler and Scholz 1983). Experiments such as this revealed the importance of early experience during development before the salmon left freshwater for the sea. Studies designed to determine how the odours of a natal stream were learned demonstrated that during the seaward migration (a period called smoltification) young salmon undergo a process very similar to imprinting and it is during this stage that the fish learn about the characteristic odours of their stream. Recent attention has focused on this period of imprinting. One particularly interesting finding has been the work demonstrating the important link between this imprinting process and increased levels of the hormone thyroxin (Morin *et al.* 1989a, b). It is now known that the olfactory epithelium of smolting masu salmon (*O. masou*) is enriched in thyroid hormone receptors compared with that of immature parr (Kudo *et al.* 1994). It has been suggested that thyroxin surges may influence the neural development in the salmon olfactory system and that this facilitates the imprinting process (Nevitt *et al.* 1994).

Another recent advance has been the isolation of an olfactory system-specific protein called N24 (Ueda and Yamauchi 1995). This protein has been found in land-locked sockeye salmon and exists in the primary olfactory neurons of various species of fish that migrate between the sea and freshwater, such as the Japanese eel (*Anguilla japonica*). It was not, however, found in non-migrating freshwater fish such as carp (*Cyprinus carpio*) or tilapia (*Orechoromis nilotics*). Ueda and Yamauchi suggest that this 24 kDa protein plays an important neuromodulatory role during the olfactory imprinting process in salmon and other migrating teleost fish. Thus we are beginning to get a clearer idea of how the olfactory imprinting process may operate and although there are still many questions to be answered we are much closer to understanding the mechanisms underlying salmon migrations.

Summary

I have reviewed experiments and observations exploring various aspects of fish orientation and used these to highlight how important spatial orientation is for many species of fish. To bring our knowledge of fish orientation behaviour up to the same level as other groups, such as insects, birds and mammals, it is now necessary to start addressing specific questions. In particular, we need to understand how and when fish use more than one compass whether these compasses form a hierarchy of back-up reference systems. Another aspect that should be addressed in more detail is the observation that fish within and between different populations show considerable individual variation in their spatial behaviour. More experimental work is required to address the nature of this variation, and the fact individual fish can vary in their use of spatial strategies should be kept in mind when interpreting results from orientation experiments testing different populations. Finally, the result that showed homing in juvenile salmon was considerably affected by the type of experimental displacement may be an important consideration for other work on fish homing behaviour, and may possibly have implications for homing work in other animal groups, such as birds and mammals.

The future outlook for the study of fish orientation behaviour looks fairly positive. Continuing advances in tracking techniques will provide us with a considerably more detailed understanding of how fish orientate around their natural home ranges, and advances in neurobiological techniques should help us further our basic knowledge of the mechanisms underlying many aspects of spatial behaviour. Finally, surprisingly little attention has been given to spatial memory mechanisms and landmark recognition at the neuronal level, and perhaps one future goal should involve searching for structures in the fish's brain that are analogous with the hippocampus of birds and mammals.

Acknowledgements

The author wishes to thank Sue Healy, Andrew Read, Joanna Girvan and Catherine Hockings for helpful comments and suggestions given at various stages during the preparation of this chapter.

6 Spatiotemporal aspects of avian long-distance migration

Peter Berthold

The phenomena and their elucidation

Far-reaching migratory movements define the birds as the most mobile group of animals, whose network of migration routes cover most of the earth's surface. Most conspicuous are the long-distance intercontinental and transoceanic migratory movements. The record holder, the Arctic tern (*Sterna paradisaea*) regularly migrates from Arctic breeding grounds to winter quarters around the Antarctic continent and may cover up to 50 000 km per year. This distance is approximately equivalent to the circumference of our planet and some individual terns may reach a lifetime mileage of more than a million kilometres (Berthold 1993). Even passerines such as the Alaskan population of the wheatear (*Oenanthe oenanthe*), which winters in southeastern Africa, can make annual journeys of about 30 000 km (Kiepenheuer 1984). In spite of these very long migratory distances birds are able to perform accurately directed migratory movements and are capable of regularly commuting between small breeding sites and wintering places or of returning to remote tiny little islands even after several years (pin-point navigation). Innumerable ringing recoveries have revealed narrow migration corridors and give evidence of remarkable breeding site, stopover area and wintering site fidelity (Zink 1973–1985). Satellite tracking has allowed us to establish the directedness of migratory journeys in actually migrating individuals (Nowak and Berthold 1991; Fig. 6.1). In addition to spatial precision, long-distance migrants in particular often show amazing temporal precision with respect to onset and course of migration as well as arrival at the breeding grounds. In such 'calendar birds', for example, the year to year variation in the date of first arrivals is often only a few days (Berthold 1993). Both spatial and temporal precision of migratory birds clearly indicate that these globetrotters are equipped with excellent and reliable spatiotemporal orientation systems. Systematic studies, initiated in the fifties, of a number of selected experimental species have elucidated, step by step, many of the basic spatiotemporal orientation mechanisms (except for those of possible true navigation in animals moving to previously inhabited areas). These mechanisms will be listed and characterised in the following section.

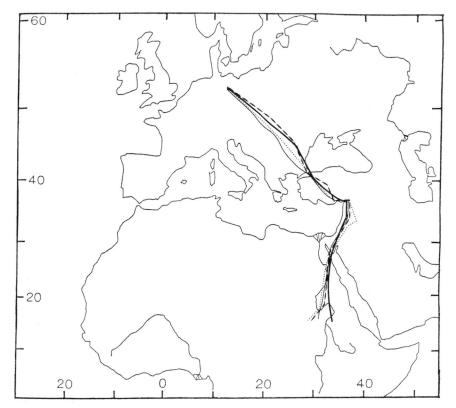

Fig. 6.1 Migratory routes of white storks (*Ciconia ciconia*) recorded by permanent satellite tracking of individuals equipped with mini-transmitters. The routes from the breeding grounds to the eastern Mediterranean are remarkably straight (from Berthold *et al.* 1993 and unpublished).

Performance guarantee: endogenous spatiotemporal programmes and biological compasses

The avian spatiotemporal orientation system (involved in migration but also in other annual processes and most likely in daily routine activities as well) comprises a set of largely interrelated items of equipment: endogenous biological clocks, genetically controlled time-programmes for the migratory process, genetically pre-programmed migration directions and thus a spatiotemporal migration vector, a set of three to five biological compasses to follow predetermined directions and to perform true navigation, which is possibly also used for return and repeated migrations after the first outward journey from the natal area (see section below on Control of return migration and subsequent migratory journeys, and the map-and-compass concept).

Endogenous biological clocks

Like other animals, birds are equipped with two types of biological or 'internal clocks' which play an important part in the spatiotemporal and physiological organisation of migration as well as in other processes: 'circadian', i.e. endogenous diurnal rhythms and 'circannual', i.e. endogenous annual rhythms or so-called internal calendars (Gwinner 1986, 1996a; Berthold 1996).

Circadian rhythms are involved in the seasonal expression of migratory activity and fat deposition during migration (providing 'fuel' for the migratory flights), in mechanisms measuring day length (environmental photoperiodism is a key factor allowing seasonal adaptation), and in synchronisation processes which adjust the approximate endogenous 'circa'-rhythms to the changing ecological requirements of the calendar year. With respect to the huge number of night migrants (most of which are otherwise diurnal), a system of two coupled self-sustained physiological circadian oscillators has been proposed in which endocrine factors are thought to shift one of the peaks of the premigratory bimodal diurnal locomotor activity pattern into the night, thereby allowing the development of nocturnal migratory activity (Gwinner 1986; Berthold 1996).

More important for the understanding of spatiotemporal aspects of avian migration treated here are the internal calendars. Thus far, the involvement of such circannual rhythms in the control of migratory events has been demonstrated for 14 bird species, and in five additional species, there is circumstantial evidence for these rhythms. They have been shown to control the onset of migration, patterns of migratory activity, migratory fattening and, most likely, food preferences and utilisation during migratory disposition as well as migratory orientation (the calendar provides a primary direction, i.e. the general orientation either towards the breeding grounds or the wintering area; Gwinner 1986, 1996b).

Circannual rhythms can easily be demonstrated. The best procedure for doing so involves transferring eggs, or preferably, very young nestlings, into constant environmental conditions (constant daily light dark cycle, e.g. 12:12 h, constant temperature, humidity and constant food supply once the birds reach independence). Despite of the lack of any seasonal cues under such experimental conditions, birds such as warblers will nevertheless produce, in proper succession, a complete set of annual events of the first migratory period, such as juvenile moult, migratory fattening and activity (represented in caged birds by nocturnal migratory restlessness, i.e. above all wing-whirring in a sitting position; Berthold 1993), winter moult, processes of return migration and characteristics of the breeding season, such as song and gonadal development (which can be examined by laparotomy, i.e. abdominal incision). In the bird's first year the timing of these annual processes corresponds to the natural seasons whereas in subsequent years they generally occur prematurely. This is due to the fact that the spontaneous period length of these circa-rhythms (7–11 months) differs considerably from that of the calendar year. Interindividual variations in the length of spontaneous periods lead to increasing desynchronisation of annual processes among captive individuals even in the same experimental chamber. After several years, some birds sing in full breeding disposition, while others are still on 'homeward migration', in moult or already performing 'autumn migration'. In long-term studies of at least 7–8 years, a complete free run of these circannual rhythms can be observed, i.e. individual processes occur at all months of the calendar year. Variation in spontaneous period lengths as well as during free run clearly demonstrate the true endogenous nature of these rhythms (Berthold 1978; Gwinner and Dittami 1990). On the other hand, they indicate that under natural conditions, these circa-rhythms must be adjusted to the seasons by different factors. Among a variety of synchronisers or 'zeitgebers', photoperiod plays the most important part. The dual system of endogenous circa-rhythms and photoperiod as a precise and reliable 'zeitgeber', provides many organisms with a viable basis for proper seasonal timing in general and for spatio-temporal orientation during migratory movements in particular (Gwinner 1986; Berthold 1996).

There is evidence that migratory processes can also be triggered endogenously without the influence of environmental factors. For example, a comparative study in about 20 European songbird species showed a very high correlation between the onset dates of migratory activity in hand-raised caged birds and the actual migration of conspecifics of the same populations in the wild. This implies that the same endogenous factors which trigger migratory activity in captive individuals initiate actual migration, and that environmental factors, if at all, are of minor importance for departure (Berthold 1990). This would explain the timing of the first migratory period of juvenile birds and in birds which winter in equatorial areas, where reliable seasonal cues are lacking (Gwinner 1990).

Endogenous time programmes

Circannual rhythms seem to fix not only the dates of onset and termination of the first migratory period in naive first-time migrants but, in addition, the course of migration and the approximate distance to be covered, through population-specific patterns of pre-programmed, genetically determined, migratory activity. This idea was first developed at the end of the eighteenth century when Naumann stated that captive long-distance migrants displayed migratory restlessness (or *zugunruhe*) over extremely long periods (Naumann 1795–1817). Clear hypotheses were advanced in the 1920s and 1930s (v. Lucanus 1923; Stresemann 1934) and these have been tested experimentally since the 1960s. First, in a variety of species and populations a clear relationship was found between time span and amount of migratory activity displayed by caged individuals and the distance to be covered by free-living conspecifics. As a rule, the longer the normal migratory distance, the more migratory restlessness is exhibited under constant experimental conditions (Gwinner 1968). Secondly, in a number of species so far investigated, the patterns of migratory restlessness appear to be adaptively pre-programmed to meet specific demands of the migratory journey. For example, European trans-Sahara migrants which cross the ecological barriers of the Mediterranean and the desert around the middle of their migratory period show peaks of activity at this time. In contrast, short-distance and partial migrants normally migrating late in the season display peaks of restlessness towards the end of their migratory period. And even extremely unusual patterns of migration as can be found in the marsh warbler (*Acrocephalus palustris*)—which leaves central Europe in about mid-July and ends migration in South Africa from December to February—are reflected in the restlessness patterns, at least to a large extent. Thus, there is increasing evidence for the fact that the temporal patterns of migratory activity may function as detailed time programmes adapted to specific migratory journeys (Berthold 1996). Two different approaches indicate that the endogenously controlled amount of migratory activity is directly related to the distance to be covered. For central European leaf-warblers (chiffchaff, *Phylloscopus collybita*, and willow warbler, *P. trochilus*), the distances travelled per time period during the autumn migration were calculated from recoveries of marked (ringed) individuals. These distances were then compared with the amounts of migratory restlessness displayed during exactly the same intervals by caged conspecifics. A final calculation of the distance the experimental birds would have covered according to their amount of restlessness showed that the birds would have ended up in their species-specific winter quarters (Gwinner 1968). In central European garden warblers (*Sylvia borin*), the total amount of nocturnal migratory restlessness (mainly expressed as wing-whirring) was registered through video recordings under infra-red illumination. The theoretical flight distance obtained by multiplying the measured average whirring time by the estimated mean flight speed corresponded well to that between the breeding grounds and the central African winter quarters (Berthold 1996).

In addition to the endogenous time programmes for migration, migrants are also equipped with corresponding programmes for the energetic demands. They comprise a specific physiological migratory disposition which includes hyperphagia as the major factor for migratory hyperlipogenesis and, most conspicuous, fat deposition which provides the fuel for the migratory flights and often leads to doubling of body mass (Farner 1955). Both the endogenously controlled patterns of migratory activity (restlessness) as well as of migratory body mass changes are extremely insensitive to environmental influences and disturbances and thus under rigid endogenous control (see section below on Adjustment and buffer mechanisms). In four cross-breeding experiments (three with blackcaps, *Sylvia atricapilla*, one with redstarts, *Phoenicurus phoenicurus* and black redstarts, *P. ochruros*) it was shown that these patterns are genetically determined. The parental stocks for studies with blackcaps consisted of central and eastern European birds, which migrate to the Mediterranean area or to southeast Africa, respectively, and display large amounts of migratory restlessness in captivity. They were crossed with conspecifics from the Canary or Cape Verde Islands or Madeira, respectively, which migrate extremely short distances or are non-migratory and thus exhibit small amounts or no restlessness at all. In the redstart study, central European redstarts, long-distance migrants wintering in central western Africa with long periods of migratory restlessness and marked fat deposition, were crossed with black redstarts, short- to middle-distance migrants, which migrate up to the Mediterranean area and show small amounts of migratory restlessness and lower fat deposition. All the F₁ hybrids showed intermediate patterns of migratory restlessness (Fig. 6.2) and, as recorded in the redstarts at least, in the pattern of fat deposition as well as in the onset of migratory activity (Berthold 1996). It can be seen from these results that the various migratory features are genetically determined species- and population-specific characteristics and it is very likely that they are quantitatively inherited. For the southern German blackcap population it was also shown that migratory activity has a high amount of phenotypic and additive genetic variation with fairly high heritability values. This variation provides the potential for rapid microevolutionary changes of migratory habits (see section below on Adaptability and the microevolutionary potential of migration programmes).

Pre-programmed directions

Until recently, there was only indirect evidence that migratory bird populations have pre-programmed migratory directions. It was based on six observations: (1) even naive first-time

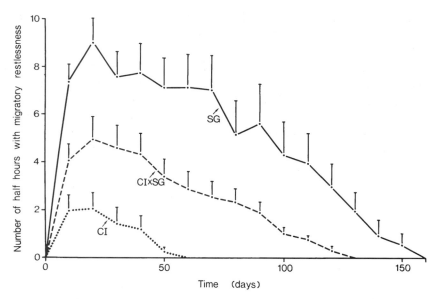

Fig. 6.2 Time course of migratory activity (restlessness) in groups of hand-raised blackcaps (*Sylvia atricapilla*) from two populations (SG: southern Germany, CI: Canary Islands) and of hybrids (CI × SG) (from Berthold and Querner 1981).

migrants tested in orientation cages normally show their typical species- or population-specific directions; (2) ringing recoveries of species in which individuals migrate alone point steadily to the same migration corridors; (3) young cuckoos (*Cuculus canorus*) migrate from Eurasia to specific African winter quarters independently of the various foster parent species with differing migratory habits; (4) displacement experiments with first-time migrants revealed migratory directions parallel to those of their parental populations; (5) facultative migrants (e.g. performing irruptive movements) also migrate quite regularly in specific directions; and (6) *Sylvia* warblers and pied flycatchers (*Ficedula hypoleuca*) show population-specific seasonal changes in their directional preferences in accordance with the course of migration even when raised in captivity (Schüz 1971; Helbig 1992; Berthold 1996).

Four recent experiments with blackcaps have produced convincing evidence for a genetic determination of primary directions in migratory birds. In a first cross-breeding experiment between migratory and resident blackcaps (from Germany and the Cape Verdes, respectively) it was shown that the urge to migrate can be transmitted genetically into part of the offspring of the non-migratory population. When hybrids displaying migratory restlessness were tested in orientation cages, they showed a significant directional preference which corresponded to the principal axis of migration in the migratory parental population. Hence, together with the migration drive, migratory directional preferences are inherited and thus are pre-programmed (Berthold *et al.* 1990b). In a second experiment, blackcaps from populations with different migratory directions were cross-bred. One population, west of a migratory divide in central Europe, migrates to western parts of the Mediterranean and Africa, the other east of the divide, to eastern parts. As expected, hand-raised individuals from both populations showed the same preferences in their migratory directions as their free-living conspecifics. Subsequently cross-bred, they produced phenotypically intermediate offspring with respect to directional preferences (Fig. 6.3). Details of the experiment indicate that migratory directions are quantitative genetic characters controlled by a number of genes (Helbig 1991). In the third experiment, blackcaps wintering in England were used. Over the past few decades, part of the central European blackcaps have developed a novel migratory habit: they migrate in northwestern instead of southerly directions and have established new wintering areas in the British Isles. Blackcaps trapped in England during the winter and tested in orientation cages in southern Germany showed a mean WNW migratory direction in the autumn. Their offspring also showed a WNW migratory direction that was statistically indistinguishable from that of the parent population (Berthold *et al.* 1992). In the fourth experiment, blackcaps wintering in England were cross-bred with German birds showing a clear preference for a southerly direction. As in the second experiment, these hybrids showed an intermediate, westerly direction (Helbig *et al.* 1994).

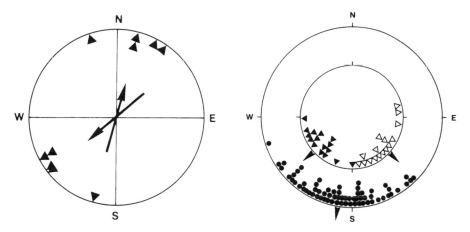

Fig. 6.3 Left: orientation behaviour of hybrids of migratory (southern Germany) and resident (Cape Verdean) blackcaps (*Sylvia atricapilla*) in orientation cages. Triangles: mean direction of individual birds during return migration (upper semicircle) and during outward migration (lower semicircle); arrows: average direction of all individuals for both periods (from Berthold *et al.* 1990b). Right: directional choice of blackcaps in orientation cages. Solid triangles: birds from southern Germany; open triangles: birds from east Austria; dots: hybrids of both populations; long solid triangles: average direction (from Helbig 1991).

Most striking among spatial programmes in migratory birds are genetically encoded seasonal changes in the migratory direction. European intercontinental migrants with African winter quarters which initially depart in westerly directions (towards the Iberian peninsula) or easterly directions (towards the eastern Mediterranean area) in order to circumvent the Alps, the Mediterranean or central parts of the Sahara, later have to turn towards more southern directions in order not to fly past the African continent. In three species so far investigated, corresponding seasonal shifts in the directional preferences were also observed in captive individuals under experimental conditions. Most revealing was the second of the previously described cross-breeding experiments. The blackcaps migrating to the east shifted their preferred direction by about 50° (in order to reach southeastern African winter quarters in the wild). The blackcaps migrating to the west and wintering in the Mediterranean area, reach their more northern wintering area without a comparative shift and did not show a shift in the experiment. The hybrids of both populations performed a smaller shift than their SE migrating parental group of only 10°, roughly intermediate between the two populations (Helbig *et al.* 1989).

Recent satellite-tracking studies in white storks regularly show straight-lined migratory routes within a narrow corridor from eastern Germany to the eastern Mediterranean in both adult and juvenile individuals. As juveniles often migrate without adults, the observations indicate that this social species is also equipped with pre-programmed migratory directions.

The genetic migration vector

As described in the previous two sections, migrants of a number of species appear to be equipped with a genetically determined time-and-direction vector. The innate spatiotemporal programming of this vector may often take at least the naive, first-time migrants to their unknown winter quarters more or less 'automatically'. Although not fully confirmed, the vector-navigation hypothesis is best supported and the most correct among a number of proposed mechanisms. In a number of critical tests no evidence was produced for one of the alternative hypotheses which proposed that migratory birds use inborn patterns of star configurations to recognise specific goal-areas for wintering. The use of star navigation thus seems unlikely. Another hypothesis, that the termination of migration is controlled energetically and not by a time programme based on migratory activity, also appears to be extremely unlikely. Migrants are regularly found to end their migratory journeys in extremely variable energetic conditions ranging from some with large fat deposits remaining to others in a state of critical depletion (Berthold 1991, 1996; Wiltschko and Wiltschko 1991).

A number of objections have been raised to the vector-navigation hypothesis in spite of the accumulation of evidence in its support. One of these concerns the accuracy of locating a suitable overwintering site and whether vector-navigation was sufficient to enable the migrant to locate a small goal. It had been thought that bad weather conditions during the migratory journey force migrants into exceptionally prolonged stopover periods and thus provoke delays of the programme so that the migratory journey would end before the typical winter area is reached. However, winter quarters of migratory bird species normally are fairly large areas, and therefore, goal-finding at the end of the migratory journey need not necessarily be restricted to small regions. Accordingly, endogenous migration programmes should be able to tolerate quite a bit of environmental disturbance before there is a risk that birds may terminate migration in atypical areas. Furthermore, bad weather periods that would prevent migrants from flying for at least a few hours within a number of days are extremely rare. Migratory movements to the wintering areas are, as a rule, fairly slow and range between about 30 km/day in short-distance migrants and about 75 km/day in long-distance migrants. These rather short daily distances may be covered within a few hours, or, more often, within one or more migratory days after an extended stopover period of a number (of up to 15) days. Because of this stop-and-go strategy migrants will rarely have difficulties synchronising migratory episodes with appropriate weather conditions. It is also likely that potential environmental changes have already affected the endogenous migration programmes through selection processes. It was once thought that the migratory activity of caged birds exceeded the migratory period of wild conspecifics. However, field research shows increasingly that the wintering of many migrants is much more of a dynamic process and that migratory movements last much longer than hitherto believed. Finally, it is true that migrants which have lost much of their fat deposits tend to prolong stopover periods for refuelling (see section below on Adjustment and buffer mechanisms). But critical fat depletion is rather the exception than the rule as migrants normally steadily increase their fat depots along with increases in migratory speed and when they approach ecological barriers. Birds suffering from exceptional fat depletion often show increased migratory activity before extending a stopover period. This increased activity may compensate for part of the delay (see section below on Adjustment and buffer mechanisms). The question has often been raised as to what happens when the end of an endogenous migration programme coincides with the arrival of a migrant in a hostile area unsuitable for wintering. We now know that migrants are capable of continuing or even reviving directed migratory movements on the basis of facultative migratory activity (see section below on Adjustment and buffer mechanisms). This also happens under deteriorating conditions in an initially suitable wintering area. For a detailed review of the objections treated here see Berthold (1996).

We do not yet know whether homeward migration—normally to the bird's original breeding area—and whether subsequent away migrations—as a rule to the previous wintering areas—are also based on vector navigation or whether they are controlled by other navigation mechanisms. Theoretical aspects of this complex of problems will be treated below in section on Control of return migration and subsequent migratory journeys, and the map-and-compass concept.

The biological compasses involved in avian migration

Like other animals, birds are capable of using so-called biological compasses for orientation. These compasses have been defined as mechanisms which provide animals with constant directions on the basis of a non-changing directional reference system. For birds, three compass systems have been ascertained, and additional environmental factors are still under debate with respect to possible compass function (Able 1991; Papi 1991; Schmidt-Koenig et al. 1991; Wallraff 1991). Most likely, the capability for using biological compasses is not restricted to migratory birds but is an ability of birds in general. However, whether migratory forms have more effective compass systems is not known (Terrill 1991). The three ascertained compasses are the sun compass, the magnetic compass and the star compass (also see Bingman, Chapter 4). The magnetic compass is thought to have evolved as a phylogenetically primitive primary compass and still appears to function as the most simple primary compass in a complex system of redundant mechanisms of avian orientation. The earth functions as a huge magnet with three main properties which, theoretically, could be used for orientation by animals: the polarity of the magnetic field, the intensity gradient from the magnetic poles to the equator, and the axial course of the field lines and their inclination in space. So far, only the use of the field lines has been demonstrated and hence this compass is also called 'inclination compass'. It allows migrants to distinguish between 'poleward' and 'equator-ward'. When crossing the equator, long-distance migrants reverse their reaction with respect to the magnetic field lines and thus can manage to continue directed migratory flights. The use of a magnetic compass has been demonstrated in at least 15 bird species thus far (Wiltschko and Wiltschko 1995).

The star compass is similarly thought to be a basic compass of nocturnal migrants, developing largely independently of any magnetic influence during ontogeny. However, in contrast to the magnetic compass, its use requires that the crucial configurations of the star patterns are learned during juvenile development. Apparently, for migrants born in the Northern Hemisphere, observing the axis of stellar rotation leads to learning the constellation of Ursa Major as a reference cue for north. The use of a star compass has so far been shown in five bird species (Wiltschko and Wiltschko 1991).

The sun compass, the first biological compass to be discovered, perhaps appears to be the most plausible. However, its use requires time compensation (provided by internal circadian clocks), learning processes (to use the azimuth as the reference cue, which has led to the additional name 'sun azimuth compass'), and it demands for regular updating to keep track of the seasonal variation of the sun's course. Although the sun compass was discovered in migratory European starlings (*Sturnus vulgaris*), very little is known about its use in migratory birds and during migration (Schmidt-Koenig *et al.* 1991). It has been demonstrated in about 10 bird species, but most studies have concentrated on the domestic pigeon (see Bingman, Chapter 4).

There are two further candidate cues that are discussed as compass mechanisms: 'sunset cues' (such as the position of the setting sun, i.e. the sunset point, horizon glow or pattern of polarised light) which appear to be highly informative for nocturnal migrants before taking off on a migratory episode. At present, it is unclear whether these cues provide something like a 'polarisation compass', are merely part of the sun compass or may just indicate the geographic direction west. The other cue under debate is infrasound. Theoretically, low frequencies produced by various sources such as mountains and oceans could provide migrants with information for orientation. Domestic pigeons, at least, are capable of perceiving infrasound, and some recent experiments suggest that it may be involved in the orientation system of that species. Whether it plays a part for migrants is not known. Wind, which has also been discussed as a directional cue for migratory birds, probably affects migration in a much more complex way than as a mere temporal compass (for review, see Berthold 1996).

Control of return migration and subsequent migratory journeys, and the map-and-compass concept

After the first migration, most migrants return more or less exactly to familiar breeding grounds or wintering areas, and many return precisely to the previously inhabited places, as mentioned above (pin-point navigation). It is clear that this high degree of accuracy cannot be achieved by vector-navigation as the genetically determined migration vector is, at least to some extent, susceptible to environmental impairment, such as wind drift, varying nutritional conditions, etc. Pin-point navigation, therefore, must be based on either different or additional orientation mechanisms. The most simple assumption would be that migrants return to previously inhabited areas by random search. However, in homing experiments with a number of species observations of the initial homeward directed orientation, as well as extremely short homing times, exclude this possibility (Wallraff 1991). Recent satellite-tracking studies of homeward migration also clearly show the directedness of returning birds towards the breeding sites (Berthold *et al.* 1993).

Another possibility is that homing is performed by direct sensory contact with the goal. For example, when domestic pigeons are clock-shifted prior to displacement experiments, they nevertheless manage to reach their lofts and often with only little delay, despite initial orientation problems. This indicates that the information necessary for successful homing is gathered *en route*. There is no evidence for, or against, this mechanism being used by migrants (Wiltschko 1992).

A third hypothesis is that goal-oriented homing to familiar breeding grounds and wintering areas could be performed through some kind of mere route reversal or path integration of the migratory route flown before. However, although this is certainly a parsimonious explanation, there are a number of objections to it. First, route reversal has thus far not been demonstrated in birds in contrast to animals of other groups like arthropods or mammals. Secondly, displacement experiments with domestic pigeons, where all useful input channels (above all in the vestibular apparatus in the middle ear) were interrupted or disturbed, did not prevent the birds from homing successfully. Therefore, route reversal and path integration are neither the essential nor the only mechanism for homeward orientation (Wallraff 1991). The same holds true for many migratory species performing loop migration, i.e. flying distinctly different routes during homeward migration (Zink 1973–1985).

Current opinion holds that it is most likely that homing of migratory birds to their breeding grounds and returning to their previous wintering areas is either based on true navigation or a map-and-compass mechanism. In the first case, they would rely on one or several navigation mechanisms so far not understood but suggested to have either a magnetic or an olfactory basis. Both explanations involve birds using gradient maps based on at least two gradients of a physical substrate which extend over a sufficiently large area. They are experienced during ontogeny and later allow for homing on the basis of bi- or multi-coordinate navigation. With respect to the map-and-compass concept, birds are thought to combine an initial compass direction to the goal area (provided by a genetically determined migration vector, by route reversal or similar mechanisms) with a gradient map which comes into play in the vicinity of the final destination (Wallraff 1991; Berthold 1996). This very complex matter still needs much more investigation.

Flexibility, adaptability and evolutionary potential of spatiotemporal migration programmes in birds

Adjustment and buffer mechanisms

As mentioned in the section above on Endogenous time programmes, both genetically determined programmes of time and pattern of migratory activity (restlessness) as well as the patterns of migratory body mass changes and of fat deposition are under rigid endogenous control and appear to be extremely insensitive to environmental influences and disturbances. This has been demonstrated in a substantial number of experiments. For instance, when large parts of such a pattern or the entire initial phase were suppressed (by complete darkness at night or body mass reduction by offering nutrient-poor diet) neither a prolongation of the patterns nor another compensatory mechanism could be detected. Such tests have further shown that the two endogenous programmes for migratory activity (restlessness) and body mass changes (fattening) are largely independent of each other. Even the complete suppression of body mass increase and thus any substantial fat deposition in the premigratory period does not prevent the normal onset and further development of migratory activity. Thus, as long as physiological limits are not exceeded, the endogenous programmes proceed according to plan, quasi-'automatically', even when the bird is faced with a wide range of environmental conditions (Berthold 1985). The situation is fundamentally different when physiological limits are exceeded. When body mass in migratory birds is dramatically reduced by starvation to a critical premigratory, i.e. more or less fat-free, level during migratory fattening, migratory activity is strongly reduced or even arrested. In such a plight both experimental birds and conspecifics in the wild react with the following emergency measures. In nights following experimental food deprivation and starvation down to a premigratory body mass level, experimental migrants showed slight but significant increases in migratory activity. In the wild this would amount to an extended migratory flight well known from birds in poor body condition, stranded in a resting area with poor feeding conditions. The motivation for this appears to be the need to find a better resting area in such a critical situation. During the refeeding phase of experimental birds, when body mass and fat deposition increased again, migratory activity decreased sharply. This reduced migratory activity during fattening appears to reflect the situation of a bird in a staging area where it can effectively refuel. In fact, lean and fat-depleted individuals are regularly found to stage, for instance, in oases in deserts for several days or even longer periods when refattening is possible whereas conspecifics with normal fat deposits regularly continue migration after a 1-day stopover (Biebach 1995).

Faith in a reliable functioning of endogenous spatiotemporal migration programmes is often shaken by the idea that such programmes which eventually lead birds into areas completely hostile to life could never have evolved. Two important points have to be considered in this context. First, if the losses were limited and negligible with respect to population maintenance this could not affect the evolutionary processes. Unfortunately, however, the loss rate due to the failure of the birds' endogenous migration programmes cannot be estimated at present, and so, any further considerations are meaningless. The second point concerns the question as to whether a migrant led to an unsuitable target area by an endogenous programme would remain helpless and eventually die or whether it would leave the area in time. We know that the latter would be the case. Even largely resident forms are well known to leave their habitat by so-called escape movements if conditions become life-threatening (Berthold 1996). Escape migrations, deficiency or contingency movements characterise some groups of migratory birds in comparable situations: facultative partial migrants as well as exclusive migrants. From a number of detailed field and laboratory studies in a series of species investigated the following rules have begun to emerge: if a target area reached on away migration provides insufficient conditions, facultative migratory activity develops and the migrants move on in their previous migratory direction (Terrill 1990). Under laboratory conditions, such facultative activity can develop within less than an hour after food removal and the increased diurnal locomotor activity can be directed into the previous migratory direction even in nocturnal migrants (Berthold 1996). In the wild, migrants can move over many hundreds of kilometres on the basis of facultative migratory activity and long-distance migrants remain reactive to deteriorating conditions of the wintering area until complete moult starts (Gwinner *et al.* 1988; Terrill 1990). Short- and middle-distance migrants, which mostly undergo only a partial moult (of body feathers) during wintering, may remain responsive throughout the wintering period. In essence, the genetically determined and rigidly endogenously controlled migration programmes and exogenously triggered facultative migratory behaviour constitute a functional entity that, in all probability, enables inexperienced first-time migrants to find a suitable wintering area as long as environmental conditions do not change dramatically (Berthold 1996).

Another aspect of flexibility—i.e. to what extent long-lived migratory bird species may be able to modify their migration strategies due to experience and learning cannot be treated for the present as the available data basis is much too small. Year-long satellite-tracking of migratory individuals will provide information to address this question in the near future.

Adaptability and the microevolutionary potential of migration programmes

Despite the fact that avian spatiotemporal migration vectors are genetically determined, and at least partially, rigidly endogenously controlled, they can be adapted rapidly to novel environmental situations, and some have shown amazingly high evolutionary potential. This adaptation is most striking in the blackcap. Since the early 1960s, i.e. within the past three decades, the number of blackcaps wintering in the British Isles has increased from a few birds to thousands of individuals. Surprisingly, this novel wintering community does not consist of the local breeding population—which still migrates exclusively to the Mediterranean area— but is composed of blackcaps from continental central Europe. There, part of the population has developed novel migratory habits: they take a WNW instead of a SW migratory direction, and have chosen a novel wintering area. A detailed investigation has shown that this behavioural change is based on microevolutionary processes. Blackcaps caught during wintering in England, transferred to southern Germany and tested in orientation cages during the following autumn migratory period oriented, as expected, toward their previous wintering area, i.e. slightly north of west. Offspring of these birds, bred in captivity in southern Germany, showed a corresponding direction indicating that this novel direction is inherited and must have evolved through selection within the past 30 years. Of about eight, partly interrelated, selective advantages, the nutritional situation in the winter improved by bird-feeders in the British Isles appears to be most important. Others include shorter migration distance, earlier return to the breeding grounds and territory occupancy and, possibly, assortative mating with individuals returning early from the same wintering area (Berthold *et al.* 1992).

In the blackcap, and to some extent in some other species, it has been shown that the control of obligate partial migration (i.e. part of a given population migrates every year, the other part is sedentary) has a strong genetic basis. Furthermore, in a two-way selective breeding experiment it was demonstrated that exclusive migratoriness or residency can rapidly be selected for within a few (about three to six) generations. Thus, obligate partial migration in this species is characterised by an extremely high microevolutionary potential with respect to marked environmental changes (Berthold *et al.* 1990a). In another experiment with blackcaps, first migratory activity was recorded in hand-raised birds from the exclusively migratory southern German population. Offspring were then bred in aviaries and heritabilities were calculated by parent–offspring regressions and full-sibling correlations. In this population, a high amount of phenotypic and additive genetic variation was found for migratory activity. This could allow rapid microevolutionary changes of migratory habits in case of directed selection. For instance, under moderate selection intensities, the investigated German blackcap population of middle-distance migrants with current wintering grounds in the Mediterranean area could evolve into a population of short-distance migrants wintering in the area of Lyon–Geneva within 10–20 generations (Berthold and Pulido 1994).

There have been many recent changes in avian migratory behaviour which may be a reaction to global warming and related phenomena. They appear to be based to a large extent on changes of endogenous migration programmes through directed selection and can be summarised in five main categories: (1) reduction of migratoriness (in many partial migrants such as the blackbird, *Turdus merula*); (2) changes of migration periods, particularly later departures and earlier returns (above all in many short- and middle-distance migrants); (3) reduction of migratory distances (in a number of species such as the greylag goose, *Anser anser*); (4) changes of migratory directions and wintering quarters (with the blackcap as the most prominent example); and (5) extension of migratoriness (a rare phenomenon, mainly connected with range expansion as in the serin, *Serinus serinus*).

If global warming progresses and greenhouse effects continue to develop, more and more profound changes within the avian migration systems are expected to occur. Most likely, improved wintering conditions within the breeding area will increase sedentariness in many partial migrants and reduce migratoriness in short-distance migrants. Such an overall increase in resident and early returning individuals will progressively diminish ecological niches available for later arriving long-distance migrants. This situation may accelerate their already widespread decline and may finally lead to a fundamental change of avian communities in higher latitudes with a substantial overall reduction of migratoriness and consequently long-distance migrants (Berthold and Querner 1995).

Toward a comprehensive theory of avian migration

According to the classical theory avian migration is of polyphyletic origin, and long-distance migration is thought to have evolved stepwise from dispersal movements through facultative partial migration and obligate partial to regular migration, and most of the orientation mechanisms are believed to be the heritage from various ancestors (Terrill 1991; Berthold 1996).

Quite recently, we obtained data that allow us to formulate a very simple but comprehensive theory which explains genesis, control, changeability and adaptability of avian migration as a whole. This theory focuses on obligate partial migration.

At least in higher latitudes, partial migratory behaviour is extremely widespread in birds. Many species, exclusively migratory in high latitudes, are partially migratory or sedentary in lower latitudes, and contain migrants and non-migrants in medium latitudes. Even largely sedentary forms (i.e. sparrows or tits) have small fractions of individuals that perform migratory movements while, on the other hand, even in the most pronounced migrants (such as swallows or warblers) occasionally individuals are found that at least try to winter successfully in the breeding area. Thus, all these forms can be considered as, and may in fact be, partial migrants with presently highly varying amounts of phenotypic migratory and non-migratory individuals. In other words, obligate partial migration could be a basic phenomenon and it could in its most extreme expression represent forms with almost exclusively migratory individuals, mainly performing long-distance migration, and on the other hand, those with almost purely resident individuals (Berthold 1996).

A detailed analysis of the data obtained from a long-term study of an obligate partially migratory population (blackcaps from southern France) and from the two-way selective breeding experiment described in the section above on Adaptability and the microevolutionary potential of migration programmes has yielded the following results. First, in the selection experiment for higher and lower frequencies of migrants we found that the amount of migratory activity in the migratory fraction increased or decreased, respectively, indicating that both traits—migratoriness and the amount of migratory activity—are connected with respect to their control. Secondly, we found that the best prediction for non-migratory behaviour among siblings in a given nest is their parents' relatively low amount of migratory activity. From these and other results we draw the conclusion that in the population studied both traits, migratoriness or the phenotypic expression of the migratory urge and the amount of migratory activity in migratory active individuals are controlled by one and the same genetic system. In this system, the amount of migratory activity appears to be quantitatively inherited and the phenotypic dichotomy migrant/non-migrant is caused by a threshold (Pulido et al. 1996). If these findings are universally valid, the entire palette of the present migratory/resident bird behaviour can easily be explained by directed selection from obligate partially migratory forms. Directed selection of long-distance migrants in favour of shorter migration routes, i.e. of smaller amounts of migratory activity, would, after some time, decrease the amount of activity below a critical threshold and then result in phenotypically non-migratory individuals. Their number would then increase until sedentariness of almost the complete population will be reached. Selection acting against sedentariness would, on the other hand, finally end up in almost exclusive migratoriness and long-distance migration (Berthold et al. 1997).

At higher latitudes, ancestors of the present bird populations have often been forced to alter their degree of migratoriness along with dramatic environmental changes, e.g. in glacial and interglacial periods. This might explain the widespread evolution of obligate partial migration as a basis for any rapid and appropriate adaptation. Transition from migratoriness to sedentariness and vice versa may be accelerated by hybridisation of related forms through increased genetic variation and, as a consequence, increased evolutionary potential, as shown by the current work with redstart species. Furthermore, one has to bear in mind that obligate partial migration is not an avian speciality but is a widespread habit well known from many other groups of invertebrates and vertebrates, such as insects, crustacea, fish and others. It is highly likely that at least some of the primitive bird species inherited the capability of performing partial migration from pre-avian ancestors (Berthold et al. 1997). If this is true, birds have had from the very beginning an ideal basic equipment for almost all kinds of migratory movements or residency. Obligate partial migration could then have established as a universal avian evolutionarily stable strategy which is not changed on principle but allows through rapid directed selection, phenotypic expressions from almost exclusive sedentariness

through short- and middle-distance migration up to the most extreme forms of intercontinental or transoceanic long-distance migration. If this view is correct, long-distance migration is not fundamentally different from most of the other types of avian migration but is just
a special section of one and the same underlying control mechanism in a long chain of varying
phenotypic expression.

7 Landmark use and the cognitive map in the rat

Etienne Save, Bruno Poucet and Catherine Thinus-Blanc

Spatial behaviours are essential to the survival of all species of mammals. In spite of the large diversity of their anatomical morphologies and natural habitats, mammals have to orient, to navigate towards specific places by using landmarks (to reach food sources or mates) and finally to return to their nests or home sites. Therefore, spatial orientation may require similar basic information processes in all species.

Although some studies have described orientation and navigation abilities of different kinds of mammals in their natural environment (bats: Müller 1966; wolves: Peters 1973; foxes: Fabrigoule and Maurel 1982; chimpanzees: Boesch and Boesch 1984; wood mice: Benhamou 1990), much of the work on spatial behaviours has been conducted in the laboratory. Dating back to the first half of the twentieth century, Tolman's behavioural experiments emphasised the excellent performance of rats in spatial problem solving and maze running (Tolman 1948). According to Tolman, such abilities could not merely be interpreted in terms of stimulus–response associations but required the use of an internal spatial representation of the environment (cognitive map). In the 1970s, O'Keefe and Nadel provided a comprehensive review of the behavioural and neurophysiological data supporting this hypothesis and formulated the cognitive map theory that has been widely influential up to now (O'Keefe and Nadel 1978). A cognitive map, within which landmarks and places are represented relative to each other (defined as allocentric coding) rather than to the organism (defined as egocentric coding) allows the animal to exhibit a flexible performance in spatial tasks. For instance, rats display an impressive ability to remember locations (Olton and Samuelson 1976), to navigate accurately towards a hidden goal by novel routes (Morris 1981), to take shortcuts (Chapuis *et al.*1987) and detours (Tolman and Honzick 1930). The use of a cognitive map is postulated when spatial performance cannot be explained by simpler mechanisms. However, although this concept is now very familiar and has been extensively used not only in mammals but also in insects or in birds (see Gallistel 1990), the principles of organisation of the cognitive map are still obscure.

For over 25 years, a huge amount of work has dealt with the neural basis of the cognitive map. The fundamental role of the hippocampus and more widely of the hippocampal formation has been revealed especially by lesion studies and single-cell recordings (O'Keefe and Nadel 1978). The most convincing argument in favour of the existence of a 'neural' cognitive map in the hippocampus came from the finding by O'Keefe and Dostrovsky that many neurons recorded from the dorsal hippocampus of freely moving rats are intensely active only when the animal's head is in a particular part of its environment. Such units are called 'place cells' (O'Keefe and Dostrovsky 1971) and a given environment is entirely mapped, represented at the cellular level (see also Sherry and Healy, Chapter 8). Thus, although other brain regions (e.g. the associative parietal cortex) may also play a part, the hippocampal circuitry is undoubtedly one major neural substrate where the cognitive map is implemented. One of the current issues is to understand how place cell firing is controlled by environmental cues; in other words, what kind of spatial information is processed by place cells.

A number of now-classical spatial tasks have been developed to test the cognitive map hypothesis in the rat. It is worth mentioning the eight-arm radial maze (Olton and Samuelson 1976), the three-table problem (Maier 1932) and the Morris navigation task in the water maze (Morris 1981). This latter experimental set-up has provided the evidence that a rat processes and stores spatial information about its environment and uses this knowledge to find direct paths. In this task, a swimming rat can escape from water by finding a safe platform in a pool filled with opaque water. As the starting position of the rat is changed from trial to trial and the platform is located beneath the surface of the water, the rat must rely on the array of visual cues located outside the swimming pool so as to infer the platform location. Analyses of the paths taken to reach the platform show that, after a few training trials, the rat swims almost directly towards the platform. Once trained in the basic task, the rat can quickly learn new goal locations each day (Whishaw 1985). Even more importantly, it shows immediate transfer when novel start points to a familiar goal place are used. This result supports the hypothesis that during navigation the rat relies on the use of a stored representation of the spatial surrounding.

However, at least one question is still unresolved: What are the constituent elements of such 'stored representations'? The nature and complexity of the type of information which controls spatial behaviours is a crucial issue that needs to be addressed to understand better not only the nature of spatial representations—by defining their constituent elements—but also their functional properties. For instance, encoding multiple spatial relationships between landmarks and places appears more likely to lead to allocentric spatial representations than using rough discrete beacons. Indeed, in almost any experimental environment rats are usually provided with many cues, originating from a variety of sources and appearing in different sensory modalities (e.g. visual, olfactory, auditory, etc.). Nevertheless, it is difficult to assess the importance of these cues when they are simultaneously available to the animal.

The issue of how this variety of environmental cues are used for orienting has been investigated by using various experimental strategies. One strategy consists in testing animals in 'cue-controlled' situations. In such situations, only a few (usually visual) cues are available. For instance, manipulations of these cues have allowed to understand how rats use them to remember places in the radial arm maze (Suzuki *et al.*1980) and simpler cross-shaped mazes (O'Keefe and Conway 1980)

Another strategy consists in testing animals in situations where relevant information is no longer available for steering a trajectory to the goal or to make a choice. Either lights are turned off after visual information could be picked up by animals, or the goal is located in a region of the apparatus where the environmental (visual) cues cannot be perceived. Successful behaviour in such situations has been interpreted as a demonstration of the animals' capabilities for planning a trajectory and anticipating the outcome of an action (Collett et al.1986).

However, besides convincing data which demonstrate that rats are able to process multiple spatial relationships, other observations suggest that, under specific conditions, they may also rely on simpler processing, e.g. on the use of a rough reference direction, or 'compass' whose precise nature remains to be determined.

The aim of this chapter, reporting results from behavioural experiments and single cell recordings in the freely moving rat, is to underline that, although rats are expected to process the relational properties of a set of prominent environmental cues, they also often rely on uncontrolled (thus, unexpected) cues. The theoretical implication of this statement is that spatial processing is not strictly confined to a precise category of environmental information but, rather, should be envisioned as an 'opportunist system', using the most appropriate cues for spatial information encoding and efficient behaviour.

'Cue-controlled' situations: What is actually controlled?

In studies involving cue-controlled situations, the experimental apparatus is usually surrounded by curtains in order to eliminate the access to distal visual cues, and a source of white noise may prevent the rats to use auditory cues. The only relevant cue can be, for instance, one or several patterned pieces of cardboard affixed to the walls of the apparatus or on the curtain. Cue-controlled environments have been used by a number of authors (e.g. O'Keefe and Conway 1980; Suzuki et al. 1980; Poucet 1985) with various cue arrangements and manipulations. Such an approach has proved fruitful for showing that: (1) animals do make use of a configuration of cues to locate a goal; (2) spatial processing is quite different according to the cue arrangement (e.g. clustered above the goal or distributed around the experimental enclosure); and (3) hippocampal lesions have a selective deleterious effect in the latter case.

Cue-controlled environments have also been used to record single unit activity from complex spike ('place') cells in the hippocampus of freely-moving rats. A distinctive feature of hippocampal place cells is that they are intensely active only when the animal is in a particular part of its environment. The location where a given place cell fires is called the 'firing field'. Although place cells are active regardless of the view the animal is facing, environmental cues have been shown to greatly influence their activity (e.g. Muller et al. 1991).

O'Keefe and Speakman (1987) trained freely-moving rats to choose the correct arm of a cross-shaped maze placed within a curtained environment, with a number of controlled spatial cues distributed around the enclosure. The location of the goal arm varied from trial to trial and the cue configuration was rotated in register with the goal. Thus, the goal position remained constant relative to the cue configuration, but changed relative to the environment beyond the curtains ('static background cues'). O'Keefe and Speakman found that place cell spatial firing was controlled by the cues within the enclosure as the firing-field locations followed the rotation of both the maze and the cue configuration. However, a smaller proportion of place cells was found to fire in relation to the static background cues or to depend on the interaction between static background cues and controlled cues.

Krimm (1994) made observations which are consistent with O'Keefe and Speakman's findings. Rats were trained in a place learning task in a Morris water maze. The pool was surrounded by curtains and the only relevant cue was a large black cardboard affixed on the wall of the pool. Following acquisition, animals were given a test trial with the cue card removed. Surprisingly, rats' performance was not altered, and they were still able to locate the submerged platform.

In the two above experiments, the goal could be located only on the basis of its spatial relationships with environmental cues (this was confirmed in both experiments by various probe trials). The question at issue concerns the nature of such cues. Obviously, the information that the experimenter controls and manipulates—the cue(s) within the enclosure—is not the only one used by the animals. One possibility is that the rats rely on the memory of the spatial layout outside the curtain (to which they had been exposed before being released in the maze or the pool) so that they can relate the starting and/or goal location to this representation. A second hypothesis is that rats make 'on-line' use of distal uncontrolled cues, i.e. outside the curtained environment while they are navigating (O'Keefe and Speakman's 'static background cues'). Such uncontrolled cues might consist, for example, of distant noises emanating from recording devices, odours from neighbouring sources and so on. Because correct performance was observed as soon as the first trial during which the cue card was removed in Krimm's experiment, these 'uncontrolled cues' might have been processed even when the cue card was present. In other words, during training rats may have constructed a global representation of visually disconnected parts of space, and then made a delayed use of the relevant distal information (no longer available when inside the enclosure). Along the second hypothesis, the rats would have relied on uncontrolled distal cues, e.g. remote auditory cues, which were still available as they were navigating towards the platform

Delayed use of spatial information

The delayed use of spatial information for orienting has been classically considered as a demonstration that animals implement 'mapping' strategies as opposed to 'guidance' strategies (O'Keefe and Nadel 1978). The possibility that animals use mapping strategies is usually tested in the following way: the subject is shown the situation from a starting point but it is only after some delay that it is allowed to choose which route to take to reach the goal. In the meantime, the visual information relevant to locate the goal has been removed. O'Keefe and Conway (1980) demonstrated that rats trained in a cross-maze in a cue-controlled environment (as in O'Keefe and Speakman's experiment; also see previous section) with the cues distributed around the enclosure (mapping situation), were able to reach successfully the goal with delays of up to 30 min between the time that they were allowed to perceive the relevant cues and the moment the response was made. In contrast, the performance of rats trained with all the cues clustered above the goal (guidance situation), was poor after even short delays (20 s). Poucet (1985) provided evidence for the same distinction in cats which were trained in a place-learning task in a cross-maze. The only relevant visual cue was located either remote from the goal (mapping situation) or above the goal (guidance situation) and the delays between the removal of the cue and the response ranged from 8 up to 60 s. While a majority of cats were still successful at long delays in the mapping situation, most cats tested in the guidance situation could not perform correctly even when the delay was the shortest (8 s).

Other situations which have not been specifically designed to study the effects of delays on performance do raise, however, a similar issue. For instance, one of us (Save 1997) trained rats in a place-learning task in a Morris water maze. During each training session, rats received four trials with the lights on and four trials with an alternation of lights on and darkness. For these latter trials, an initial period of light (light phase) was followed by a period of darkness (dark phase) until the rat reached the platform. One group had a short light phase (SHORT group) corresponding to the moment that immediately follows release of the rat into the pool and during which it begins swimming. The other group had a longer light phase (LONG group) corresponding to twice the short period (Fig. 7.1a). The analysis of escape latencies and navigation accuracy (deviation with respect to the trajectory in light) revealed that the SHORT rats were impaired in maintaining an accurate trajectory in darkness whereas the LONG rats remained remarkably accurate (Fig. 7.1b). However, over long distances in darkness, LONG rats deviated gradually from the trajectory begun in light. This may reflect the fact that in the dark, the rats used not only the memory of their initial location to plan their travel direction to the platform but also the path integration or dead reckoning system (Etienne *et al.*, Chapter 3; Gallistel 1990). This navigational system is based on the processing of internal cues such as vestibular, somatosensory, proprioceptive cues. One major drawback of the path integration system is that it accumulates angular errors, thus limiting the accuracy of navigation beyond short distances. Reference to external cues is required to correct such errors and update the representation as a function of the trajectory's features.

Another experiment aimed at examining rats' abilities to integrate two visually disconnected parts of space into an overall representation also addresses the issue of the delayed use of spatial information (Schenk *et al.* 1997). Rats were allowed a full view of distant environmental cues from the periphery of a 'homing board' (Fig. 7.2, left panel). When they were in the central region of the board, they were prevented from seeing these landmarks (either the light was turned off or curtains around the central region prevented the rats from visually perceiving the environment). For a control group, the light was always off. The goal was a hole in the floor of the apparatus, which was connected to the home cage, under the board. The task consisted of escaping through one of the four holes at a fixed spatial position relative to the visually disconnected landmark array. Consequently, an accurate localisation of the correct hole implied that animals could construct and use a representation including two visually disconnected environments: the dark or bare arena containing the goal location and the distant cue array. Training was followed by probe trials during which escape was not possible, in order to rule out the use of cues emanating from the goal hole. The amount of time spent in the hole sectors (Fig. 7.2, right panel) was recorded. Although the poor performance of one of the groups (tested in the 'free-access' condition; see legend of Fig. 7.2) is difficult to interpret, it is clear that rats were capable of locating an inconspicuous goal located in an environment visually disconnected from relevant spatial information. In addition, the control group which never had visual access to the spatial layout did not demonstrate any preference for the sector containing the goal hole.

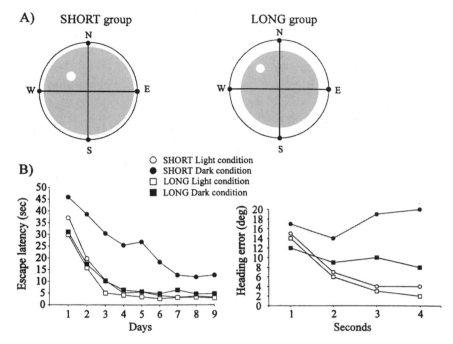

Fig. 7.1 (a) Experimental design. Each diagram represents a view from above of the water maze. Rats were trained to reach the platform (white circle) located in the NW quadrant from three starting places (N, S and W) with the light on (Light condition) and with an alternation of light and darkness (Dark condition). In this latter condition, the peripheral 'light area' corresponded to a narrow ring for the SHORT group, and to a wider ring for the LONG group (shown on the figure). Light was automatically turned off by the computer when the rat entered the central 'dark area' and the room remained in complete darkness as long as the animal swam in this area. (b) Results. The left panel shows the mean escape latency (in seconds) to reach the platform throughout training in both the Light and Dark conditions for each group. The SHORT group displayed higher escape latency than the LONG group in the Dark condition ($P<0.001$) and than its own performance in the Light condition ($P<0.001$). The right panel shows the heading error (defined as the angle between the start point-target azimuth and the animal's vector originating from the release point, irrespective of the direction of deviation) during 4 successive seconds of swimming after release of the animal in the pool at the end of training. SHORT rats were less accurate than LONG rats in the Dark condition ($P<0.001$) but not in the Light condition.

All together, these data demonstrate unambiguously that, provided animals have had the opportunity to perceive the visual layout of the environment for some duration, they are able to reach a goal when such information is no longer available. More importantly with regard to our concern, the failure of rats which had been exposed to a short light duration (Save's experiment) or which could never see the environment (Schenk *et al.* 1997) leads us to rule out the possibility that uncontrolled distal non-visual information may have been used by the animals; this is a conclusion apparently at odds with that drawn from the studies presented in the preceding section. It is difficult to determine why, although both kinds of cues are generally available, the rats rely only on prominent distal cues in some situations whereas in others they rely only on static background cues. This probably reflects the environmental differences and, in particular the reliability of the different categories of cues across situations (see Conclusions). However, although background cues are extremely difficult to control, it remains possible to neutralise their influence through the use of specific procedures. The following section presents, in some detail, such a procedure.

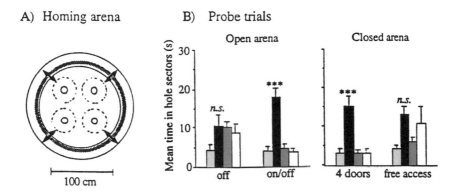

Fig. 7.2 (a) The two-compartment table. In one situation (open arena) the inner region was defined by switching off the room lights each time the animals entered it ('on/off' group). A control group ('off') was trained in total darkness (under infra-red light). In another condition (closed arena), the inner region was defined by a white curtain with fringes touching the surface of the table. In such a case, animals could access the arena from any direction by passing through the fringes ('free access' group). In another 'closed arena' condition (represented on the figure), a wall defined the arena which could be access only through four doors ('four-doors' group). (b) Time spent in the hole sectors during the 72 s probe trial with no hole connected. A control group had been trained in constant darkness ('off') in the open arena. As expected, they did not show any preference for the region of the escape hole. In contrast, rats from the 'on/off' group spent significantly more time around the escape hole. The same result was found in the closed arena condition for the 'four-door' group. In contrast, confusion between holes was recorded when access was unrestricted through the fringes ('free access' group). However, that group improved performance level up to that of the four-door group with additional training (reproduced from Schenk *et al.* 1995 with kind permission of Kluwer Academic Publishers).

Use of 'uncontrolled' distal cues

Among the wide range of environmental information that animals can use to orient, the geometrical features of the environment appear to be spontaneously selected (Poucet *et al.* 1986; Thinus-Blanc *et al.* 1987) and even predominate over conspicuous patterned cues. For instance, when a rat is required to orient in a rectangular chamber, it mainly relies on the shape of the chamber and neglects potential cues provided by either discrete inserts placed at corners or salient visual patterns placed on walls (Cheng and Gallistel 1984). However, because of the symmetry of the layout (such as the two opposite corners of the rectangular chamber), the goal location remains ambiguous and determining which corner contains the inconspicuous goal requires additional information. This issue has been addressed by one of us (Poucet, in preparation) in two experiments. The first was a purely behavioural examination of the navigation behaviour of rats in a rectangular environment. The second experiment was a unit-recording experiment conducted in rats freely moving in a rectangular arena.

In the behavioural experiment, rats were trained in a water maze navigation task. The apparatus was a rectangular pool visually isolated from the rest of the laboratory by a cylindrical curtain. The pool, filled with water made opaque by the addition of powdered chalk, was placed on a large table that was rotated 90° each day so as to make static background cues outside the curtaining irrelevant. Inside the pool, there was a small submerged platform initially located in the centre of the arbitrarily defined northeast quadrant.

Each day, the rats were tested in one four-trial session (two trials from each starting point). Following each daily session, a single probe trial lasting 60 s was conducted during which the platform was removed from the pool. The general schedule of the experiment is shown in Fig. 7.3. The experiment consisted of three distinct stages, each one consisting of five consecutive sessions. During stage 1, a large black cue card covered the entire wall of the long axis opposite the corner where the goal platform was located. Because the entire apparatus was rotated from day to day, rats could rely on two major classes of spatial information to locate the goal, namely: (1) the geometrical shape of the pool, and (2) the black cue card location. During stage 2, the black cue card was removed from the pool. In stage 3, Poucet attempted to rule out the use of static background cues stemming from the environment outside the curtained area by rotating the entire pool by 90° between the last (fourth) trial of the session with the platform in the pool and the probe trial with the platform removed. Therefore, if rats used both static background cues and the geometrical shape of the pool during the training trials, they could only rely on the geometrical shape of the pool during the probe trial.

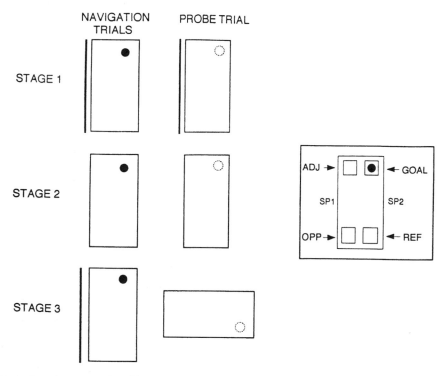

Fig. 7.3 A schematic representation of the arrangement used during each stage of the water maze navigation experiment. The pool was rotated 90°, 180° or 270° between daily sessions, and therefore the arrangements shown above represent only one of four possible dispositions. The goal platform (shown as a black circle) was kept in constant register relative to the large black cue card (shown as a black solid line) and overall rectangular shape of the pool during stage 1. The cue card extended along the whole wall of the pool. The location of the removed goal platform during probe trials is shown as a dotted line circle. The insert on the right side of the figure shows the two starting points SP1 and SP2 as well as the relative locations of the square-shaped areas that were used to measure times in quadrants.

The swim path of all trials was monitored and recorded by means of a video camera mounted above the pool. For the purpose of the present experiment, the main analysis consisted in comparing the time spent by the animal in four regions of the apparatus (Fig. 7.3). These regions were defined as small quadrants 15 cm square that were respectively: (1) GOAL: a quadrant defined as a square-shaped area centred on the goal platform location; (2) OPP: the quadrant diagonally opposite to the GOAL quadrant (3) ADJ: the quadrant in the corner directly adjacent (along the short axis of the rectangle) to the corner containing the GOAL quadrant and (4) REF: the quadrant directly adjacent (along the short axis of the rectangle) to the corner containing the OPP quadrant. According to the stage of the experiment, the quadrants of interest for analysis were: (1) GOAL versus OPP, to demonstrate the discriminability of the goal corner relative to the symmetric corner, and (2) OPP versus REF (or GOAL + OPP versus ADJ + REF), to demonstrate any preference for the symmetrically 'correct' quadrant relative to a corner almost equally distant from the goal but not equivalent on geometrical grounds.

The results of stage 1 (Fig. 7.4a) showed that rats quickly learned the location of the goal platform. Analyses of navigation paths during the first trial of each daily session and during probe trials revealed that navigation was mainly based on the use of the black cue card. This conclusion is suggested by the fact that the rats spent more time in the GOAL quadrant than in either the OPP or REF quadrants. In addition, no difference was observed in time spent in the OPP quadrant relative to the REF quadrant either during the first trials of each daily session or during the probe trial. Overall, the results of stage 1 suggest that the rats did not confuse the two symmetrical corners of the rectangle presumably because they used the cue card to disentangle the goal location from the opposite corner.

During stage 2 (Fig. 7.4b), no cue card was available to help the rats determine the location of the goal platform. Nevertheless, rats again displayed good performance during navigation trials, and their behaviour during probe trials clearly demonstrated that they had learned the goal location. Under these circumstances evidence was also found that rats' behaviour was initially based, at least partly, on the use of the geometrical shape of the pool. An analysis of navigation performance on the first trial of each daily session showed that rats spent the same amount of time in the GOAL and OPP quadrants, and spent more total time in GOAL + OPP quadrants as opposed to REF + ADJ quadrants. This result suggests therefore that, in the absence of a cue card and of a clear indication of the goal location relative to the laboratory (as the whole pool was rotated from day to day), rats relied mainly on the shape of the apparatus to find the goal platform on the first trial of each daily session. However, the preference for the two symmetrically 'correct' corners of the pool (i.e. GOAL and OPP quadrants) vanished within each daily session On the probe trial the rats would spend most of their time in the correct goal quadrant and visit equally the OPP and REF quadrants. This result indicates that by the end of each session the rats had come to associate the goal location with some uncontrolled static background cues likely to help the discrimination of the two opposite corners of the rectangular box.

During stage 3 (Fig. 7.4c), the pool was rotated not only from one daily session to another but also between the last (fourth) navigation trial of a given session and the probe trial that immediately followed. Thus, during the probe trial, rats could not use any uncontrolled static background cues from the laboratory to determine which one of the two opposite corners was

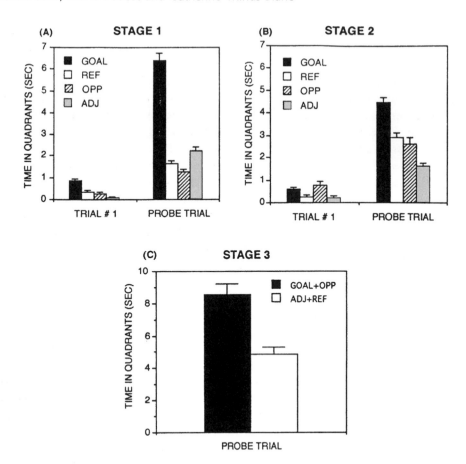

Fig. 7.4 Water maze navigation during the three stages of the experiment. (a) Stage 1. Mean time ($\pm$SE) spent in quadrants during the first navigation trial and during the final probe trial of each daily session. During both trial 1 and the probe trial, rats preferentially chose the correct goal quadrant compared with all other quadrants ($P<0.001$), and did not spend more time in the opposite quadrant relative to the reference quadrant. (b) Stage 2. Mean time ($\pm$SE) spent in quadrants during the first navigation trial and during the final probe trial of each daily session. During trial 1 of each daily session, rats spent more time in the two symmetrically 'correct' quadrants (GOAL+OPP versus REF+ADJ: $P<0.001$), and no difference between GOAL and OPP was observed. In contrast, the final probe trial of each daily session resulted in a significant preference for the GOAL quadrant compared with all other quadrants ($P<0.001$), and no difference between OPP and REF. (c) Stage 3. Mean time ($\pm$SE) spent in quadrants during the final probe trial of each daily session of stage 3. Rats spent more time in the two symmetrically 'correct' quadrants, GOAL+OPP, relative to the two symmetrically incorrect quadrants, REF+ADJ ($P<0.001$).

the most likely to contain the goal platform. The quadrant analysis revealed that, under these circumstances, rats displayed a consistent preference for the GOAL + OPP quadrants as opposed to the REF + ADJ quadrants. Thus, preventing the rat from associating the goal location with a consistent static background cue results in a clear preference for the geometrically 'correct' quadrants of the pool.

The behavioural results reported above show that rats use the geometry of the environment only when they cannot use either a salient visual cue or a directional cue stemming from the outside of the cue-controlled environment. One of the questions that arises from these results is the extent to which the geometrical shape of the recording environment could be used by the hippocampal place cell system to indicate the rat's position. To address this question, Poucet investigated the positional firing patterns of place cells recorded from rats while they could move freely in a rectangle-shaped arena. As there was no specific cue within the rectangular arena, only the shape of the apparatus was a useful cue for localisation. Under these circumstances, however, the situation was ambiguous because the symmetrical shape of the rectangle did not allow discrimination between the corner positions by itself. Therefore, the expectation was that place cell firing fields might occupy two symmetric positions across successive recording sessions.

In the present single-cell recording experiments, place units were recorded in both light and dark conditions, so as to address the contribution of visual information to place cell firing. A rat exploring a rectangular environment should be able, in principle, to deduce its position on the basis of the visual appearance of the environment and/or on the basis of its possible movements with respect to the long and short walls. Therefore, place cells recorded from a rat repeatedly introduced into a rectangular arena in darkness should fire at a consistent location. If the rat is disoriented, however, the cell should fire in symmetric locations within the rectangle. Furthermore, some time delay should be required before place field firing is established, as the rat first has to explore the box to determine where the long and short walls are located. Even though movement information can influence place fields, there remains a need for information about direction, presumably supplied by the stable framework of the room within which recording occurs. This can be tested by rotating the rectangular box and determining if the place fields rotate as well.

The methods were substantially the same as those used in past studies (Poucet et al. 1994; Save et al. 1996; Cressant et al. 1997). The recording chamber was a rectangular box with no top. The arena was visually isolated from the rest of the laboratory by a cylindrical curtain. To permit estimation of positional firing rates everywhere in the cylinder, rats were food-deprived and trained in a 'pellet-chasing' task in which they have to retrieve food pellets scattered into the cylinder. As the food pellets land in unpredictable places, the rat learns to run almost constantly over the whole floor surface. After training, rats were surgically implanted with a movable array of electrode wires aimed at the dorsal hippocampus. In addition to spike data, the head position of the rat was tracked by locating a red LED positioned on the mid-line about 1 cm above the head and somewhat forward of the rat's eyes.

Once a unit was isolated, it was recorded with the rectangular arena in the standard (STD) position (see Fig. 7.5). Additional sessions were made with the arena rotated either 45°, 90°, 180° or 270° relative to the laboratory frame. Also some sessions were recorded with the lights turned off. It is important to notice that the rat was not disconnected from the recording cable between consecutive sessions so as to ensure the stability of the electrophysiological signal. Rather, it was brought out of the rectangle apparatus and put in a small 'waiting' cage 50 cm from the rectangular arena within the curtained environment while the experimenter performed the appropriate rotation of the arena. One consequence of this procedure is that the rat was not disoriented between successive recording sessions.

Recordings were made from 12 dorsal hippocampal units, electrophysiologically classified as complex-spike place cells. All cells had one place field in the arena; each was active only when the rat's head was in a specific part (the 'field') of the arena and was virtually silent elsewhere. All cells reacted in a very similar way to the various manipulations that were made.

Figure 7.5 shows the effects of rotating the field on the spatial firing pattern for one place cell recorded for 12 consecutive sessions. As can be seen, rotation of the rectangular arena by 180° from the standard position did not alter the firing pattern of the cell, nor did it change the position of the firing field. In other words, the firing field position does not appear to be tied to a specific local cue within the rectangular apparatus. Rather, as the arena did not provide a cue likely to permit discrimination of the two opposite sides of the rectangle, the location of the cell firing field appears to be controlled by some external uncontrolled cues fixed relative to the environment.

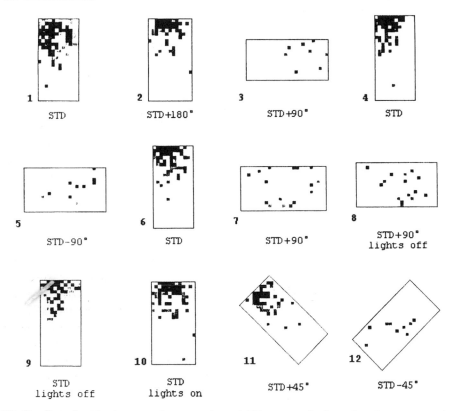

Fig 7.5 The effects of rotating the rectangular arena on the spatial firing pattern of a place cell. To obtain a positional firing rate distribution, the total time the red light was detected in each pixel and the total number of spikes in each pixel were accumulated for the session duration. The rate in each pixel was the number of spikes divided by the dwell time. Grey-shaded firing rate maps were used to visualise positional firing rate distributions. The initial position of the arena is referred to as standard (STD) and all rotated positions are relative to this initial arrangement.

The results obtained with 90° rotations of the arena stand in sharp contrast with those obtained when a 180° rotation is made. In all cells, the rotation of the arena by 90° from the standard position produced a dramatic reduction in the firing rate of the cell. In the firing rate maps shown in Fig. 7.5, the decrease of the cell firing rate is seen as an almost complete vanishing of the firing field. It is important to notice that this effect is reversible, that is when two 90° rotations are made in succession (therefore resulting in the alignment of the arena with its standard position), the cell resumes firing and a clear firing field can be observed at the location it occupied initially (before any 90° rotation). Such effects can be observed both with the lights on and with the lights off. This indicates that the cue used to anchor the cell firing field is non-visual. Unfortunately, it is impossible to determine the exact nature of this cue at this time. Finally, the cell shown in Fig. 7.5 was also recorded during a 45° counterclockwise rotation session that followed a recording session conducted with the box in the standard position. It is clear that this rotation did not result in any major change in the firing pattern of the cell. In contrast a 90° clockwise rotation conducted after the last 45° counterclockwise rotation (which results in a 45° clockwise rotation of the rectangle relative to the laboratory frame) again resulted in a cessation of cell firing.

These results have several important implications. First, they indicate that place cells can fire appropriately in a consistent place even when such a place is signalled only by the shape of the apparatus. Secondly, under the non-disorientation procedure used in the present experiment, the system makes use of a reference direction fixed relative to the laboratory frame (i.e. relative to a static background cue). One, therefore, is led to put forward the hypothesis that the navigational system responsible for setting the angular coordinate 'selects' some, as yet, unknown feature of the environment as a stable anchor so that when the rectangle is not in register with the stable reference direction, a mismatch is detected. All cells recorded under this circumstance stopped firing, an alteration indicative of a 'complete remapping' which might be taken to reflect the effect of such a detected mismatch (Quirk et al. 1990; Bostock et al. 1991).

Conclusions

The main conclusion from these studies is that animals can simultaneously use different categories of cues for navigation. In some experiments, these cues are those that are manipulated by the experimenter. For example, the animals failed to locate the hidden goal when they were either consistently tested in total darkness (Schenk et al. 1997) or prevented from seeing the surrounding for a sufficient duration (Save 1997). This observation allows us to rule out that an uncontrolled distal cue (e.g. compass information, overall reference direction) had been used. In contrast, in other experiments, animals tend to rely on uncontrolled background cues (Krimm 1994), or on both controlled and uncontrolled cues (O'Keefe and Speakman 1987). In addition, when proximal controlled information does not unambiguously specify the goal position (Poucet's experiment, stage 2), then rats use static background cues. Indeed, if an unusual change of the position of the apparatus with respect to the external environment is made (Poucet's stage 3), the frame of reference provided by external background cues cannot be used to locate the goal. The geometrical properties of the field then become the only relevant spatial information for place navigation.

These conclusions call for several remarks. The first one concerns the respective properties of the information conveyed by an array of visual cues and of the non-visual uncontrolled information that appears to be used in some cases. Although auditory and olfactory cues may provide some spatial information to the rats (Tomlinson and Johnston 1991), their reliance on them is probably limited. For instance, there is no evidence that rats can rely on a configuration of distinct auditory or olfactory cues to display complex spatial behaviour. Because the informational content of odours and sounds in terms of distance and direction is likely to be unstable and subject to interference, rats may use them only as an indication of a rough overall directional reference. In contrast, vision allows precise processing of spatial information (Thinus-Blanc and Gaunet 1997). It remains true, however, that the rough frame of reference provided by non-visual uncontrolled cues can be used by animals. Such an overall direction of reference may be essential to ensure the spatial consistency of distinct parts of the environment. For example, it may be useful for relating to each other, regions of space that do not share common landmarks.

The fact that the animals take into account different categories of cues suggests that they are able to use multiple frames of reference. This would allow the animal to compensate for the irrelevancy of one given frame (when the apparatus is rotated for instance in Poucet's experiment, stage 3) by the reliance on another frame. Such an idea is consistent with the results of a recent unit recording study by Gothard *et al.* (1996) showing that hippocampal place cells can be bound to distinct reference frames (involving landmarks, static background cues, starting point). Most interestingly, some cells (termed 'disjunctive' cells) were found to encode locations separately with respect to different frames of reference. However, Gothard *et al.* did not find evidence for a hypothetical population of cells (termed 'conjunctive' cells) whose activity would reveal an interaction between reference frames. In contrast, the activity of place cells recorded by Poucet seems to be bound to both the framework depending on the static background cues and the geometrical features of the rectangle, as these cells stopped firing when the rectangular arena was not aligned with the external frame of reference.

To conclude, the present results show that rats often tend to rely on 'uncontrolled' cues that appear to be used as an overall reference direction. Such cues provide robust and reliable information that allows the animal to navigate efficiently. In contrast, visual cues and in particular those emanating from the proximal layout provide animals with more precise spatial information. The counterpart of this precision is that the appearance of these cues is more likely to change as a function of the subject's movements within the apparatus. Extracting spatial invariants from the versatile appearance of the environment requires probably a more important cognitive effort because the information to be processed is plentiful.

Finally, it is tempting to analyse the impact of different categories of cues on spatial behaviour in terms of hierarchy. However, the reliance on such or such category is heavily dependent on the specific constraints of the task and on the animal's motivational state, etc. Therefore a hierarchical distinction between different categories of spatial cues may not be functionally valid and generalisable.

8 Neural mechanisms of spatial representation

David Sherry and Sue Healy

Our modern understanding of the neural basis of spatial orientation begins with a theory about the function of the mammalian hippocampus. In their book, *The hippocampus as a cognitive map*, John O'Keefe and Lynn Nadel (1978) proposed that the hippocampus was a neural structure dedicated to creating and maintaining a mental map of space. This theory rested on two observations. The first was that some complex spike cells in the rat hippocampus, so called because of their pattern of electrical discharge, were selectively active when the animal was in certain places in its environment (O'Keefe and Dostrovsky 1971). The receptive fields of these cells were locations in space. When the animal left the place where the place cell was active, the cell became electrically quiet. The locations in which place cells fired were of various shapes and sizes and different cells were usually active in different places (Fig. 8.1).

The second important observation for the cognitive map theory was that damage to the hippocampus disrupted spatial orientation in rats. Animals with lesions of the hippocampus, or with their hippocampus removed, could not find their way around, even in familiar environments (Morris *et al.* 1982).

Since the theory of the hippocampus as a cognitive map was first proposed there has been an enormous amount of research on the hippocampus, on spatial orientation and on the relation between the two. What follows is a brief survey of current ideas and research findings in this rapidly changing field. Embedded in this survey are several general themes. It is now clear that the hippocampus does not act exclusively as a cognitive map of space. It also clear that some important neurons involved in spatial orientation, the 'head direction cells', lie outside the hippocampus. Furthermore, whatever the hippocampus does, it does not do it alone but in concert with other parts of the brain and there is growing understanding of the reciprocal communication that occurs between the hippocampus and other brain areas. Finally, there is a renewed interest in how best to capture theoretically the essential features of spatial orientation. The idea of the cognitive map, first proposed by Tolman (1948), has been an important and influential stimulus to research. But it is really more a metaphor than a theory. Research on path integration, landmark use, the sun compass and snapshot orientation (described in other chapters of this book) are attempts to specify more concretely exactly what makes up a 'cognitive map' of space.

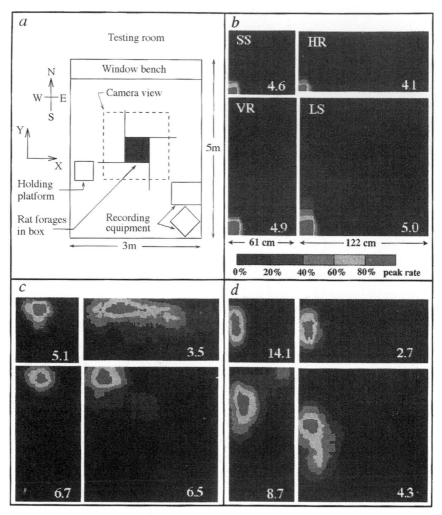

Fig. 8.1 The receptive fields of hippocampal place cells. Rats were observed in an enclosure which could be varied in size, from a small square (SS), to a horizontal rectangle (HR), vertical rectangle (VR) or a large square (LS) by moving the walls of the enclosure. The location of the rat, recorded by a video camera above the enclosure, was combined with recordings of the firing rates of place cells to produce firing rate maps like those shown for the three cells b, c and d. The peak firing rate of place cell b occurred at a fixed distance from the west and south walls for all enclosures. Peak firing rate for cell c was at a fixed distance from the north and west walls. Place cell d had a peak firing rate at a fixed distance from the west wall and at a proportion of the distance between the north and south walls. Shading indicates the location of the rat when the firing rate of the cell reached the indicated percentage of its peak firing rate. The actual peak rates, in spikes per second, are shown in the bottom right of each enclosure. Cells b and c were recorded from CA1, cell d from CA3. From O'Keefe and Burgess (1996).

Neuroanatomy

Its distinctive anatomy is probably responsible in some degree for the remarkable level of interest in the function of the hippocampus. Various properties have been attributed to the internal circuitry of the hippocampus. Lesion studies have a played a central part in attempts to understand the function of the hippocampus, one of the most well-known being the classic study by Scoville and Milner of the patient H.M. (Scoville and Milner 1957). H.M. became amnesiac following a surgical procedure performed to control epilepsy. The operation involved bilateral removal of part of the temporal lobe and included much of the hippocampus. Clinical case studies and lesion studies with rats and non-human primates continue to be a major source of information about hippocampal function, and a general picture of hippocampal anatomy is required to understand the results of this research, and the difference of opinion over how these results should be interpreted.

Connections within the hippocampal formation

Although there is variation among mammals in the size and shape of the hippocampus, its intrinsic circuitry is very distinctive and is conserved across species (Fig. 8.2). The primary input to the hippocampus, the perforant path, originates in the neighbouring entorhinal cortex and terminates on the granule cells of the dentate gyrus. Mossy fibres, consisting of the axons of dentate gyrus granule cells, project on to pyramidal cells in the CA3 field of the 'hippocampus proper'. The CA designation, for cornu Ammonis, derives from de Garengeot's 1724 remark that the external shape of the human hippocampus resembles the horns of Ammon, an Egyptian god sometimes depicted endowed with rams' horns (Lewis 1923). Axons of CA3 pyramidal cells project to other cells within CA3 and also make up the Schaffer collaterals which project to pyramidal cells in CA1. This sequence of projections from the entorhinal cortex to dentate gyrus to CA3 to CA1 constitutes the 'trisynaptic circuit' of the hippocampus. Cells in CA1 project in turn to cells in the subicular complex, which have projections back to the entorhinal cortex.

The intrinsic circuitry of the hippocampus as described above is largely unidirectional. Although hippocampal cells project to many subcortical regions outside the hippocampus, the sequence of synaptic activation within the hippocampus, nevertheless, follows a route from the entorhinal cortex to CA1 (Amaral 1987). This anatomical organisation, combined with physiological data on the sequential activation of cells within the hippocampus, led to the proposal that the hippocampus was organised in lamellae—thin layers—arranged orthogonal to the long axis of the hippocampus (Anderson et al. 1971). Because each lamella would contain a complete path of synaptic activation (from entorhinal cortex to dentate gyrus to CA3 to CA1) it was proposed that the hippocampus consisted of a series of parallel modular units. More recent anatomical evidence, however, shows that projections traversing the long axis of the hippocampus are as important in the three-dimensional organisation of the hippocampus as projections contained within the plane of the putative lamellae (Amaral and Witter 1989). It is also clear that the classical view of the hippocampal trisynaptic circuit, described above, is a simplification. Direct inputs from the entorhinal cortex to CA1 and CA3 have been identified, along with direct output from CA1 to the entorhinal cortex (Jones 1993).

Finally, why 'hippocampus'? Because according to Guilio Cesare Aranzi (1530–1589), 'In its length it extends toward the anterior parts and the front of the brain and is provided with a flexous figure of varying thickness. This recalls the image of a Hippocampus, that is, of a little sea-horse' (Lewis 1923, p. 217).

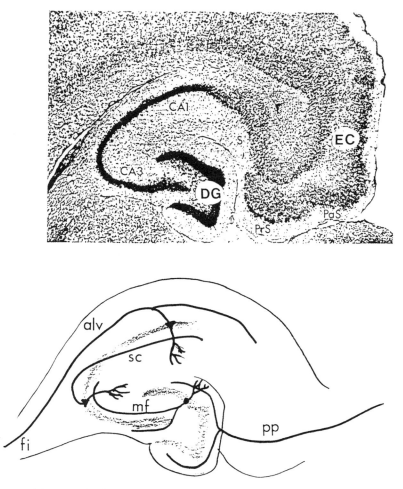

Fig. 8.2 Anatomy of the mammalian hippocampus. A horizontal section of the rat hippocampus is shown in the upper part of the figure. The most conspicuous features of this thionin-stained section are the cell bodies of granule cells in the dentate gyrus (DG), pyramidal cells in the CA cell fields (CA1, CA3) and the neuronal layers of the entorhinal cortex (EC). A drawing of the section in the lower part of the figure shows the perforant path (pp) and trisynaptic circuit. Other abbreviations: alv, alveus; fi, fimbria; mf, mossy fibres; PaS, parasubiculum; PrS, presubiculum; S, subiculum; sc, Schaffer collateral. Photomicrograph from Amaral and Witter (1989).

Hippocampal input and output

Apart from entorhinal input, the dentate gyrus and CA cell fields receive few direct inputs from the cortex. Cortical inputs converge instead on the subiculum and entorhinal cortex, whence they are passed on to the hippocampus. By this route the hippocampus receives highly processed input from most sensory modalities. Most of the rat entorhinal cortex receives input from the olfactory bulb, not surprisingly, perhaps, given the importance of olfaction in the behaviour of rats. However, the hippocampus does receive extensive subcortical inputs directly, including cholinergic projections from the septal region to the dentate gyrus, CA3, subicular complex and entorhinal cortex, hypothalamic projections to dentate gyrus and CA3, and thalamic projections to the subicular complex, entorhinal cortex and CA1.

Output from the subiculum and entorhinal cortex is a major pathway by which the hippocampus influences cortical activity. The perirhinal cortex, the cortex of the temporal pole, the caudal parahippocampal gyrus and the caudal cingulate gyrus all receive projections from the subicular complex or entorhinal cortex and it is from these way stations that the hippocampal signals ultimately reach temporal, parietal and frontal cortex (Amaral 1987)

Subcortical outputs occur primarily through the fimbria and include projections to the septal nuclei, nucleus accumbens, thalamus and mamilliary nuclei. A major source of output through the fimbria is the alveus, made up of the axons of CA1 pyramidal cells. There is recent evidence that projections from Ammon's horn to the lateral septal nuclei may be topographically organised (Risold and Swanson 1996). Because different regions within the lateral septal nucleus exert influences on different kinds of behaviour, such as ingestion and male and female sexual behaviour, this topographical organisation of hippocampal projections raises the possibility that different parts of the hippocampus selectively influence different categories of behaviour. There are also extensive commissural connections between the cell fields of the left and right hippocampus.

Hippocampal place cells

Hippocampal place cells show patterns of electrical discharge that depend on where the animal is in space (O'Keefe and Dostrovsky 1971). Recording electrodes in the cell fields of the hippocampus, usually of a laboratory rat, can be combined with video-recordings of the animal's location in an enclosure, to reveal how the pattern of electrical discharge of a single place cell varies with the animal's location (Fig. 8.1). Some cells have relatively invariant place fields that do not change as the size and shape of the enclosure confining the animal is changed (O'Keefe and Burgess 1996). The place fields of other cells enlarge, contract, split in two, and sometimes disappear as the shape and size of the immediate environment changes.

Despite the remarkable properties of place cells and a number of interesting theoretical proposals, there is no generally accepted account of the function of place cells in spatial orientation. O'Keefe and Burgess (1996) favour the view that place cells encode distance from edges as a normal or Gaussian distribution of cell activity with the mean at a fixed distance from the edge. 'Distance' in this model can be linear distance or relative distance, for example, 20% of the way across an enclosure. Place cells are sensitive to more than one edge and the sum of the normal curves encoding distance gives rise to the shape of a cell's place field. A rather different model suggests that place cells may be part of a system of path integration (McNaughton et al. 1996; see also Etienne et al., Chapter 3). According to this hypothesis, information from the animal's self-generated motion is integrated with place cell output to produce path integration with periodic positional fixes on known landmarks.

Head direction cells

Another family of cells is also sensitive to orientation in space but unlike hippocampal place cells, these cells exhibit maximum rates of electrical discharge when the animal's head is pointing in a particular direction. Head direction (HD) cells are found outside the hippocampus in the dorsal presubiculum, the posterior parietal cortex, retrosplenial cortex and anterior thalamus. HD cells are not sensitive to whether the head is raised or lowered above the horizon or rolls to the left or right, but instead show maximum firing rates when the animal points its head to a particular azimuth, or point on the horizon.

Taube and Burton (1995) observed how the preferred direction of HD cells changed as rats moved from a familiar cylindrical enclosure, along a passageway with two right-angled turns, and into a novel rectangular enclosure (Fig. 8.3). The preferred direction of most cells was remarkably stable, changing only 6–30° after negotiating the passageway and entering the novel, differently shaped rectangular environment. Cells maintained their firing direction when they returned to the cylinder. In the cylindrical enclosure, however, rotating a familiar conspicuous cue card by 90° caused the preferred direction of HD cells to rotate in the same direction by 45–90°. When animals next left the cylindrical enclosure and moved along the passageway toward the rectangle, HD cells tended to revert immediately to the preferred direction they had formerly shown in the cylinder, passageway and rectangle. Taube and Burton (1995) note that when recordings were available from multiple HD cells, the cells tended to stay in register as the animal moved, and to shift in register in response to changes in the position of the landmark.

This pattern of results suggests that HD cells receive both idiothetic input that allows them to maintain a stable compass bearing in novel environments, and landmark input that allows them to maintain a preferred firing direction with respect to familiar landmarks after these landmarks are moved (Taube *et al.* 1996). Idiothetic information, generated by self-motion, is an essential component of navigation by path integration, or dead reckoning (see Etienne *et al.*, Chapter 3). Idiothetic input generated by movement of the rat out of the cylinder, around corners in the passageway and into the rectangle would provide sufficient information for HD cells to maintain a stable firing direction *en route* and in a novel environment. Change in preferred firing direction following change in the position of a landmark, however, also shows that HD cells are affected by landmark information. In a simple path integration system, heading errors tend to increase with distance travelled, and path integration therefore requires periodic fixes on the animal's position, using either familiar landmarks or some known frame of reference. The convergence of idiothetic and landmark signals on HD cells suggests that they may be a component of a path integration navigation system in rats (see also McNaughton *et al.* 1996).

Genetic variation in hippocampal mossy fibres

Mossy fibre projections from dentate gyrus granule cells enter CA3 at various levels. Some terminate just above the pyramidal cell layer on the apical dendrites of CA3 neurons, some terminate within and just below the pyramidal cell on the basal dendrites of these cells (Fig. 8.2). The latter projections, called the intra- and infrapyramidal mossy fibre projections (IIP-MF) show remarkable variation among inbred strains of mice (Fig. 8.4). The length and size of IIP-MF is correlated with performance on spatial maze tasks by these mouse strains (Schwegler and Lipp 1995). On the radial arm maze, for example, with extramaze cues available and delays imposed between successive choices, the number of errors on the maze

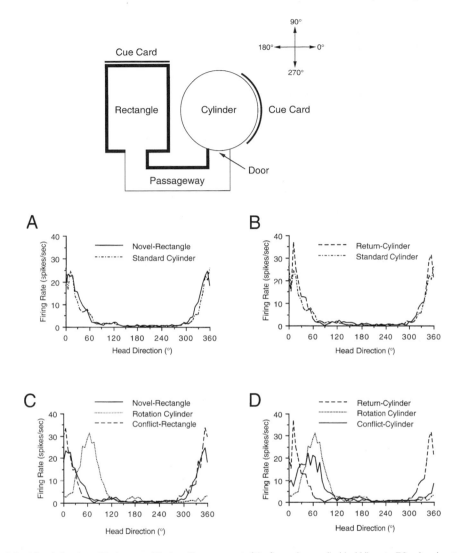

Fig. 8.3 A head direction cell in the postsubiculum. The upper part of the figure shows cylindrical (diameter 76 cm) and rectangular (51 × 68 cm) enclosures with large moveable cue cards, connected by a passageway. (a) The preferred firing direction of the cell did not change when the animal moved from the standard cylinder to the novel-rectangle. (b) The cell maintained its firing direction when the animal left the rectangular enclosure and re-entered the cylinder (return-cylinder). (c) A 90° rotation of the cylinder cue card produced a 60° rotation in the same direction of the preferred firing direction of the cell in the cylinder (rotation cylinder). When the animal entered the passageway and proceeded to the rectangle, the preferred firing direction of the cell returned to its initial orientation as soon as the animal entered the passageway (conflict-rectangle). (d) The preferred firing direction of the cell maintained its orientation to the rotated cylinder cue card when the animal returned to the cylinder from the rectangle (conflict-cylinder). Novel-rectangle and return-cylinder data are shown for comparison in (c) and (d). From Taube and Burton (1995).

and size of IIP-MF for nine inbred mouse strains was highly correlated (Schwegler and Lipp 1995). Although this correlational result does not necessarily indicate that variation in IIP-MF is the cause of the observed differences in maze performance, further studies show similar effects when the size of IIP-MF is manipulated experimentally. In the mouse strain DBA/2, which normally has short mossy fibre projections (Fig. 8.4) and poor spatial learning,

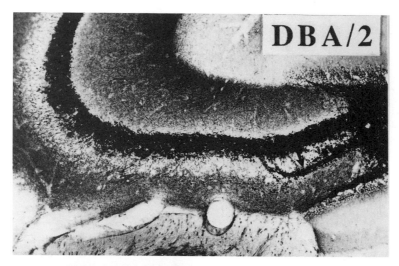

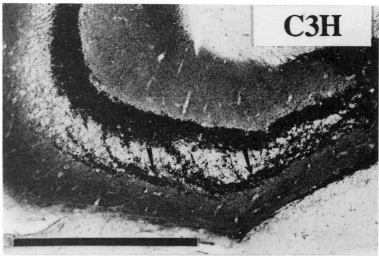

Fig. 8.4 Infrapyramidal mossy fibres (arrows) in horizontal sections of the hippocampus for two inbred mouse strains, DBA/2 and C3H. The extent of mossy fibre projections is shown in this section using Timm's stain. Scale bar equals 0.5 mm. From Lipp and Schwegler (1989).

thyroxine administered postnatally causes an increase in the size of IIP-MF. In these thyroxine-treated animals, IIP-MF size and radial maze performance was again found to be highly correlated.

The size of IIP-MF projections is not correlated with performance on a variety of non-spatial tasks and non-spatial versions of the radial-arm maze. On a Y-maze discrimination task, however, in which the mouse must learn that small metal plates indicate which maze arm to choose to avoid a puff of air, successful performance among mouse strains is correlated with the size of IIP-MF (Schwegler and Lipp 1995). Thus, although genetic variation in IIP-MF clearly influences spatial ability, it also has effects on at least one task with no obvious spatial component.

The hippocampus and spatial behaviour

What part, then, do the folded interleaved layers of hippocampal cells and their synaptic connections play in cognition? Despite the long history of interest in the hippocampus and the volume of research findings available, there is no consensus on the matter.

> The general finding that rats without a hippocampus were impaired on those tasks that required the utilisation of spatial and contextual information stands in contrast with the spared performance that was found in learning about and handling (even complex) non-spatial information (Jarrard 1993, p. 9).

> . . . spatial memory in rodents, as well as conscious recollection and explicit memory expression in humans, are prime examples of a fundamental declarative memory function mediated across species by the hippocampus (Eichenbaum 1996, p. 193).

This lack of a clear understanding of the function of the hippocampus despite rather good understanding of its structure, prompted the anatomist W.M. Cowan to propose that one function mediated by the hippocampus was 'the sense of frustration' (Swanson 1979). This situation persists because some well-designed behavioural experiments lead to the first conclusion quoted above, while others lead to the second. Two examples illustrate this.

The existence of place cells is tantalising evidence that the hippocampus has something to do with locations in space, but is not conclusive by itself. More complete evidence comes from experiments showing that rats with hippocampal lesions are impaired in spatial orientation but not in other tasks. Such animals perform poorly in radial-arm mazes, requiring many more choices than control animals to visit each arm of the maze to collect food. Rats with hippocampal damage also have difficulty in learning the location of a hidden escape platform in the water maze, something control animals do readily (Morris et al. 1982).

The water maze consists of a circular pool of water with a single submerged platform. The rat cannot see the platform because the water has been made cloudy with powdered milk or small pellets that float on the surface. When swimming in the pool, the rat usually has a clear view of the room and 'extra-maze' cues surrounding the pool. 'Maze' is actually a misnomer for this apparatus, because the rat is free to swim anywhere in the pool until it finds the platform and climbs on to it. The water maze can be used in various ways. In a typical experiment, a rat learns over successive trials that there is a platform to be found in the pool, and then is given test trials in which the platform is removed. Its memory for the spatial location of the platform can be assessed by recording the amount of time it spends swimming in the quadrant of the pool that formerly contained the platform and by quantifying the length and shape of the path the animal takes. A variety of experiments have shown that animals learn the location of the platform with respect to prominent extra-maze cues, although learning to search, for example by avoiding the wall of the pool, is also an important component of successful water maze performance (Cain and Saucier 1996). In an early experiment with this apparatus Morris et al. (1982) found that rats with hippocampal lesions performed poorly in comparison with control animals in learning the location of the escape platform (Fig. 8.5). Hippocampal rats showed little deficit in locating the platform when it protruded slightly above the water's surface, indicating that lesions of the hippocampus did not impair vision or other components of the task. Other experimental evidence shows that hippocampal lesions do not disrupt the ability of rats to learn a variety of complex non-spatial tasks (Jarrard 1995).

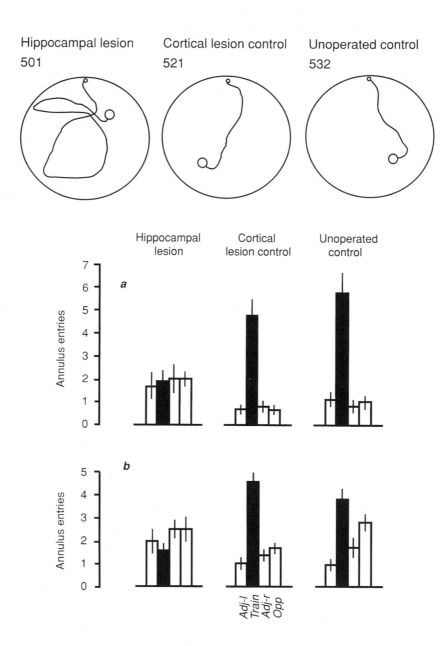

We will turn next to an experiment that provides evidence for the view that the function of the hippocampus cannot be exclusively spatial. Bunsey and Eichenbaum (1996) trained rats on a series of odour associations in which rats had to dig through a layer of sand and ground rat chow in a small cup to obtain a food reward. Scents could be added to the sand and chow mixture to create samples and test items with distinctive odours. Rats were then trained that if the first sample cup they were given carried odour A, then in the pair of cups presented next, food would be found in the cup carrying odour B, but not the cup carrying odour Y (Fig. 8.6). If the sample cup carried odour X, then in the pair of cups presented next, food would be found in the cup carrying odour Y, but not the cup carrying odour B. Once this association had been learned (A→B, not Y; X→Y, not B) rats were trained on a second association. For this task odours B and Y were used as samples. Odour B in the sample cup indicated that food would be found in the cup with odour C but not in the cup with odour Z. Odour Y in the sample indicated the presence of food in the cup carrying odour Z, not the cup with odour C.

The tests of interest were whether or not the rats treated these associations as transitive and symmetrical. That is, when presented with a sample cup with odour A, how would the rat behave when given a choice between cups with odours C and Z? If it treated the associations as transitive (A→B, B→C), it should choose C. In another test, the animal encountered odour C in a sample cup, and was offered a subsequent choice between cups with odours B and Y. If the rat treated the associations as symmetrical (B↔C), it should choose B. It is important to note that these transitivity and symmetry tests consisted of combinations of samples and choices that were novel to the rat.

Rats with neurotoxic lesions that destroyed the dentate gyrus and CA cell fields learned the basic associations. Their performance was slightly below that of control animals, but the difference was not statistically significant (Bunsey and Eichenbaum 1996). There was a dramatic difference, however, between hippocampally lesioned animals and controls on the transitivity and symmetry tests. Rats with an intact hippocampus showed odour preferences that would be expected if they treated the associations as transitive and symmetrical. Hippocampally lesioned animals showed no odour preference in choice tests on transitivity or symmetry tests (Fig. 8.6).

These results show that damage to the rat hippocampus disrupts performance on a task that has no obvious spatial component. The deficit seems more one of inability to combine remembered associations in order to make an appropriate choice, a deficit reminiscent of the impairments found in human amnesiacs with hippocampal damage (Zola-Morgan *et al.*

Fig. 8.5 The effects of hippocampal lesions on behaviour in the Morris water maze. The large circles represent the water maze and the small circles represent the location of the hidden platform. Swim paths are shown for rats with: the entire hippocampus removed by aspiration; a lesion of the neocortex overlying the hippocampus; and control procedures (Control). Parts (a) and (b) of the Figure show the behaviour of rats in test trials in which the platform was removed from the water maze. (a) Shows test trials following experience with a hidden platform, and (b) shows test trials following experience with a visible platform that protruded above the water surface. The graphs show the number of times the rat entered an imaginary ring, or annulus, equal in size to the platform located in each of four quadrants of the water maze. Annulus entries for the familiar location of the platform (Train, dark bars) are shown, along with annulus entries for the adjacent quadrant on the left (Adj-l), the adjacent quadrant on the right (Adj-r) and the opposite quadrant. Animals with hippocampal lesions do not swim preferentially over the former location of the platform, while cortical and control animals do so reliably. From Morris *et al.* (1982).

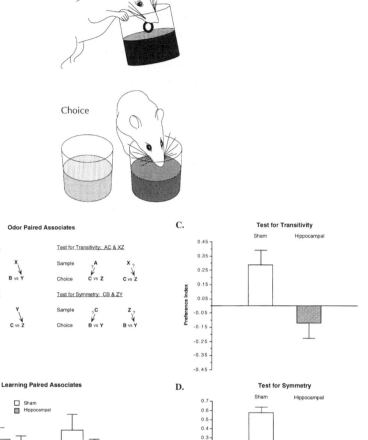

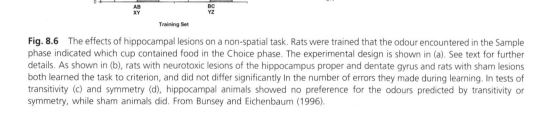

Fig. 8.6 The effects of hippocampal lesions on a non-spatial task. Rats were trained that the odour encountered in the Sample phase indicated which cup contained food in the Choice phase. The experimental design is shown in (a). See text for further details. As shown in (b), rats with neurotoxic lesions of the hippocampus proper and dentate gyrus and rats with sham lesions both learned the task to criterion, and did not differ significantly In the number of errors they made during learning. In tests of transitivity (c) and symmetry (d), hippocampal animals showed no preference for the odours predicted by transitivity or symmetry, while sham animals did. From Bunsey and Eichenbaum (1996).

1986). It is results of this kind, along with research on non-human primates and clinical studies of people with hippocampal damage, that lead to the conclusion that the function of the hippocampus is much broader than spatial memory or spatial orientation. Instead, these results suggest that the hippocampus is fundamentally involved in a class of memory that Squire (1992) has called declarative memory. The properties of declarative memory vary somewhat, depending on whether the term is being used in connection with rodents, non-human primates or people, but it usually refers to memory for events and the conditional and contextual relations among events. Memory for spatial locations is regarded as one outcome of the operation of declarative memory, not different in any important way from memory for odour associations of the kind described by Bunsey and Eichenbaum (1996) or any other domain of declarative memory. Declarative memory is usually contrasted with memory functions that are spared by damage to the hippocampus such as the formation of simple associations, learning of habits and procedures, and phenomena such as priming in which the operation of memory is implicit and does not involve directed retrieval of remembered information.

There are a number of possible explanations for these clearly contradictory conclusions about the function of the hippocampus. One is that hippocampus means different things to different researchers. A hippocampal lesion in one experiment may involve damage to CA cell fields and the fimbria and the subiculum, while in another experiment only lesions restricted to the CA cell fields or dentate gyrus qualify as hippocampal lesions. In addition, techniques such as aspiration or electrolytic lesioning destroy both neurons and fibres of passage—bundles of axons projecting from one part of the brain to another—that happen to pass through the lesion site. 'Hippocampal' lesions can thus interrupt communication between parts of the brain that may not normally depend on intact hippocampal circuitry for their operation. This particular problem can be solved, however, by lesioning with neurotoxic chemicals such as ibotenic acid that destroy hippocampal neurons but leave axonal projections such as the alveus undamaged (Fig. 8.2). Differences in procedure and anatomical specification of the hippocampus may partly explain discrepant experimental results on the role of the hippocampus in behaviour. However, proponents of both the declarative memory and spatial memory interpretations of hippocampal functions can support their conclusions with the effects on behaviour of lesions restricted to neurons in one or more of the CA cell fields (Squire 1992) or CA cell fields plus dentate gyrus granule cells (Jarrard 1993).

Another possible reason for the persistence of differing views of the function of the hippocampus is that researchers concerned with the spatial memory model work primarily with rodents while those seeking a broader view of hippocampal function try to account for results obtained with rodents, non-human primates, and clinical patients with a single model. The hippocampus may do different things in different species. Spatial functions may frequently be observed in rodents because spatial orientation is the primary declarative memory problem most animals, including rodents, deal with. Evolutionary change in the brain and cognitive function may have had the effect that the hippocampus serves more complex functions in animals with more complex cognitive organisation, such as primates and humans. This does not explain, however, results showing deficits in non-spatial memory in rodents.

Finally, results described further in the section on Comparative analyses, below, show that differences in relative hippocampal size between species and between the sexes are related to differences in the use of space. Greater hippocampal size is observed in animals that search for caches of stored food, range widely in search of mates, or, in the case of avian brood parasites, search for host nests. The spatial memory hypothesis of hippocampal function would seem to account for these results more readily than the declarative hypothesis. These results could be accommodated by the declarative hypothesis by supposing that spatial memory is just one among many outcomes of declarative memory, except that differences in sociality, mating system, sex, mode of development, diet and a host of other variables are not good predictors of relative hippocampal size in animals (Sherry *et al.* 1992). If declarative memory was the function of the hippocampus it might be expected that species differences of many kinds could lead to species differences in declarative memory and hence relative hippocampal size. It is clear that a generally accepted account of the function of the hippocampus lies in the future.

The avian hippocampus

If the plethora of experimental work on the mammalian hippocampus has not yet allowed us to reach a consensus on its function, there may be some value to viewing the hippocampus in a different way. One possibility is to examine the role of a similar structure in a non-mammalian brain. After all, the use of 'simpler', analogous systems to investigate learning and memory has provided us with fundamental insights, currently unobtainable from humans, or even rats. Sea hares (*Aplysia*), honey-bees (*Apis mellifera*) and fruit flies (*Drosophila*) are among the best known examples (e.g. Byrne 1985; Tully and Quinn 1985; Menzel 1990).

Bingman and co-workers were the first to take seriously the possibility that the avian hippocampus (also called the dorsomedial forebrain) might also play a part in the processing of spatial information. Subsequently, there has been a two-pronged approach to the investigation of avian hippocampal structure and function: (1) a neurobiological course, which includes attempts to characterise the neuroanatomical structure of the hippocampus (e.g. Székely and Krebs 1996), and also employs lesion and electrophysiological techniques (e.g. Wieraszko and Ball 1993); (2) use of the Comparative Method, which attempts to determine whether variation in hippocampal structure is correlated with variation in spatial information processing. Although not always viewed as being complementary by their proponents, it is through both disciplines that we are now in the position to suggest both that the avian hippocampus is heavily involved in the processing of spatial information and that it shares structural and functional characteristics with the mammalian hippocampus.

Support for homology between the avian and mammalian hippocampus comes from cytoarchitectural, immunocytochemical and ontogenetic studies (e.g. Källén 1962), although the two structures are morphologically unalike in many ways (see Figs 8.2 and 8.7). However, in its topological relationship to the lateral ventricle (Craigie 1935), diversity of cell types (Mollá *et al.* 1986; Montagnese *et al.* 1996), sources of afferents and efferents (Benowitz and Karten 1976; Krayniak and Siegel 1978; Casini *et al.* 1986; Bingman *et al.* 1989; Székely and Krebs 1996), laminar organisation (Durward 1932; Craigie 1935) and neurochemical distribution (Shimizu and Karten 1990; Erichsen *et al.* 1991; Krebs *et al.* 1991; Montagnese *et al.* 1993) there is good evidence for anatomical homology between avian and mammalian hippocampus. In addition, long-term potentiation, that putative basis of memory most frequently studied in the mammalian hippocampus, has been observed in both pigeon and songbird hippocampus (Wieraszko and Ball 1991, 1993).

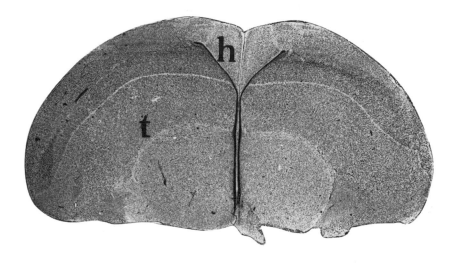

Fig. 8.7 A coronal section through the forebrain of a magpie (*Pica pica*). H = hippocampal region, T = telencephalon.

The hippocampus and homing in pigeons

Support for functional similarity between the avian and mammalian hippocampus comes from a variety of lesion studies which have focused on two groups of birds: pigeons and food-storing songbirds. The overwhelming consensus from all of this work is that the avian hippocampus plays a part in spatial information processing.

Hippocampal lesions in pigeons (*Columba livia*) appear to have little effect on performance of conventional learning and memory tasks, such as delayed-matching-to-sample (DMTS) and recognition tasks (Macphail and Reilly 1989; Good and Macphail 1994*a*) whereas on other tasks involving a spatial component (e.g. spatial DNMTS), hippocampal pigeons were found to perform more poorly than control birds (Reilly and Good 1987; Good and Macphail 1994*b*). Performance by hippocampal black-capped chickadees (*Parus atricapillus*) and dark-eyed juncos (*Junco hyemalis*), two songbird species, on a DMTS task requiring memory for the object colour, was not different to performance prior to surgery but performance on a very similar task requiring memory for object location declined in both species post-surgery (Hampton and Shettleworth 1996*a*; Fig. 8.8).

The choice of homing pigeons and food-storing passerines as model systems in which to examine the function of the avian hippocampus has come about because both groups perform behaviours which appear to demand greater spatial information processing than that

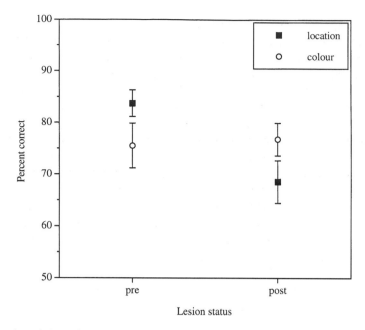

Fig. 8.8 Pre- and post-lesion performance on a spatial task and a colour task by a storing species and a non-storing species. From Hampton and Shettleworth (1996a).

required of congeneric species. The spatial processing demand in homing may seem self-evident and, indeed, has received more than four decades of attention (see Bingman, Chapter 4). However, one of the striking features of pigeon homing is the wide variety of mechanisms the bird may use in order to home successfully. The use of any of these mechanisms (e.g. a magnetic compass, an olfactory gradient, a sun compass, knowledge of familiar landmarks) on its own or in concert enable successful navigation. All, therefore, have some spatial component, but it appears to be the acquisition and use of information about familiar landmarks which involve the hippocampus.

In a series of experiments with hippocampal-lesioned pigeons, Bingman and colleagues have managed to determine what role the hippocampus plays in pigeon homing. In an early study, homing pigeons with hippocampal lesions did not home from release sites more than 30 km from the home loft, whether or not the release site was familiar (Bingman *et al.* 1984). However, although the birds failed to home they did leave the release site in a homeward direction. Released from within 800 m of the home loft hippocampal birds simply explored the loft area but made no attempt to enter their home loft. These results are not dissimilar from those obtained by Schmidt-Koenig and Walcott (1978) when they covered pigeons' eyes with frosted lenses. They, too, found that although birds headed homewards, once in the vicinity of the loft they did not enter their home loft. A later experiment showed that if birds were given sufficient postoperative experience of the home-loft (seeing out of it, not flying) they were able to return home from both familiar and unfamiliar distant release sites. However, hippocampal-lesioned birds given postoperative experience of a new loft were unable to return to it successfully (Bingman *et al.* 1985, 1987, 1988).

These data appeared to support the hypothesis that the hippocampus was not necessary for successful navigation from distant release sites whether or not they were familiar but that an intact hippocampus was required for homing based on memory of landmarks, visual or otherwise, local to the home loft. A study involving radiotracking of pigeons by Bingman and Mench (1990) added further support: hippocampal pigeons released 10 km from the home loft were impaired in homing performance and their flight patterns were much more less homeward oriented than those of control birds. All of these studies involved birds that had been trained previously in an attempt to determine how the hippocampus might be involved in the use of spatial information, with the assumption that lesions would either impair a memory store, or, impair the retrieval of spatial information from such a store.

The question then arises as to whether hippocampal lesions affect the ability of pigeons to *acquire* spatial information. Two different kinds of experiment have been carried to investigate this question involving either retraining adult birds or training naive, young birds following hippocampal lesioning. In both cases, lesioned birds were unable to learn either a familiar landmark map or a navigational map (see Bingman, Chapter 4; Bingman *et al.* 1990; Bingman and Yates 1992). The hippocampus in homing pigeons, then, appears to be involved in both the acquisition and the storage/recall of spatial information. Data on variation in hippocampal structure among different strains of domestic pigeons offer support for this idea: homing pigeons have larger hippocampal volumes than do either fantails or strassers. Both of these latter strains have been bred for attractive morphological character-istics rather than homing ability (Rehkämper *et al.* 1988).

The hippocampus and food storing

Relative to the many years of work on pigeon homing, the notion that food storing may also require spatial memory is a comparatively recent one. Food storing is a behaviour performed by many different species, ranging from ants and bees to magpies, squirrels and bears. Marsh tits (*Parus palustris*), for example, may store 50–100 seeds in a morning, placing each in a different location several metres apart and may not retrieve this food for several days or weeks (Cowie *et al.* 1981; Stevens and Krebs 1986). For a long time it was assumed that birds were retrieving food using smell or by hiding it in the same places over and over. The idea that these birds could *remember* where they had hidden their food seemed far too extraordinary for animals with such small brains. Over the last decade, however, it has been shown that not only do marsh tits remember a prodigious number of different locations, they can remember what kind of food was stored and even that they have removed and eaten a cache (Shettleworth 1995).

Lesions to the hippocampus of food-storing birds have been found to affect the birds' ability to retrieve food accurately while leaving intact their storing behaviour and the motivation to retrieve (black-capped chickadees, *Parus atricapillus*: Sherry and Vaccarino 1989; nutcrackers, *Nucifraga caryocatactes*: Krushinskaya 1966). On two laboratory tasks involving a spatial component, spatial non-matching-to-sample and continuous spatial alternation, black-capped chickadees with hippocampal lesions performed less well than did control birds (Hampton and Shettleworth 1996b). However, these results do not fit the picture quite as neatly as it may appear for two reasons. The first is that hippocampal pigeons do not perform worse than controls on a similar spatial alternation task (Reilly and Good 1987), and the second is that pre-operative performance of the juncos on the alternation task is better than that of the chickadees. If solving this task is dependent on spatial information processing and the hippocampus is the brain region processing this kind of information, then it is to be expected that animals with hippocampal lesions would perform more poorly post-lesion. However, far from performing worse post-lesion on an alternation task, hippocampal pigeons are more likely to perform better as indeed are hippocampal rats (Jackson and Strong 1969). Hampton and Shettleworth (1996b) suggest, on the basis of these data, that perhaps an intact hippocampus interferes with the processing of information necessary for good performance on alternation tasks. If this was the case, the larger hippocampus of the black-capped chickadee might possibly lead to even poorer performance by intact chickadees on such a task than intact juncos: just the result Hampton and Shettleworth found. This is clearly not a sufficient interpretation of the data as it does not additionally explain why performance of both species dropped following hippocampal lesions. Further testing comparing storing and non-storing species using other learning and memory testing paradigms will be needed to explain these apparently contradictory results.

The Comparative Method

To the best of our knowledge, the vast majority of the contributions of the mechanisms underlying learning and memory have been based on the assumption that we can infer function from dysfunction. This is no less true in the search for understanding the neural basis of spatial representation: experimental lesions have long played a major part in attempts to answer the question of where in the brain spatial representations may be processed and/or stored. However, all experiments using lesion techniques, whether chemical or mechanical, are open to the criticism that a region other than that aimed at has also been affected in some way (see Gaffan 1994). This is particularly likely when the area in question is the mammalian hippocampus, located as it is deep in the brain and with its many internal and external connections.

Over the past decade another methodological approach has been brought into play which has given us a complementary method of investigating the likelihood that the hippocampus is the brain region crucial to the neural representation of space. This method, the Comparative Method, is used by evolutionary biologists to investigate adaptations shaped by natural selection (Harvey and Pagel 1991). In particular, it enables us to determine whether different species have arrived at a similar solution to a common problem by selective processes or via shared ancestry. Ever since Darwin this technique has been used to identify evolutionary trends across a range of taxonomic groups by showing that variation in one behavioural, morphological or physiological feature is closely correlated with variation in the biological or physical environment. For example, we may like to know why some species have larger brains than others. Hypotheses advanced over the last three decades have proposed that increases in brain size or weight are due variously to changes in: body weight (see review in Gould 1975), body surface area (Gould 1975), basal metabolic rate (Martin 1981), gestation length (Hofman 1983) and ecological correlates (e.g. Harvey et al. 1980). However, only this last hypothesis, that variation in brain size is closely correlated with variation in behavioural or ecological variables, has withstood statistical analyses.

Success in discovering relationships such as that between diet and brain size in primates

(Mace *et al.* 1980) and developmental pattern and brain size in birds (Bennett and Harvey 1985) notwithstanding, to those interested in understanding brain function, these kinds of relationships may appear to offer no additional insight because it is well known that different parts of the brain perform different functions. More recent work has focused on relationships between variation in behaviour and ecology and parts of the brain that have fairly well defined functions, particularly those areas dealing with sensory information. It is, however, investigations of the hippocampus that concern us here. A number of comparative studies appear to provide support for the role of the hippocampus in the processing of spatial information, especially in birds.

Comparative analyses

Most of these comparative analyses have investigated the relationship between variation in food storing and variation in hippocampal volume. A fundamental assumption in all of this work is that an increase in hippocampal volume endows a superior functional capacity of some description, for example, more or faster information processing capabilities. This assumption is based on the fact that neural tissue is expensive to operate, maintain and repair, as evidenced by its high and constant demand for oxygen and glucose as well as the observation that recovery from damage is often slow or non-existent. It should also be noted that the demonstration of a change in hippocampal volume does not tell us how this has been accomplished. One or several constituents of the hippocampus may have been modified, such as neuron number, number of glial cells, number of dendritic spines, number of synapses and so on. Volumetric changes are just the beginning: careful, detailed neuroanatomical analyses are then required.

Two large interspecific studies have shown that the presence of food storing is positively correlated with hippocampal volume in songbirds: food storing species have relatively larger hippocampal volumes (for their brain size) than do non-storing species (Krebs *et al.* 1989; Sherry *et al.* 1989). Neither of these studies found a significant proportion of the variation in hippocampal volume to be explained by a range of other ecological variables, for example, diet, nesting dispersion, developmental strategy or mating system. One variable that one might have expected to entail a greater demand for spatial information processing and thus be associated with an increase in relative hippocampal volume was that of migration. However, two studies failed to find a correlation between variation in hippocampal volume and the distance different species travel on migration (Sherry *et al.* 1989; Healy *et al.* 1991).

The Parid and Corvid families both offer the opportunity to examine more closely the relationship between food storing and hippocampal volume as within both families there is variation in the degree of food storing, ranging from species such as jackdaws, *Corvus monedula* (Goodwin 1986) and great tits, *Parus major* (Perrins 1979), which store little or not at all, through species like marsh tits, *P. palustris* (Cowie *et. al.* 1981) and magpies, *Pica pica* (Birkhead 1990), which store tens or hundreds of food items and retrieve most caches after a few hours or days to species such as willow tits, *P. montanus* (Haftorn 1956) and Clark's nutcrackers, *Nucifraga columbiana* (Tomback 1977), which may store many thousands of items and not retrieve them for several months. Four studies have now shown that degree of food storing (number of food items and length of time cached) is positively correlated with variation in hippocampal volume: those species which store more and for longer have larger relative hippocampal volumes (Corvidae: Healy and Krebs 1992; Basil *et al.* 1996; Paridae: Hampton *et al.* 1995; Healy and Krebs 1996). In all of these studies the number of food items cached is positively correlated with the length of time food is cached. It is not possible, therefore, to distinguish whether it is one or both of these features of the food storing behaviour that is associated with an enlarged hippocampus. Experimental tests comparing the ability of storers and non-storers to remember small numbers of locations over increasing periods of time have produced conflicting results: the enlarged hippocampus does not obviously enable the food storer to remember spatial information longer than the non-storer (Olson 1991; Healy 1995).

Very little is known of the relationship between food storing and the hippocampus in mammals, although thus far the mammalian data are consistent with the avian results. In a comparison between two species of kangaroo rats (Merriam's kangaroo rats, *Dipodymus merriami,* and bannertail kangaroo rats, *D. spectabilis*), Jacobs and Spencer (1994) found that the scatterhoarding species had larger hippocampal volumes than those species which hoard their food in large stockpiles or larders. Given the debate over homology between the avian and mammalian hippocampal structures, it would surely be illuminating to know more about the relationship between food storing and the hippocampus in mammals.

As noted by Squire (1993), even the combination of a correlation between hippocampal volume and food storing and of deficits in performance on cache retrieval by food storers with hippocampal lesions is not sufficiently convincing evidence that the avian hippocampus is necessarily involved in spatial memory. It may be that the hippocampus is involved with some other learning or memory capacity, for example, the ability to remember many items or the ability to reduce effects of interference between similar items (Shapiro and Olton 1994). Demonstrating that similar variation in hippocampal structure was correlated with variation in other ecological variables that also appear to demand an increase in spatial information processing would strengthen the case for the hippocampus being the site where this information is processed. Some of this evidence is provided by sex differences in the hippocampus.

Sex differences

One situation in which it appears that animals are faced with differences in demand for spatial memory is the practice by some birds of brood parasitism. In brown-headed cowbirds, *Molothrus ater*, for example, the female lays one egg a day each in a different host nest, preferring to lay the egg in a nest already containing at least one host egg. Prior to laying eggs she searches for suitable host nests, returning the following day or later. The male brown-headed cowbird does not help the female in her search for host nests and so does not appear to require the same degree of spatial memory capacity as his mate. Sherry *et al.* (1993) found that while female brown-headed cowbirds do, indeed, have a relatively larger hippocampus than conspecific males, there is no sex difference in hippocampal volume in two closely related icterid species, the redwinged blackbird, *Agelaius phoeniceus,* and the common grackle, *Quiscalus quiscala.* These species do not practise brood parasitism.

More recently, Reboreda *et al.* (1996) compared three species of cowbird, two of which practise brood parasitism, shiny cowbirds, *Molothrus bonariensis,* in which the female, but not the male, searches for nests, and screaming cowbirds, *M. rufoaxillaris,* in which both sexes search for nests together. The third species, bay-winged cowbirds, *M. badius,* are themselves parasitised by screaming cowbirds. Reboreda *et al.* found that relative hippocampal volume was larger in both of the parasitic species than in the bay-winged cowbird. They also found that a difference between the sexes in hippocampal structure existed only in the shiny cowbird, as they had predicted from the behavioural observations.

Sex differences in cognitive capacities of mammals, especially humans, has long been a controversial one. Tying these differences into neural variation has also been problematic. One of the consistent behavioural differences between men and women, however, is seen in the performance of certain spatial tasks: men usually perform better than do women (see Kimura 1992). Solving of spatial tasks also may differ between the sexes (e.g. Galea and Kimura 1993). However, while there is an abundance of differences in their brains, there is no evidence that the differences in spatial abilities between the sexes are correlated with variation in hippocampal volume.

In other mammals, it appears there may be a relationship between variation in demand for spatial information processing and sex differences in hippocampal structure. It has been proposed that variation in home range size may require an increase in spatial information processing and that this will be correlated with changes in hippocampal structure. It was also suggested that polygynous males will tend to cover more ground in their search for females than monogamous males. Therefore, we might expect to see that polygynous males both perform better than monogamous males on spatial memory tasks and that they have larger hippocampal volumes. The little evidence there is, to date, is consistent with this hypothesis. Gaulin and Fitzgerald (1986, 1989) showed sex differences in the solving of laboratory maze problems by meadow voles (*Microtus pennsylvanicus*), but not by prairie voles (*M. ochrogaster*). Male meadow voles are polygynous whereas male prairie voles are monogamous. Jacobs *et al.* (1990) have shown that there are sex differences in hippocampal volume between the montane vole *M. montanus* and the pine vole *M. pinetorum*: male montane voles are polygynous and pine male voles are monogamous. These vole studies point strongly towards the possibility that range size has been a major factor in the determination of hippocampal structure in mammals. It would be of interest to show a similar relationship in other mammals.

Development

All of the preceding discussion has been based on behavioural and neural differences in adults. However, the onset of many behaviours requiring increased spatial information processing often occurs before the animal reaches sexual maturity.

Food storing, for example, begins soon after the young birds have fledged, when they are several weeks old (Clayton 1992; Haftorn 1992). It is possible, therefore, to determine when the difference in hippocampal volume observed between adults of storing and non-storing species arises. Two studies have shown that there is no difference in relative hippocampal volume between pre-fledging juveniles from storing and non-storing species (magpies and jackdaws: Healy and Krebs 1993, marsh tits and blue tits, *P. caeruleus*: Healy *et al.* 1994; Fig 8.9). There is also no difference in relative hippocampal volume between juveniles and adults of the non-storing species whereas adults of the storing species have significantly larger hippocampal volumes than conspecific juveniles. Experimental manipulation of food-storing experience in hand-raised marsh tits has demonstrated that hippocampal enlargement does not occur until the bird has had experience of food-storing (Clayton and Krebs 1994).

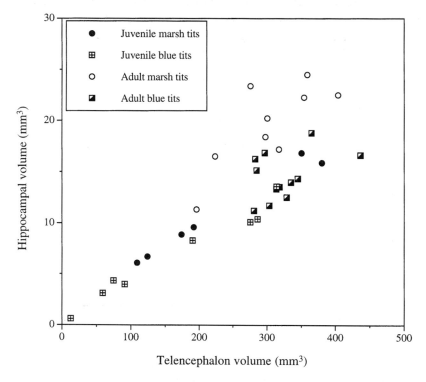

Fig. 8.9 Development of the hippocampus in storing (marsh tits) and non-storing species (blue tits). From Healy *et al.* (1994).

Migration, too, occurs some time after fledging. Indeed, the young bird setting out on its first migration is 3–4 months old. Although neither Healy *et al.* (1991) nor Sherry *et al.* (1989) found a correlation between migration distance and variation in hippocampal volume this is, perhaps, not very surprising. After all, there is no evidence to show that memory for landmarks observed *en route* is used by migrants. However, many migrants are astonishingly accurate at returning to breeding territories, stopover sites and overwintering areas (e.g. Moreau 1972; Loevei 1989). Healy *et al.* (1996) have suggested that they are able to return to these sites with such great fidelity because they remember the local landmarks associated with each site. If this is the case, we would expect to see hippocampal variation associated with experience of migration, not the distance the birds travel, and this is just what was observed.

Experienced garden warblers (*Sylvia borin*), which migrate from central Europe to tropical Africa, have relatively larger hippocampal volumes than naive birds (Fig. 8.10). However, this apparent effect of experience on hippocampal volume is possibly confounded with effects of age. Experienced birds are, after all, also older. To investigate whether age had any effect on hippocampal structure, birds from both age groups were kept in captivity for a year. While there was no effect of captivity on hippocampal volume in the older, experienced birds, there was some increase in hippocampal volume in the naive, younger birds. We cannot be sure whether this volumetric increase in the young birds was due to some effect of the captive environment or to increasing age. We do know that increasing age does not necessarily affect hippocampal volume as there was no change in hippocampal volume with increasing age in a closely related, non-migrant, the Sardinian warbler (*S. melanocephala*).

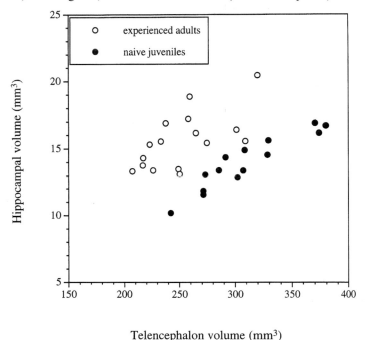

Fig. 8.10 Hippocampal volume in garden warblers: adults with migration experience and naive juveniles. From Healy *et al.* (1996).

It appears that the hippocampus is more plastic in some species than others and these species are those which have an increased demand for spatial information processing. Although Clayton and Krebs (1994) showed that increases in hippocampal volume required food-storing experience it seems that this response is not a quantitative one: birds given more frequent opportunities to store when very young do not have larger hippocampal volumes than those birds storing a single item (Clayton 1996). Unlike the warblers in which the hippocampus increased in size without migration experience, young marsh tits deprived of food-storing experience appeared to have *smaller* hippocampal volumes than their experienced conspecifics. Interestingly, young blue tits and marsh tits trained on a food-finding task akin to storing were able to learn and to solve the task equally well but only the hippocampus of the marsh tits increased in volume (Clayton 1995).

There appears to be some developmental plasticity in hippocampal structure in both garden warblers and marsh tits, not seen in close relatives living less spatially-rich lives. Our current knowledge of the relationship between food storing, migration and variation in hippocampal structure during development invites much more detailed investigation.

Seasonal changes

Not only does food storing begin after the young birds leave the nest, there is some field evidence to suggest that storing varies seasonally: birds store more in the autumn and winter, much less in the spring and summer (e.g. Smith *et al.* 1992). Smulders *et al.* (1995) have shown that hippocampal volume in the black-capped chickadee also varies seasonally and is at its largest during October, when the birds are storing most. Barnea and Nottebohm (1994) showed that while new neurons appear in the hippocampus of the black-capped chickadee throughout the year there is a peak in recruitment in October, coinciding with the volumetric changes seen by Smulders *et al.* and the behavioural changes. However, there does not appear to be a straightforward relationship between the number of hippocampal neurons and volume as the total number of hippocampal neurons does not appear to change through the year (Barnea and Nottebohm 1994). This parallels the result found by Healy and Krebs (1993), that although there were substantial volumetric differences between juvenile and adult food storers, there was no significant difference in neuron numbers. This would suggest that volume changes in the avian hippocampus may be due to changes in dendritic arborisation or in the number or size of support cells.

The replacement of old neurons through neurogenesis may occur within 6 weeks. If the hippocampus is involved in spatial information processing it is unlikely to be the site of storage for those longer-lasting memories.

Senescence

Long-lasting though some of our memories may be, ageing has a marked effect on our ability to learn and to remember new information. For the purposes of this chapter, the interest in ageing is twofold: first, ageing animals show deficits in spatial learning and memory and secondly, structural changes occur in the hippocampus which are correlated with these behavioural changes.

Young and old rats tested on a variety of laboratory tasks, for example, radial arm mazes, the Morris water-bath and the circular platform task (in which the rat has to choose the single hole which leads to a dark escape chamber) perform differently: old rats acquire the task more slowly and are less adept at remembering locations of food or of escape holes or platforms (Barnes 1979; Barnes and McNaughton 1985). Performance on a non-spatial versions of the radial maze task or the Morris water maze are not, however, correlated with age nor can the spatial deficits be explained by other correlates of ageing, for example, animals moving more slowly (Barnes *et al.* 1987). Acquisition of a T-maze discrimination task in which the rat had to learn which of two arms was always baited did not appear to differ between young and old rats but subsequent analysis of the data suggested that the old rats were using a non-spatial strategy to solve the task (Barnes *et al.* 1980).

A number of age-related changes occur in the mammalian hippocampus which appear to be correlated with these behavioural changes. For example, electrophysiological studies have shown that there are age-related changes in long-term potentiation or long-term enhancement (LTE) in the hippocampus. Experiments testing anaesthetised rats and rats with chronic recording implants show changes in features such as time taken to reach asymptotic levels of

LTE (slower in older rats) and decay rate of synaptic strength (faster in older rats) (Landfield *et al.* 1978; Barnes 1979; Barnes and McNaughton 1980). This latter result was correlated with spatial memory performance of old rats: the highest rates of decay of synaptic strength were found in older rats with the poorest spatial memory. This evidence has led Barnes (1988) to suggest both that LTE may underlie spatial information processing in the hippocampus and that this processing ability declines with age.

It is difficult to be sure how important a part senescence plays in the lives of most animals as they are more likely to succumb first to predation or starvation. However, the ageing data add yet more weight to the hypothesis that the hippocampus plays a major part in the processing of spatial information.

Conclusions

With the publication of their book, *The hippocampus as a cognitive map*, O'Keefe and Nadel (1978) set in train a considerable amount of investigation into the relationship between the hippocampus and the processing of spatial information that shows little sign of slowing two decades later. Both before and since this publication alternative theories for hippocampal function have been put forward that vary in the degree to which they can explain the behavioural data, primarily provided from lesion experiments. Although the waters seem considerably muddier than they appeared 20 years ago, the weight of comparative evidence seems to support a part for the hippocampus in spatial information processing. Indeed, in rats and in birds, the evidence is consistent with the idea that a major role of the hippocampus involves the representation of space. It is not clear why this explanation suits the rat and avian data rather well but not the results from studies of humans and non-human primates. Whether there really has been an evolutionary change in hippocampal function or whether the answer lies in the differences in the methodology used to test performance remains to be seen.

Acknowledgements

We would like to thank Peter Cain and Case Vanderwolf for their many helpful comments on the manuscript.

References

Able, K. P. (1991). The development of migratory orientation mechanisms. In *Orientation in birds* (ed. P. Berthold), pp. 166–79. Birkhäuser Verlag, Basel.

Able, K. P. (1993). Orientation cues used by migratory birds: a review of cue-conflict experiments. *Trends in Ecology and Evolution*, **8**, 367–71.

Able, K. P. (1996). The debate over olfactory navigation by homing pigeons. *Journal of Experimental Biology*, **199**, 121–4.

Alyan, S. and Jander, R. (1994). Short-range homing in the house mouse, *Mus musculus*: Stages in the learning of directions. *Animal Behaviour*, **48**, 285–98.

Amaral, D. G. (1987). Memory: anatomical organization of candidate brain areas. In *Handbook of physiology*, Section 1: *The nervous system*. Vol. V. *Higher functions of the brain*, Part 1 (ed. B. Mountcastle, F. Plum and S. R. Geiger), pp. 211–94. American Physiological Society, Bethesda, MD.

Amaral, D. G. and Witter, M. P. (1989). The three-dimensional organization of the hippocampal formation: a review of anatomical data. *Neuroscience*, **31**, 571–91.

Anderson, P., Bliss, V. P. and Skrede, K. K. (1971). Lamellar organization of hippocampal excitatory pathways. *Experimental Brain Research*, **13**, 222–38.

Armstrong, J. D., Braithwaite, V. A. and Ryecroft, P. (1996). A flat-bed passive integrated transponder antenna array for monitoring behaviour of Atlantic salmon parr and other fish. *Journal of Fish Biology*, **48**, 539–41.

Armstrong, J. D., Braithwaite, V. A. and Huntingford, F. A. (1997). Spatial strategies of wild Atlantic salmon parr: exploration and settlement in unfamiliar areas. *Journal of Animal Ecology*, **66**, 203–11.

Arnold, G. P. and Metcalfe, J. D. (1989). Fish migration: orientation and navigation or environmental transport? *Journal of Navigation*, **42**, 367–74.

Aronson, L. R. (1951). Orientation and jumping behaviour in the Gobiid fish *Bathygobius soporator*. *American Museum of Noviscotia*, **1486**, 1–22.

Aronson, L. R. (1971). Further studies on orientation and jumping behaviour in the Gobiid fish *Bathygobius soporator*. *Annals of the New York Academy of Science*, **188**, 378–92.

Baerends, G. P. (1941). Fortpflanzungsverhalten und Orientierung der Grabwespe *Ammo-is* Jur. *Tijdschrift voor Entomologie*, **84**, 68–275.

Balda, R. P. and Turek, R. J. (1984). The cache-recovery system as an example of memory capabilities in Clark's nutcracker. In *Animal cognition* (ed. H. L. Roitblat, T. G. Bever and H. S. Terrace), pp. 513–32. Lawrence Erlbaum Associates, Hillsdale, NJ.

Barnea, A. and Nottebohm, F. (1994). Seasonal recruitment of hippocampal neurons in adult free-ranging black-capped chickadees. *Proceedings of the National Academy of Sciences USA*, **91**, 11217–21.

Barnes, C. A. (1979). Memory deficits associated with senescence: A neurophysiological and behavioral study in the rat. *Journal of Comparative and Physiological Psychology*, **93**, 74–104.

Barnes, C. A. (1988) Aging and the physiology of spatial memory. *Neurobiology of Aging*, **9**, 563–8.

Barnes, C. A. and McNaughton, B. L. (1980). Physiological compensation for loss of afferent synapses in rat hippocampal granule cells during senescence. *Journal of Physiology (London)*, **309**, 473–85.

Barnes, C. A. and McNaughton, B. L. (1985). An age comparison of the rates of acquisition and forgetting of spatial information in relation to long-term enhancement of hippocampal synapses. *Behavioral Neuroscience*, **99**, 1040–8.

Barnes, C. A., Nadel, L. and Honig, W. K. (1980). Spatial memory deficit in senescent rats. *Canadian Journal of Psychology*, **34**, 29–34.

Barnes, C. A., Green, E. J., Baldwin, J. and Johnson, W. E. (1987). Behavioral and neurophysiological examples of functional sparsing in senescent rat. *Canadian Journal of Psychology*, **41**, 131–40.

Barrows, E. M. (1976). Mating behavior in halictine bees (Hymenoptera: Halictidae): I, Patrolling and age-specific behavior in males. *Journal of the Kansas Entomological Society*, **49**, 105–19.

Basil, J. A., Kamil, A. C., Balda, R. P. and Fite, K. V. (1996). Differences in hippocampal volume among food storing corvids. *Brain Behavior and Evolution*, **47**, 156–64.

Becker, L. (1958). Untersuchungen über das Heimfindevermögen der Bienen. *Zeitschrift für Vergleichende Physiologie*, **41**, 1–25.

Biegler, R. and Morris, R. G. M. (1996). Landmark stability: studies exploring whether the perceived stability of the environment influences spatial representation. *Journal of Experimental Biology*, **199**, 187–93.

Benhamou, S. (1990). An analysis of movements of the wood mouse *Apodemus sylvaticus* in its home range. *Behavioural Processes*, **22**, 235–50.

Benhamou, S. and Séguinot, V. (1995). How to find one's way in the labyrinth of path integration models. *Journal of Theoretical Biology*, **174**, 463–6.

Bennett, A. T. D. (1993). Spatial memory in a food storing corvid. I. Near tall landmarks are primarily used. *Journal of Comparative Physiology A*, **173**, 193–207.

Bennett, P. M. and Harvey, P. H. (1985). Relative brain size and ecology in birds. *Journal of Zoology (London)*, **207**, 151–69.

Benowitz, L. I. and Karten, H. J. (1976). The tractus infundibuli and other afferents to the parahippocampal region of the pigeon. *Brain Research*, **102**, 174–80.

Benvenuti, S. and Brown, I. A. (1989). The influence of olfactory deprivation on homing of experienced and inexperienced American pigeons. *Behaviour*, **111**, 113–28.

Benvenuti, S. and Fiaschi, V. (1983). Pigeon homing: Combined effect of olfactory deprivation and visual impairment. *Comparative Biochemistry and Physiology*, **76A**, 719–23.

Benvenuti, S., Fiaschi, V., Gagliardo, A. and Luschi, P. (1990). Pigeon homing: a comparison between groups raised under different conditions. *Behavioral Ecology and Sociobiology*, **27**, 93–8.

Benvenuti, S., Ioalé, P., Gagliardo, A. and Bonadonna, F. (1992). Effects of zinc sulphate-induced anosmia of homing behaviour of pigeons. *Comparative Biochemistry and Physiology*, **103A**, 519–26.

Benvenuti, S., Ioalé, P. and Nacci, L. (1994). A new experiment to verify the spatial range of pigeons' olfactory map. *Behaviour*, **131**, 277–92.

Berthold, P. (1978). Circannuale Rhythmik: Freilaufende selbsterregte Periodik mit lebenslanger Wirksamkeit bei Vögeln. *Naturwissenschaften*, **65**, 546.

Berthold, P. (1985). Endogenous components of annual cycles of migration and moult. *Proceedings of the XVIII International Ornithology Congress*, Moscow, 1982 (ed. V.D. Ilyichev and V. M. Gavrilov), pp. 922–30. Nauka, Moscow.

Berthold, P. (1990). Wegzugbeginn und Einsetzen der Zugunruhe bei 19 Vogelpopulationen—eine vergleichende Untersuchung. Proc. Int. 100. DO-G Meeting, Current Topics Avian Biology, Bonn 1988. *Journal für Ornithologie*, **131**, 217–22.

Berthold, P. (1991). Spatiotemporal programmes and genetics of orientation. In *Orientation in birds* (ed. P. Berthold), pp. 86–105. Birkhäuser Verlag, Basel.

Berthold, P. (1993). *Bird migration. A general survey*. Oxford University Press, Oxford.

Berthold, P. (1996). *Control of bird migration*. Chapman & Hall, London.

Berthold, P. and Pulido, F. (1994). Heritability of migratory activity in a natural bird population. *Proceedings of the Royal Society of London, Series B*, **257**, 311–5.

Berthold, P. and Querner, U. (1981). Genetic basis of migratory behaviour in European warblers. *Science*, **212**, 77–9.

Berthold, P. and Querner, U. (1995). Microevolutionary aspects of bird migration based on experimental results. *Israel Journal of Zoology*, **41**, 377–85.

Berthold, P., Mohr, G. and Querner, U. (1990a). Steuerung und potentielle Evolutionsgeschwindigkeit des obligaten Teilzieherverhaltens: Ergebnisse eines Zweiweg-Selektionsexperiments mit der Mönchsgrasmücke (*Sylvia atricapilla*). *Journal für Ornithologie*, **131**, 33–45.

Berthold, P., Wiltschko, W., Miltenberger, H. and Querner U. (1990b). Genetic transmission of migratory behavior into a nonmigratory bird population. *Experientia*, **46**, 107–8.

Berthold, P., Helbig, A. J., Mohr, G. and Querner U. (1992). Rapid microevolution of migratory behaviour in a wild bird species. *Nature*, **360**, 668–9.

Berthold, P., Nowak, E. and Querner, U. (1993). *White stork satellite-tracking in Europe and Africa: a progress report*. IUCN specialist group on storks, ibises and spoonbills Newsletter 1/2, pp. 3–5.

Berthold, P., Helbig, A. J., Mohr, G., Pulido, F. and Querner, U. (1997). Vogelzug—moderne Phänomenologie und experimentelle Analyse der Steuerungssysteme und Evolutionsvorgänge. Jahrbuch der Max Planck Gesellschaft, München.

Berthoz, A., Israël, I., Georges-François, P., Grasso R. and Tsuzuku T. (1995). Spatial memory of body linear displacement: What is being stored? *Science*, **269**, 95–8.

Biebach, H. (1995). Stopover of migrants flying across the Mediterranean Sea and the Sahara. *Israel Journal of Zoology*, **41**, 387–92.

Bingman, V. P. and Ioalè, P. (1989). Initial orientation of anosmic homing pigeons based on information gathered at familiar release sites remains homeward directed following clock shift. *Behaviour*, **110**, 205–18.

Bingman, V. P. and Jones, T.-J. (1994). Hippocampal lesions disrupt sun compass directional learning in homing pigeons. *Journal of Neuroscience*, **14**, 6687–94.

Bingman, V. P. and Mench, J. A. (1990). Homing behavior of hippocampus and para-hippocampus lesioned pigeons following short-distance release. *Behavioural Brain Research*, **40**, 227–38.

Bingman, V. P. and Yates, G. (1992). Hippocampal-lesions impair navigational learning in experienced homing pigeons. *Behavioral Neuroscience*, **106**, 229–32.

Bingman, V. P., Bagnoli, P., Ioalé, P. and Casini, G. (1984). Homing behavior in pigeons after telencephalic ablations. *Brain, Behavior and Evolution*, **24**, 94–106.

Bingman, V. P., Ioalé, P., Casini, G. and Bagnoli, P. (1985). Dorsomedial forebrain ablations and home loft association behavior in homing pigeons. *Brain, Behavior and Evolution*, **26**, 1–9.

Bingman, V. P., Ioalé, P., Casini, G. and Bagnoli, P. (1987). Impaired retention of preoperatively acquired spatial reference memory in homing pigeons following hippo-campal ablation. *Behavioural Brain Research*, **24**, 147–56.

Bingman, V. P., Ioalé, P., Casini, G. and Bagnoli, P. (1988). Hippocampal ablated homing pigeons show a persistent impairment in the time taken to return home. *Journal of Comparative Physiology A*, **163**, 559–63.

Bingman, V. P., Bagnoli, P., Ioalé, P. and Casini, G. (1989). Behavioral and anatomical studies of the avian hippocampus. In *The hippocampus, new vistas*, Vol. 52, *Neurology and neurobiology* (ed. V. Chan-Palay and C. Koehler), pp. 379–94. Liss, New York.

Bingman, V. P., Ioalé, P., Casini, G. and Bagnoli, P. (1990). The avian hippocampus: Evidence for a role in the development of the homing pigeon navigational map. *Behavioral Neuroscience*, **104**, 906–11.

Bingman, V. P., Ioalé, P., Casini, G., Bagnoli, P. and Strasser, R. (1994). Critical importance of the hippocampus for local navigational learning in young homing pigeons. *Society for Neuroscience Abstracts*, **20**, 1012.

Bingman, V. P., Jones, T.-J., Strasser, R., Gagliardo, A. and Ioalé, P. (1995). Homing pigeons, hippocampus and spatial cognition. In *Behavioural brain research in naturalistic and semi-naturalistic settings*, Proceedings of the NATO Advanced Study Institute, Acquafredda di Maratea, Italy, Sept 10–20, 1994 (ed. E. Alleva, A. Fasolo, H.-P. Lipp, L. Nadel and L. Ricceri), pp. 207–38. Kluwer Academic Publishers, Dordrecht.

Bingman, V. P., Gagliardo, A. and Ioalé, P. (1996). Hippocampal participation in the sun compass orientation of phase-shifted homing pigeons. *Journal of Comparative Physiology A*, **179**, 695–702.

Birkhead, T. (1990). *The magpies*. T. & A. D. Poyser, London.

Bisetzky, A. R. (1957). Die Tänze der Bienen nach einem Fussweg zum Futterplatz. *Zeitschrift für Vergleichende Physiologie*, **40**, 264–88.

Bles, W., de Jong, J. M. B. V. and De Wit, G. (1984). Somatosensory compensation for loss of labyrinthine function. *Acta Otolaryngology*, **97**, 213–21.

Boesch, C. and Boesch, H. (1984). Mental maps in wild chimpanzees: an analysis of hammer transports for nut-cracking. *Primates*, **25**, 160–70.

Bostock, E., Muller, R. U. and Kubie, J. L. (1991). Experience-dependent modifications of hippocampal place cell firing. *Hippocampus*, **1**, 193–206.

Bourke, A. F. G. and Franks, N. R. (1995). *Social evolution in ants*. Princeton University Press, Princeton, NJ.

Bovet, J. (1992). Mammals. In *Animal homing* (ed. F. Papi), pp. 321–61. Chapman & Hall, London.

Braithwaite, V. A. (1993). When does previewing the landscape affect pigeon homing. *Ethology*, **95**, 141–51.

Braithwaite, V. A. and Guilford, T. (1991). Viewing familiar landscapes affects pigeon homing. *Proceedings of the Royal Society of London, Series B*, **245**, 183–6.

Braithwaite, V. A. and Newman, J. A. (1994). Exposure to familiar visual landmarks allows pigeons to home faster. *Animal Behaviour*, **48**, 1482–4.

Braithwaite, V. A., Armstrong, J. D., McAdam, H. M. and Huntingford, F. A. (1996). Can juvenile Atlantic salmon use multiple cue systems in spatial learning? *Animal Behaviour*, **51**, 1409–15.

Brown, G. E., Chivers, D. P. and Smith, R. J. F. (1995). Localized defecation by pike: a response to labelling by cyprinid alarm pheromone? *Behavioral Ecology and Socio-biology*, **36**, 105–10.

Brünnert, U., Kelber, A. and Zeil, J. (1994) Ground-nesting bees determine the location of their nest relative to a landmark by other than angular size cues. *Journal of Comparative Physiology A*, **175**, 363–9.

Burkhalter, A. (1972). Distance measuring as influenced by terrestrial cues in *Cataglyphis bicolor*. In *Information processing in the visual system of arthropods* (ed. R. Wehner), pp. 303–8. Springer-Verlag, Berlin.

Bunsey, M. and Eichenbaum, H. (1996). Conservation of hippocampal memory function in rats and humans. *Nature*, **379**, 255–7.

Buzzard, C. N. (1936). De l'organisation du travail chez les abeilles. *Bulletin de Societé Apiculture Alpes-Maritimes*, **15**, 65–70.

Byrne, J. H. (1985). Neural and molecular mechanisms underlying information storage in *Aplysia*: Implications for learning and memory. *Trends in Neurosciences*, **8**, 478–82.

Cain, D. P. and Saucier, D. (1996). The neuroscience of spatial navigation: focus on behavior yields advances. *Reviews in the Neurosciences*, **7**, 215–31.

Cain, P., Gerin, W. and Moller, P. (1994). Short-range navigation of the weakly electric fish, *Gnathonemus petersii* L. (Mormyridae, Teleostei), in novel and familiar environments. *Ethology*, **96**, 33–45.

Carey, F. G. and Scharold, J. V. (1990). Movements of blue sharks (*Prionace glauca*) in depth and course. *Marine Biology*, **106**, 329–42.

Cartwright, B. A. and Collett, T. S. (1982). How honeybees use landmarks to guide their return to a food source. *Nature*, **295**, 560–4.

Cartwright, B. A. and Collett, T. S. (1983). Landmark learning in bees. *Journal of Comparative Physiology A*, **151**, 521–43.

Cartwright, B. A. and Collett, T. S. (1987). Landmark maps for honeybees. *Biological Cybernetics*, **57**, 85–93.

Casini, G., Bingman, V. P. and Bagnoli, P. (1986). Connections of the pigeon dorsomedial forebrain studied with WGA-HRP and H-3 proline. *Journal of Comparative Neurology*, **245**, 454–70.

Chappell, J. and Guilford, T. (1995). Homing pigeons primarily use the sun compass rather than fixed directional visual cues in an open-field arena food-searching task. *Proceedings of the Royal Society of London, Series B*, **260**, 59–63.

Chapuis, N., Durup, M. and Thinus-Blanc, C. (1987). The role of exploratory experience in a shortcut in golden hamsters (*Mesocricetus auratus*). *Animal Learning and Behavior*, **15**, 174–8.

Cheng, K. (1986). A purely geometric module in the rat's spatial representation. *Cognition*, **23**, 149–78.

Cheng, K. (1988). Some psychophysics of the pigeon's use of landmarks. *Journal of Comparative Physiology A*, **162**, 815–26.

Cheng, K. (1989). The vector sum model of pigeon landmark use. *Journal of Experimental Psychology: Animal Behavior Processes*, **15**, 366–75.

Cheng, K. (1990). More psychophysics of the pigeon's use of landmarks. *Journal of Comparative Physiology A*, **166**, 857–63.

Cheng, K. (1994). The determination of direction in landmark-based spatial search in pigeons: A further test of the vector sum model. *Animal Learning and Behavior*, **22**, 291–301.

Cheng, K. (1995). Landmark-based spatial memory in the pigeon. In *The Psychology of Learning and Motivation*, Vol. 33 (ed. D. L. Medin), pp. 1–21. Academic Press, San Diego, CA.

Cheng, K. and Gallistel, C. R. (1984). Testing the geometric power of an animal's spatial representation. In *Animal cognition* (ed. H. L. Roitblat, T. G. Bever and H. S. Terrace), pp. 409–23. Lawrence Erlbaum Associates, Hillsdale, NJ.

Cheng, K. and Sherry, D. (1992). Landmark-based spatial memory in birds (*Parus atricapillus* and *Columba livia*): The use of edges and distances to represent spatial positions. *Journal of Comparative Psychology*, **106**, 331–41.

Cheng, K. and Spetch, M. L. (1995). Stimulus control in the use of landmarks by pigeons in a touch-screen task. *Journal of the Experimental Analysis of Behavior*, **63**, 187–201.

Cheng, K., Collett, T. S. and Wehner, R. (1986). Honeybees learn the colour of landmarks. *Journal of Comparative Physiology A*, **159**, 69–73.

Cheng, K., Collett, T. S., Pickhard, A. and Wehner, R. (1987). The use of visual landmarks by honeybees: Bees weight landmarks according to their distance from the goal. *Journal of Comparative Physiology A*, **161**, 469–75.

Chittka, L. and Geiger, K. (1995). Honeybee long-distance orientation in a controlled environment. *Ethology*, **99**, 117–26.

Chittka, L., Kunze, J., Shipman, C. and Buchmann, S. L. (1995). The significance of landmarks for path integration in homing honeybee foragers. *Naturwissenschaften*, **82**, 341–3.

Clarke, T. A. and Wagner, P. J. (1976). Vertical distribution and other aspects of the ecology of certain mesopelagic fishes taken near Hawaii. *Fisheries Bulletin*, **74**, 635–45.

Clayton, N. S. (1992). Ontogeny of food-storing and associated retrieval in marsh tits, *Parus palustris*. *Behaviour*, **122**, 11–25.

Clayton, N. S. (1995). Development of memory and the hippocampus—comparison of food-storing and nonstoring birds on a one-trial associative memory task. *Journal of Neuroscience*, **15**, 2796–807.

Clayton, N. S. (1996). Development of food-storing and the hippocampus in juvenile marsh tits (*Parus palustris*). *Behavioural Brain Research*, **74**, 153–9.

Clayton, N. S. and Krebs, J. R. (1994). Hippocampal growth and attrition in birds affected by experience. *Proceedings of the National Academy of Sciences USA*, 91, 7410–14.

Collett, T. S. (1987). The use of visual landmarks by gerbils: reaching a goal when landmarks are displaced. *Journal of Comparative Physiology A*, **160**, 109–13.

Collett, T. S. (1992). Landmark learning and guidance in insects. *Philosophical Transactions of the Royal Society of London, B*, **337**, 295–303.

Collett, T. S. (1995). Making learning easy: the acquisition of visual information during orientation flights of social wasps. *Journal of Comparative Physiology A*, **177**, 737–47.

Collett, T. S. (1996). Insect navigation en route to the goal: multiple strategies for the use of landmarks. *Journal of Experimental Biology*, **199**, 227–35.

Collett, T. S. and Baron, J. (1994). Biological compasses and the coordinate frame of landmark memories in honeybees. *Nature*, **368**, 137–40.

Collett, T. S. and Kelber, A. (1988). The retrieval of visuo-spatial memories by honeybees. *Journal of Comparative Physiology A*, **163**, 145–50.

Collett, T. S. and Land, MF (1975). Visual spatial memory in a hoverfly. *Journal of Comparative Physiology A*, **100**, 59–84.

Collett, T. S. and Lehrer, M. (1993). Looking and learning: a spatial pattern in the orientation flight of the wasp *Vespula vulgaris*. *Proceedings of the Royal Society of London, Series B*, **252**, 129–34.

Collett, T. S. and Rees, J. A. (1997). View-based navigation in hymenoptera: multiple strategies of landmark guidance in the approach to a feeder. *Journal of Comparative Physiology A*, **181**, 47–58.

Collett, T. S., Cartwright, B. A. and Smith, B. A. (1986). Landmark learning and visuo-spatial memories in gerbils. *Journal of Comparative Physiology A*, **158**, 835–51.

Collett, T. S., Dillmann, E., Giger, A. and Wehner, R. (1992). Visual landmarks and route-following in desert ants. *Journal of Comparative Physiology A*, **170**, 435–42.

Collett, T. S., Fry, S. N. and Wehner, R. (1993). Sequence learning by honeybees. *Journal of Comparative Physiology A*, **172**, 693–706.

Collett, T. S, Baron, J. and Sellen, K. (1996). On the encoding of movement vectors by honeybees. Are distance and direction represented independently? *Journal of Comparative Physiology A*, **179**, 395–406.

Corlett, J. (1992). The role of vision in the planning and guidance of locomotion through the environment. In *Vision and motor control* (ed. L. Porteau and D. Elliott), pp. 375–97. Elsevier, Amsterdam.

Cowie, R. J., Krebs, J. R. and Sherry, D. F. (1981). Food storing by Marsh Tits. *Animal Behaviour*, **29**, 1252–9.

Craigie, E. H. (1935). Studies on the brain of the kiwi (*Apteryx australis*). *Journal of Comparative Neurology*, **56**, 223–357.

Cressant, A., Muller, R. U. and Poucet, B. (1997). Failure of centrally placed objects to control the firing fields of hippocampal place cells. *Journal of Neuroscience*, **17**, 2531–42.

Dabouineau, L. and Rivault, C. (1995) Ontogenetic development of spatial orientation in first- and second-instar cockroach larvae (*Blattella germanica* (L.), Dictyoptera). *Ethology*, **101**, 148–59.

Dill, M., Wolf, R. and Heisenberg, M. (1993). Visual pattern recognition in *Drosophila* involves retinotopic matching. *Nature*, **365**, 751–3.

Dittman, A. H. and Quinn, T. P. (1996). Homing in Pacific salmon: mechanisms and ecological basis. *Journal of Experimental Biology*, **199**, 83–91.

Dodson, J. J. (1988). The nature and role of learning in the orientation and migratory behavior of fishes. *Environmental Biology of Fishes*, **23**, 161–82.

Downhower, S. F. and Windsor, D. (1971). Use of land marks in orientation by bank swallows. *BioScience*, **21**, 570–2.

Durward, A. (1932). Observations on the cell masses in the cerebral hemisphere of the New Zealand kiwi (*Apteryx australis*). *Journal of Anatomy*, **46**, 437–77.

Dyer, F. C. (1993). How honey bees find familiar feeding sites after changing nesting sites with a swarm. *Animal Behaviour*, **46**, 813–6.

Dyer, F. C. and Dickinson, J. A. (1996). Sun-compass learning in insects: representation in a simple mind. *Current Directions in Psychology*, **5**, 67–72.

Dyer, F. C. and Gould, J. L. (1981). Honey bee orientation: A backup system for cloudy days. *Science*, **214**, 1041–2.

Dyer, F. C. and Gould, J. L. (1983). Honey bee navigation. *American Scientist*, **71**, 587–97.

Eichenbaum, H. (1996). Is the rodent hippocampus just for 'place'? *Current Opinion in Neurobiology*, **6**, 187–95.

Eickwort, G. C. (1977). Male territorial behaviour in the mason bee *Hoplitis anthocopoides* (Hymenoptera: Megachilidae). *Animal Behaviour*, **25**, 542–54.

Erichsen, J. T., Bingman, V. P. and Krebs, J. R. (1991). The distribution of neuropeptides in the dorsomedial telencephalon of the pigeon (*Columba livia*): a basis for regional subdivisions. *Journal of Comparative Neurology*, **314**, 478–92.

Esch, H. and Burns, J. E. (1995). Honeybees use optic flow to measure the distance of a food source. *Naturwissenschaften*, **82**, 38–40.

Esch, H. E. and Burns, J. E. (1996). Distance estimation by foraging honeybees. *Journal of Experimental Biology*, **199**, 155–62.

Essler, H. and Kotrschal, K. (1994). High resolution analysis of swim path patterns of intact and olfaction-deprived minnows (*Phoxinus phoxinus*) stimulated with food and potential predator odour. *Journal of Fish Biology*, **45**, 555–67.

Etienne, A. S. (1978). Energy versus time dependent parameters in the determination of a behavioural sequence in the *Aeschna* larva. *Journal of Comparative Physiology A*, **127**, 89–96.

Etienne, A. S., Maurer, R., Saucy, F. and Teroni, E. (1986). Short distance homing in the golden hamster after a passive outward journey. *Animal Behaviour*, **34**, 696–715.

Etienne, A. S., Maurer, R. and Saucy, F. (1988). Limitations in the assessment of path dependent information. *Behaviour*, **106**, 81–111.

Etienne, A. S., Teroni, E., Hurni, C. and Portenier, V. (1990). The effect of a single light cue on homing behaviour of the golden hamster. *Animal Behaviour*, **39**, 17–41.

Etienne, A. S., Joris-Lambert, S., Reverdin, B. and Teroni, E. (1993). Learning to recalibrate the role of dead reckoning and visual cues in spatial navigation. *Animal Learning and Behavior*, **21**, 266–80.

Etienne, A. S., Joris-Lambert, S., Dahn-Hurni, C. and Reverdin, B. (1995a). Optimizing visual landmarks: two and three dimensional minimal landscapes. *Animal Behaviour*, **49**, 165–79.

Etienne, A. S., Joris-Lambert, S., Maurer, R., Reverdin, B. and Sitbon, S. (1995*b*). Optimizing distal landmarks: Horizontal versus vertical structures and relation to background. *Behavioural Brain Research*, **68**, 103–16.

Etienne, A. S., Maurer, R. and Séguinot, V. (1996). Path integration in mammals and its interaction with visual landmarks. *Journal of Experimental Biology*, **199**, 201–9.

Etienne, A. S., Georgakopoulos, J., Griffin, A. and Manter, R. Dead reckoning, landmarks and the representation of space in a comparative perspective. In *Wayfinding: Cognitive Maps and Spatial Processes* (ed. R. Golledge). Johns Hopkins University Press, Baltimore (in press).

Fabrigoule, C. and Maurel, D. (1982). Radio-tracking of foxes' movements related to their home range, a cognitive map hypothesis. *Quarterly Journal of Experimental Psychology*, **34B**, 195–208.

Farner, D. S. (1955). The annual stimulus for migration. Experimental and physiological aspects. In *Recent studies of avian biology* (ed. A. Wolfson), pp. 198–237. University of Illinois Press, Urbana.

Free, J. B. (1987). *Pheromones of social bees*. Cornell University Press. Ithaca, New York.

Frisch, K. von (1953). *The dancing bees* (trans. D. Ilse). Harcourt Brace Jovanovich, San Diego, CA.

Frisch, K. von (1965). *Tanzsprache und Orientierung der Bienen*. Springer-Verlag, Berlin.

Frisch, K. von (1967). *The dance language and orientation of bees*. Oxford University Press, London.

Frisch, K. von (1974). *Animal architecture*. Harcourt Brace Jovanovich, New York.

Gaffan, D. (1994). Scene-specific memory for objects: a model of episodic memory impairment in monkeys with fornix transection. *Journal of Cognitive Neuroscience*, **6**, 305 20.

Galea, L. M. and Kimura, D. (1993). Sex differences in route-learning. *Personality and Individual Differences*, **14**, 53–65.

Gallistel, C. R. (1990). *The organization of learning*. Bradford Brooks/MIT Press, Cambridge, MA.

Gallistel, C. R. (1994). Space and time. In *Animal learning and cognition*, Vol. 9. *Handbook of perception and cognition* (ed. N. J. Mackintosh), pp. 221–53. Academic Press, London.

Garcia de Leaniz, C. (1989). Site fidelity and homing of Atlantic salmon parr in a small Scottish stream. In *Salmonid migration and distribution* (ed. E. Brannon and B. Jonsson), pp. 70–80. University of Washington, Seattle.

Gaulin, S. J. C. and Fitzgerald, R. W. (1986). Sex differences in spatial ability: An evolutionary hypothesis and test. *American Naturalist*, **127**, 74–88.

Gaulin, S. J. C. and Fitzgerald, R. W. (1989). Sexual selection for spatial-learning ability. *Animal Behaviour*, **37**, 322–31.

Georgakopoulos, J. and Etienne, A. S. (1994). Identifying location by dead reckoning and external cues. *Behavioural Processes*, **31**, 57–74

Gibson, R. J. (1993). The Atlantic salmon in fresh water: spawning, rearing and production. *Reviews in Fish Biology*, **3**, 39–73.

Girvan, J. R. and Braithwaite, V. A. (1997). Orientation mechanisms in different populations of the three spined stickleback. In *Orientation and Navigation – birds, humans and other animals*. Royal Institute of Navigation, Paper No. 16. Oxford.

Glasauer, S., Amorim, M.-A., Vitte, E. and Berthoz, A. (1994). Goal-directed linear locomotion in normal and labyrinthine-defective subjects. *Experimental Brain Research*, **98**, 323–35.

Goff, G. P. and Green, J. M. (1978). Field studies of the sensory basis of homing and orientation to the home site in *Ulvaria subbifurcata*. *Canadian Journal of Zoology*, **56**, 2220–4.

Good, M. and Macphail, E. M. (1994*a*). Hippocampal lesions in pigeons (*Columba livia*) disrupt reinforced preexposure but not overshadowing or blocking. *Quarterly Journal of Experimental Psychology*, **47B**, 263–91.

Good, M. and Macphail, E. M. (1994*b*). The avian hippocampus and short-term-memory for spatial and nonspatial information. *Quarterly Journal of Experimental Psychology*, **47B**, 293–317.

Goodale, M. A., Ellard, C. G. and Booth, L. (1990). The role of image size and retinal motion in the computation of absolute distance by the Mongolian gerbil (*Meriones unguiculatus*). *Vision Research*, **30**, 399–413.

Goodwin, D. (1986). *Crows of the world*. British Museum (Natural History), London.

Goodyear, C. P. and Bennett, D. H. (1979). Sun compass orientation of immature bluegill. *Transactions of the American Fisheries Society*, **108**, 555–9.

Görner, P. (1958). Die optische und kinästhetische Orientierung der Trichterspinne *Agelena labyrinthica* (CL.). *Zeitschrift für Vergleichende Physiologie*, **41**, 111–53.

Gotceitas, V. and Godin, J.-G. J. (1992). Effects of location of food delivery and social status on foraging-site selection by juvenile Atlantic salmon. *Environmental Biology of Fishes*, **35**, 291–300.

Gothard, K. M., Skaggs, W. E., Moore, K. M. and McNaughton, B. L. (1996). Binding of hippocampal CA1 activity to multiple reference frames in a landmark-based navigation task. *Journal of Neuroscience*, **16**, 823–835.

Gould, S. J. (1975). Allometry in primates, with emphasis on scaling and the evolution of the brain. *Contributions to Primatology*, **5**, 244–92.

Gould-Beierle, K. and Kamil, A. K. (1996). The use of local and global cues by Clark's nutcrackers (*Nucifraga columbiana*). *Animal Behaviour*, **52**, 519–28.

Green, J. M. and Fisher, R. (1977). A field study of homing and orientation to the home site in *Ulvaria subbifurcata* (Pisces: Stichaeidae). *Canadian Journal of Zoology*, **55**, 1551–6.

Greggers, U. and Mauelshagen, J. (1997). Matching behavior of honeybees in a multiple-choice situation: the differential effect of environmental stimuli on the choice process. *Animal Learning and Behavior* (in press).

Grüter, M. and Wiltschko, R. (1990). Pigeon homing: The effect of local experience on initial orientation and homing success. *Ethology*, **84**, 239–55.

Gwinner, E. (1968). Artspezifische Muster der Zugunruhe bei Laubsängern und ihre mögliche Bedeutung für die Beendigung des Zuges im Winterquartier. *Zeitschrift für Tierpsychologie*, **25**, 843–53.

Gwinner, E. (1986). *Circannual rhythms*. Springer-Verlag, Berlin.

Gwinner, E. (1990). Circannual rhythms in bird migration: Control of temporal patterns and interactions with photoperiod. In *Bird migration* (ed. E. Gwinner), pp. 257–68. Springer-Verlag, Berlin.

Gwinner, E. (1996*a*). Circadian and circannual programmes in avian migration. *Journal of Experimental Biology*, **199**, 39–48.

Gwinner, E. (1996*b*). Circannual clocks in avian reproduction and migration. *Ibis*, **138**, 47–63.

Gwinner, E. and Dittami, J. (1990). Endogenous reproductive rhythms in a tropical bird. *Science*, **249**, 906–8.

Gwinner, E., Schwabl, H. and Schwabl-Benzinger, I. (1988). Effects of food-deprivation on migratory restlessness and diurnal activity in the garden warbler (*Sylvia borin*). *Oecologia*, **77**, 321–6.

Haftorn, S. (1992). Ontogeny of food storing in titmice. *Ibis*, **134**, 69–71.

Haftorn, S. (1956). Contribution to the food biology of tits especially about storing of surplus food. Part III. The Willow-Tit (*Parus atricapillus* L.). *Det Kgl Norske Videnskabers Selskabs Skrifter*, **3**.

Halvorsen, M. and Stabell, O. (1990). Homing behaviour of displaced stream-dwelling brown trout. *Animal Behaviour*, **39**, 1089–93.

Hampton, R. R. and Shettleworth, S. J. (1996a). Hippocampal lesions impair memory for location but not color in passerine birds. *Behavioral Neuroscience*, **110**, 831–5.

Hampton, R. R. and Shettleworth, S. J. (1996b). Hippocampus and memory in a food-storing and in a nonstoring bird species. *Behavioral Neuroscience*, **110**, 946–64.

Hampton, R. R., Sherry, D. F., Shettleworth, S. J., Khurgle, M. and Ivy, G. (1995). Hippocampal volume and food storing in three species of parids. *Brain, Behavior and Evolution*, **45**, 54–61.

Harrison, J. F., Fewell, J. H., Stiller, T. M. and Breed, M. D. (1989). Effects of experience on use of orientation cues in the giant tropical ant. *Animal Behaviour*, **37**, 869–71.

Hartmann, G. and Wehner, R. (1995). The ant's path integration system: A neural architecture. *Biological Cybernetics*, **73**, 483 97.

Harvey, P. H. and Pagel, M. (1991). *The comparative method in evolutionary biology*. Oxford University Press, Oxford.

Harvey, P. H., Clutton-Brock, T. H. and Mace, G. M. (1980). Brain size and ecology in small mammals and primates. *Proceedings of the National Academy of Sciences USA*, **77**, 4387–9.

Hasler, A. D. and Scholz, A. T. (1983). *Olfactory imprinting and homing in salmon*. Springer-Verlag, Berlin.

Hasler, A. D. and Wisby, W. J. (1951). Discrimination of stream odors by fishes in relation to parent stream behavior. *American Naturalist*, **85**, 223–38.

Hawryshyn, C. W., Arnold, M. G., Bowering, E. and Cole, R. L. (1990). Spatial orientation of rainbow trout to plane-polarized light: The ontogeny of E-vector discrimination and spectral sensitivity characteristics. *Journal of Comparative Physiology A*, **166**, 565–74.

Healy, S. D. (1995). Memory for objects and positions: delayed-non-matching-to-sample in tits. *Quarterly Journal of Experimental Psychology*, **48B**, 179–91.

Healy, S. D. and Krebs, J. R. (1992). Food storing and the hippocampus in corvids: amount and size are correlated. *Proceedings of the Royal Society of London, Series B*, **248**, 241–5.

Healy, S. D. and Krebs, J. R. (1993). Development of hippocampal specialisation in a food-storing bird. *Behavioural Brain Research*, **53**, 127–31.

Healy, S. D. and Krebs, J. R. (1996). Food storing and the hippocampus in Paridae. *Brain, Behavior and Evolution*, **47**, 195–9.

Healy, S. D., Krebs, J. R. and Gwinner, E. (1991). Hippocampal volume and migration in birds. *Naturwissenschaften*, **78**, 424–6.

Healy, S. D., Clayton, N. S. and Krebs, J. R. (1994). Development of hippocampal specialisation in two species of tit (*Parus* spp.). *Behavioural Brain Research*, **61**, 23–8.

Healy, S. D., Gwinner, E. and Krebs, J. R. (1996). Hippocampal volume in migrating and non-migrating warblers: effects of age and experience. *Behavioural Brain Research*, **81**, 61–8.

Helbig, A. J. (1991). Inheritance of migratory direction in a bird species: a cross-breeding experiment with SE- and SW-migrating blackcaps (*Sylvia atricapilla*). *Behavioral Ecology and Sociobiology*, **28**, 9–12.

Helbig, A. J. (1992). Population differentiation of migratory directions in birds: comparison between ringing results and orientation behaviour of hand-raised migrants. *Oecologia*, **90**, 483–8.

Helbig, A. J., Berthold, P. and Wiltschko, W. (1989). Migratory orientation of blackcaps (*Sylvia atricapilla*): population-specific shifts of direction during the autumn. *Ethology*, **82,** 307–15.

Helbig, A. J., Berthold, P., Mohr, G. and Querner, U. (1994). Inheritance of a novel migratory direction in central European blackcaps. *Naturwissenschaften*, **81**, 184–6.

Helfman, G. S., Meyer, J. L. and McFarland, W. N. (1982). The ontogeny of twilight migration patterns in grunts (Pisces: Haemulidae). *Animal Behaviour*, **30**, 317–26.

Hermer, L. and Spelke, E. S. (1994). A geometric process for spatial representation in young children. *Nature*, **370**, 57–9.

Hoffmann, K. (1954). Versuche zu der im Richtungsfinden der Vögel enthaltenen Zeitschäzung. *Zeitschrift für Tierpsychologie*, **11,** 453–75.

Hofman, M. A. (1983). Energy metabolism, brain size and longevity in mammals. *Quarterly Review of Biology*, **58**, 495–512.

Holland, K. N., Brill, R. W. and Chang, R. K. C. (1990). Horizontal and vertical movements of Pacific blue marlin captured and released using sportfishing gear. *Fisheries Bulletin*, **88**, 397–402.

Huntingford, F. A. and Wright, P. J. (1989). How sticklebacks learn to avoid dangerous feeding patches. *Behavioural Processes*, **19**, 181–9.

Ioalé, P., Wallraff, H. G., Papi, F. and Foà, A. (1983). Long-distance releases to determine the spatial range of pigeon navigation. *Comparative Biochemistry and Physiology*, **76A,** 733–42.

Ioalé, P., Nozzolini, M. and Papi, F. (1990). Homing pigeons do extract directional information from olfactory stimuli. *Behavioral Ecology and Sociobiology*, **26**, 301–5.

Jacobs, L. F. and Spencer, W. (1994). Natural space-use patterns and hippocampal size in kangaroo rats. *Brain, Behavior and Evolution*, **44**, 125–32.

Jacobs, L. F., Gaulin, S. J. C., Sherry, D. F. and Hofman, G. E. (1990). Evolution of spatial cognition—sex specific patterns of spatial behavior predict hippocampal size. *Proceedings of the National Academy of Sciences USA*, **87**, 6349–52.

Jackson, W. J. and Strong, P. N. (1969). Differential effects of hippocampal lesions upon sequential tasks and maze learning by the rat. *Journal of Comparative and Physiological Psychology*, **68**, 442–50.

Jamon, M. (1994). An analysis of trail-following behaviour in the wood mouse, *Apodemus sylvaticus*. *Animal Behaviour*, **47**, 1127–34.

Janzen, D. H. (1971). Euglossine bees as long-distance pollinators of tropical plants. *Science*, **171**, 203–5.

Janzen, D. H. (1974). The deflowering of central America. *Natural History*, **83**, 48–53.

Jarrard, L. E. (1993). On the role of the hippocampus in learning and memory in the rat. *Behavioral and Neural Biology*, **60**, 9–26.

Jarrard, L. E. (1995). What does the hippocampus really do? *Behavioural Brain Research*, **71**, 1–10.

Jones, M. A. and Bingman, V. P. (1996). A neural network analysis of navigational learning in homing pigeons. *Forma*, **11**, 103–14.

Jones, R. S. G. (1993). Entorhinal-hippocampal connections: a speculative view of their function. *Trends in Neurosciences*, **16**, 58–64.

Junger, W. (1991*a*). Waterstriders (*Gerris paludum* F.) compensate for drift with a discontinuously working visual position servo. *Journal of Comparative Physiology A*, **169**, 633–9.

Junger, W. (1991*b*). Die sensorischen und neuronalen Grundlagen der Driftkompensation beim Wasserläufer *Gerris paludum*. Doctoral thesis, University of Tübingen, Germany.

Källén, B. (1962). Embryogenesis of brain nuclei in the chick telencephalon. *Ergebnisse der Anatomie und Entwicklungsgeschichte Weisbaden*, **36**, 62–82.

Kalmijn, A. J. (1982). Electric and magnetic field detection in elasmobranch fishes. *Science*, **218**, 916–8.

Kamin, L. J. (1969). Selective association and conditioning. In *Fundamental issues in associative learning* (ed. N. J. Mackintosh and W. K. Honig), pp. 42–64. Dalhousie University Press, Halifax, Nova Scotia.

Karnofsky, E. B., Atema, J. and Elgin, R. H. (1989). Field observations of social behaviour, shelter use and foraging in the lobster, *Homarus americanus*. *Biological Bulletin*, **176**, 239–46.

Kaye, H., Gambini, B. and Mackintosh, N. J. (1988). A dissociation between one-trial overshadowing and the effect of a distractor on habituation. *Quarterly Journal of Experimental Psychology*, **40B**, 31–47.

Kayton, M. (1990). *Navigation: land, sea, air and space*. IEEE Press, New York.

Keenleyside, M. H. A. (1962). Skin-diving observations of Atlantic salmon and brook trout in the Miramichi River, New Brunswick. *Journal of the Fisheries Research Board Canada*, **19**, 625–34.

Keeton, W. T. (1970). Do pigeons determine latitudinal displacement from the sun's altitude? *Nature*, **227**, 626–7.

Kennedy, G. J. A. (1981). Individual variation in homing tendency in the European minnow, *Phoxinus phoxinus* (L). *Animal Behaviour*, **29**, 621–5.

Kelber, A. and Zeil, J. (1990). A robust procedure for visual stabilisation of hovering flight position in guard bees of *Trigona* (*Tetragonisca*) *angustula* (Apidae, Meliponinae). *Journal of Comparative Physiology A*, **167**, 569–77.

Kelber, A. and Zeil, J. (1997). *Tetragonisca* guard bees take expanding and contracting patterns as indicating unintended displacement in space. *Journal of Comparative Physiology A*, **181**, 257–65.

Kieffer, J. D. and Colgan, P. W. (1992). The role of learning in fish behaviour. *Reviews in Fish Biology and Fisheries*, **2**, 125–43.

Kiepenheuer, J. (1984). The magnetic compass mechanism of birds and its possible associa-tion with the shifting course directions of migrants. *Behavioral Ecology and Sociobiology*, **14**, 81–99.

Kiepenheuer, J., Neumann, M. F. and Wallraff, H. G. (1993). Home-related and home-independent orientation of displaced pigeons with and without olfactory access to environmental air. *Animal Behaviour*, **45**, 169–82.

Kimura, D. (1992). Sex-differences in the brain. *Scientific American*, **267**, 119–25.

Kirschvink, J. L., Walker, M. M., Chang, S.-B. R. and Dizon, A. E. (1985). Chains of single domain magnetite particles in chinook salmon, *Oncorhynchus tschawytscha*. *Journal of Comparative Physiology A*, **157**, 375–81.

Kleerekoper, H., Matis, J., Gensler, P. and Maynard, P. (1974). Exploratory behaviour of goldfish (*Carassius auratus*). *Animal Behaviour*, **22**, 124–32.

Kramer, G. (1959). Recent experiments on bird orientation. *Ibis*, **101**, 399–416.

Krayniak, P. F. and Siegel, A. (1978). Efferent connections of the hippocampus and adjacent regions in the pigeon. *Brain, Behavior and Evolution*, **15**, 372–88.

Krebs, J. R., Sherry, D. F., Healy, S. D., Perry, V. H. and Vaccarino, A. L. (1989). Hippocampal specialization of food-storing birds. *Proceedings of the National Academy of Sciences USA*, **86**, 1388–92.

Krebs, J. R., Erichsen, J. T. and Bingman, V. P. (1991). The distribution of neurotransmitter-related enzymes in the dorsomedial telencephalon of the pigeon (*Columba livia*). *Journal of Comparative Neurology*, **314**, 467–77.

Kreithen, M. L. and Quine, D. B. (1979). Infrasound detection by the homing pigeon: A behavioural audiogram. *Journal of Comparative Physiology*, **129**, 1–4.

Krimm, M. (1994). Rôle de l'expérience visuelle précoce et des aires visuelles corticales dans le traitement des informations spatiales. Doctoral dissertation. University Aix-Marseille II.

Krushinskaya, N. L. (1966). Some complex forms of feeding behaviour of nutcracker *Nucifraga caryocatactes*, after removal of old cortex. *Journal of Evolutionary Biochem-istry and Physiology*, **11**, 563–8.

Kudo, H., Tsuneyoshi, Y., Nagae, M., Adachi, S., Yamauchi, K., Ueda, H. and Kawamura, H. (1994). Detection of thyroid hormone receptors in the olfactory system and brain of wild masu salmon *Onochrynchus masou* (Brevoort) during smolting by *in vitro* auto-radiography. *Aquaculture and Fisheries Management*, **25**, 171–82.

LaBar, G. W. (1971). Movement and homing of Cutthroat Trout (*Salmo clarki*) in clear and bridge creeks, Yellowstone National Park. *Transactions of the American Fisheries Society*, **1**, 41–9.

Land, M. F. and Layne, J. (1995). The visual control of behaviour in fiddler crabs: II. Tracking control systems in courtship and defence. *Journal of Comparative Physiology A*, **177**, 91–103.

Landfield, P. W., McGaugh, J. L. and Lynch, G. (1978). Impaired synaptic potentiation processes in the hippocampus of aged, memory-deficient rats. *Brain Research*, **150**, 85–101.

Lednor, A. and Walcott, C. (1988). Orientation of homing pigeons at magnetic anomalies. The effects of experience. *Behavioral Ecology and Sociobiology*, **22**, 3–8.

Lehrer, M. (1993). Why do bees turn back and look? *Journal of Comparative Physiology A*, **172**, 549–63.

Lehrer, M. and Collett, T. S. (1994). Approaching and departing bees learn different cues to the distance of a landmark. *Journal of Comparative Physiology A*, **175**, 171–7.

Levin, L. E., Belmonte, P. and González, O. (1992). Sun-compass orientation in the characid *Cheirodon pulcher*. *Environmental Biology of Fishes*, **35**, 321–5.

Lewis, F. T. (1923). The significance of the term hippocampus. *Journal of Comparative Neurology*, **35**, 213–30.

Linsenmair, K. E. (1967). Konstruktion und Signalfunktion der Sandpyramide der Reiterkrabbe *Ocypode saratan* Forsk. (Decapoda Brachyura Ocypodidae). *Zeitschrift für Tierpsychologie*, **24**, 403–56.

Lipp, H.-P. (1992). Chaos and fuzzy systems in der Schweizer Armee: ein Fall für Brieftauben. In *Informationstechnik und Armee*, Vol. 31 (ed. Bauem), pp. 4/1–16). EDMZ, Bern.

Lipp, H. -P. and Schwegler, H. (1989). Structure variations of the hippocampal mossy fiber system and avoidance learning. In *The hippocampus – new vistas* (ed. V. Chan-Palay and C. Köhler), pp. 395–410. Alan R. Liss, New York.

Loevei, G. L. (1989). Passerine migration between the Palaearctic and Africa. In *Current Ornithology*, 6 (ed. D. M. Power), pp. 143–74. Academic Press, London.

Loyacano, H. A. and Chappell, J. A. (1977). Sun-compass orientation in juvenile largemouth bass, *Micropterus salmoides*. *Transactions of the American Fisheries Society*, **106**, 77–9.

Lucanus, F. von (1923). *Die Rätsel des Vogelzuges*. Beyer and Söhme, Langensalza.

Ludlow, A. M. (1996). *Territorial behaviour in the longfin damsel fish (Stegastes diencaeus)*. MSc Thesis. Lehigh University. Lehigh, USA.

Luschi, P. and Dall'Antonia, P. (1993). Anosmic pigeons orient from familiar sites by relying on the map-and-compass mechanism. *Animal Behaviour*, **46**, 1195–203.

Mace, G. M., Harvey, P. H. and Clutton-Brock, T. H. (1980) Is brain size an ecological variable? *Trends in Neurosciences*, **3**, 193–6.

Mackintosh, N. J. (1976). Overshadowing and stimulus intensity. *Animal Learning and Behavior*, **4**, 186–92.

Mackintosh, N. J. and Reese, B. (1979). One-trial overshadowing. *Quarterly Journal of Experimental Psychology*, **31**, 519–26.

Macphail, E. M. and Reilly, S. (1989). Rapid acquisition of a novelty versus familiarity concept by pigeons (*Columba livia*). *Journal of Experimental Psychology: Animal Behavior Processes*, **15**, 242–52.

Maier, N. R. F. (1932). A study of orientation in the rat. *Journal of Comparative Psychology*, **14**, 387–99.

March, J., Chamizo, V. D. and Mackintosh, N. J. (1992). Reciprocal overshadowing between intra-maze and extra-maze cues. *Quarterly Journal of Experimental Psychology*, **45B**, 49–63.

Margules, J. and Gallistel, C. R. (1988). Heading in the rat: Determination by environmental shape. *Animal Learning and Behavior*, **16**, 404–10.

Mather, J. A. (1991). Navigation by spatial memory and use of visual landmarks in octopuses. *Journal of Comparative Physiology A*, **168**, 491–7.

Martin, R. D. (1981). Relative brain size and metabolic rate in terrestrial vertebrates. *Nature*, **293**, 57–60.

Matsuura, M. and Yamane, S. (1984). *Biology of the Vespine wasps*. Springer-Verlag, Berlin.

Maurer, R. (1993). L'intégration du chemin ou navigation à l'estime chez l'animal. Formalisation de modéles neuromimétiques. Doctoral thesis, University of Geneva.

Maurer, R. and Séguinot, V. (1995). What is modelling for? A critical review of the models of path integration. *Journal of Theoretical Biology*, **175**, 457–75.

Mayne, R. (1974). A systems concept of the vestibular organs. In *Handbook of sensory physiology*, Vol. VI/II (ed. H. H. Kornhuber), pp. 493–580. Springer-Verlag, Berlin.

McNaughton, B. L., Chen, L. L. and Markus, E. J. (1991). 'Dead reckoning', landmark learning, and the sense of direction: a neurophysiological and computational hypothesis. *Journal of Cognitive Neuroscience*, **3**, 190–202.

McNaughton, B. L., Barnes, C. A., Gerrard, J. L., Gothard, K., Jung, M. W., Knierim, J. J., Kudrimoti, H., Qin, Y., Skaggs, W. E., Suster, M. and Weaver, K. L. (1996). Deciphering the hippocampal polyglot: the hippocampus as a path integration system. *Journal of Experimental Biology*, **199**, 173–85.

Menzel, R. (1990). Learning, Memory, and 'Cognition' in Honey Bees. In *Neurobiology of Comparative Cognition* (ed. R. P. Kesner and D. S. Olton), pp. 237–92. Lawrence Erlbaum Associates, NJ.

Menzel, R., Geiger, K., Chittka, L., Joerges, J., Kunze, J. and Müller, U. (1996). The knowledge base of bee navigation. *Journal of Experimental Biology*, **199**, 141–6.

Merkel, R. W. (1994). An adaptive value of spatial learning and memory in the blackeye goby, *Coryphopterus nicholsi*. *Animal Behaviour*, **47**, 1462–4.

Milinski, M. (1994). Long-term memory for food patches and implications for ideal free distributions in sticklebacks. *Ecology*, **75**, 1150–6.

Miller, R. B. (1954). Movements of Cutthroat Trout after different periods of retention upstream and downstream from their homes. *Journal of the Fisheries Research Board, Canada*, **11**, 550–8.

Mittelstaedt, H. and Mittelstaedt, M. L. (1973). Mechanismen der Orientierung ohne richtende Aussenreize. *Fortschritte der Zoologie*, **21**, 46–58.

Mittelstaedt, H. and Mittelstaedt, M. L. (1982). Homing by path integration. In *Avian navigation* (ed. F. Papi and H. G. Wallraff), pp. 290–7. Springer-Verlag, Berlin.

Mollá, R., Rodriguez, J., Calvet, S. and Garcia-Verdugo, J. M. (1986). Neuronal types of the cerebral cortex of the adult chicken *Gallus gallus*. A golgi study. *Journal für Hirnforschung*, **27**, 381–90.

Montagnese, C. M., Krebs, J. R., Székely, A. D. and Csillag, A. (1993). A sub-population of large calbindin-like immunopositive neurones is present in the hippocampal formation in food-storing but not in non-storing species of bird. *Brain Research*, **614**, 291–300.

Montagnese, C. M., Krebs, J. R. and Meyer, G. (1996). The dorsomedial and dorsolateral forebrain of the zebra finch, *Taeniopygia guttata*—a golgi-study. *Cell And Tissue Research*, **283**, 263–82.

Moreau, R. E. (1972). *The Palaearctic-African bird migration systems*. Academic Press, London.

Morin, P.-P., Dodson, J. J. and Doré, F. Y. (1989a). Cardiac responses to natural odorants as evidence of a sensitive period for olfactory imprinting in young Atlantic salmon, *Salmo salar*. *Canadian Journal of Fisheries and Aquatic Sciences*, **46**, 122–30.

Morin, P.-P., Dodson, J. J. and Doré, F. Y. (1989b). Thyroid activity concominant with olfactory learning and heart rate changes in Atlantic salmon, *Salmo salar*, during smoltification. *Canadian Journal of Fisheries and Aquatic Sciences*, **46**, 131–6.

Morris, R. G. M. (1981). Spatial localization does not require the presence of local cues. *Learning and Motivation*, **12**, 239–60.

Morris, R. G. M., Garrud, P., Rawlins, J. N. P. and O'Keefe, J. (1982). Place navigation impaired in rats with hippocampal lesions. *Nature*, **297**, 681–3.

Müller, H. G. (1966). Homing and distance orientation in bats. *Zeitschrift für Tierpsychologie*, **23**, 403–21.

Müller, M. and Wehner, R. (1988). Path integration in desert ants, *Cataglyphis fortis*. *Proceedings of the National Academy of Sciences USA*, **85**, 5287–90.

Müller, M. and Wehner, R. (1994). The hidden spiral: systematic search and path integration in desert ants, *Cataglyphis fortis*. *Journal of Comparative Physiology A*, **175**, 525–30.

Muller, R. U., Kubie, J. L., Bostock. E. M., Taube, J. S. and Quirk, G. J. (1991). Spatial firing correlates of neurons in the hippocampal formation of freely moving rats. In *Brain and space* (ed. J. Paillard), pp. 296–333. Oxford University Press, London.

Myrberg, A. A., Montgomery, W. L. and Fishelson, L. (1988). The reproductive behaviour of *Acanthus nigrofuscus* (Forskal) and other surgeonfishes (Fam. Acanthuridae) off Eilat, Israel (Gulf Aqaba, Red Sea). *Ethology*, **79**, 31–61.

Naumann, J. A. (1795–1817). *Naturgeschichte der Land- und Wasser-Vögel des nördlichen Deutschlands und angränzender Länder*. Osterloh & Aue, Köthen.

Neese, V. (1988). Die Entfernungsmessung der Sammelbiene: Ein energetisches und zugleich sensorisches Problem. *Biona-Report*, **6**, 1–15.

Nevitt, G. A., Dittman, D. A., Quinn, T. P. and Moody, W. J. (1994). Evidence for a peripheral olfactory memory in imprinted salmon. *Proceedings of the National Academy of Sciences USA*, **91**, 4288–92.

Noda, M., Gushima, K. and Kakuda, S. (1994). Local prey search based on spatial memory and expectation in the planktivorous reef fish, *Chromis chrysurus* (Pomacentridae). *Animal Behaviour*, **47**, 1413–22.

Nowak, E. and Berthold, P. (1991). Satellite tracking: a new method in orientation research. In *Orientation in birds* (ed. P. Berthold), pp. 307–21. Birkhäuser Verlag, Basel.

O'Keefe, J. (1976). Place units in the hippocampus of the freely moving rat. *Experimental Neurology*, **51**, 78–109.

O'Keefe, J. and Burgess, N. (1996). Geometric determinants of the place fields of hippocampal neurons. *Nature*, **381**, 425–8.

O'Keefe, J. and Conway, D. H. (1980). On the trail of the hippocampal engram. *Physiological Psychology*, **8**, 229–38.

O'Keefe, J. and Dostrovsky J. (1971). The hippocampus as a spatial map: Preliminary evidence from unit activity in the freely moving rat. *Brain Research*, **34**, 171–5.

O'Keefe, J. and Nadel, L. (1978). *The hippocampus as a cognitive map*. Oxford University Press, Oxford.

O'Keefe, J. and Speakman, A. (1987). Single unit activity in the rat hippocampus during a spatial memory task. *Experimental Brain Research*, **68**, 1–27.

Olson, D. (1991). Species differences in spatial memory among Clark's nutcrackers, pigeons and scrub jays. *Journal of Experimental Psychology: Animal Behavior Processes*, **17**, 363–76.

Olton, D. S. and Samuelson, R. J. (1976). Remembrances of places passed: spatial memory in rats. *Journal of Experimental Psychology: Animal Behavior Processes*, **2**, 97–116.

Papi, F. (1991). Olfactory navigation. In *Orientation in Birds* (ed. P. Berthold), pp. 52–85. Birkhäuser Verlag, Basel.

Papi, F. (1995). Recent experiments on pigeon navigation. In *Behavioral brain research in naturalistic and semi-naturalistic settings* (ed. E. Alleva, A. Fasolo, H.-P. Lipp, L. Nadel and L. Ricceri), pp. 225–38. Kluwer Academic Publishers, Dordrecht.

Papi, F., Fiore, L., Fiaschi, V., Benvenuti, S. and Baldaccini, N. E. (1972). Olfaction and homing in pigeons. *Monitore Zoologico Italiano (N. S.)*, **6**, 85–95.

Pastergue-Ruiz, I. and Beugnon, G. (1994). Spatial sequential memory in the ant *Cataglyphis cursor*. In *Les Insectes Sociaux. Proceedings of the 12th Congress of the International Union. Study social insects* (ed. A. Lenoir, G. Arnold and M. Lepage), p. 490. University Paris Nord, Paris.

Pavlov, I. P. (1927). *Conditioned reflexes* (trans. G. V. Anrep). Oxford University Press, London.

Perrins, C. M. (1979). *British tits*. The New Naturalist Series (eds. M. Davies, J. Gilmour and K. Mellanby). Collins, London.

Peters, R. P. (1973). Cognitive maps in wolves and men. In *Environmental design research*, Vol. 2 (ed. W. F. E. Preiser), pp. 247–53. Dowden, Hutchinson and Ross, Stroudsberg, Pennsylvania.

Piéron, H. (1904). Du rle sens musculaire dans l'orientation des fourmis. *Bulletin of the Institute of General Psychology*, **4**, 168–87.

Pitcher, T. J. (1993). *Behaviour of teleost fishes*, 2nd edn. Chapman & Hall, London.

Polak, M. (1993). Landmark territoriality in the neotropical paper wasps *Polistes canadensis* (L.) and *P. carnifex* (F.) (Hymenoptera: Vespidae). *Ethology*, 95, 278–90.

Poucet, B. (1985). Choices of routes through a complex spatial environment by cats. *Animal Behaviour*, **33**, 1026–8.

Poucet, B., Chapuis, N., Durup, M. and Thinus-Blanc, C. (1986). A study of exploratory behavior as an index of spatial knowledge in hamsters. *Animal Learning and Behavior*, **14**, 93–100.

Poucet, B., Thinus-Blanc, C. and Muller, R. U. (1994). Place cells in the ventral hippocampus of rats. *Neuroreport*, **5**, 2045–8.

Pulido, F., Berthold, P. and van Noordwijk, A. J. (1996). Frequency of migrants and migratory activity are genetically correlated in a bird population: evolutionary implications. *Proceedings of the National Academy of Sciences USA*, **93**, 14642–7.

Quinet, Y. amd Pasteels, J. M. (1996). Spatial specialization of the foragers and foraging strategy in *Lasius fuliginosus* (Latreille) (Hymenoptera, Formicidae). *Insectes Sociaux*, **43**, 333–46.

Quinn, T. P. (1984). Homing and straying in Pacific salmon. In *Mechanisms and migration in fishes* (ed. J. D. McCleave, G. P. Arnold, J. J. Dodson and W. H. Neill), pp. 357–62. Plenum Press, New York.

Quinn, T. P. (1992). Fishes. In *Animal homing* (ed. F. Papi), pp. 145–211. Chapman & Hall, London.

Quinn, T. P. and Ogden, J. C. (1984). Field experience of compass orientation in migrating juvenile Grunts (*Haemulidae*). *Journal of Experimental Marine Biology and Ecology*, **81**, 181–92.

Quirk, G. J., Muller, R. U. and Kubie, J. L. (1990). The firing of hippocampal place cells in the dark depends on the rat's recent experience. *Journal of Neuroscience*, **10**, 2008–17.

Reboreda, J. C., Clayton, N. S. and Kacelnik, A. (1996). Species and sex-differences in hippocampus size in parasitic and nonparasitic cowbirds. *Neuroreport*, **7**, 505–8.

Reese, E. S. (1989). Orientation behaviour of butterflyfishes (family Chaetodontidae) on coral reefs: spatial learning of route specific landmarks and cognitive maps. *Environmental Biology of Fishes*, **25**, 79–86.

Rehkämper, G., Haase, E. and Frahm, H. D. (1988). Allometric comparison of brain weight and brain structure volumes in different breeds of the domestic pigeon, *Columba livia f. d.* (fantails, homing pigeons, strassers). *Brain, Behavior and Evolution*, **31**, 141–9.

Reilly, S. and Good, M. (1987). Enhanced DRL and impaired forced-choice alternation performance following hippocampal lesion in the pigeon. *Behavioural Brain Research*, **26**, 185–97.

Rescorla, R. A. (1967). Pavlovian conditioning and its proper control procedures. *Psychological Review*, **74**, 71–80.

Reynolds, G. S. (1961). Attention in the pigeon. *Journal of the Experimental Analysis of Behavior*, **4**, 203–8.

Ribi, W. A. and Ribi, L. (1979). Natural history of the Australian digger wasp *Sphex cognatus* Smith (Hymenoptera, Sphecidae). *Journal of Natural History*, **13**, 693–701.

Risold, P. Y. and Swanson, L. W. (1996). Structural evidence for functional domains in the rat hippocampus. *Science*, **272**, 1484–6.

Robinson, G. E. and Dyer, F. C. (1993). Plasticity of spatial memory in honey bees: reorientation following colony fission. *Animal Behaviour*, **46**, 311–20.

Robinson, G. E., Underwood, B. A. and Henderson, C. E. (1984). A highly specialized water-collecting honey bee. *Apidologie*, **15**, 355–8.

Rodriguez, F., Duran, E., Vargas, J.P., Torres, B. and Salas, C. (1994). Performance of goldfish trained in allocentric and egocentric maze procedures suggests presence of a cognitive mapping system in fishes. *Animal Learning and Behavior*, **22**, 409–20.

Roitblat, H. L., Tham, W. and Golub, L. (1982). Performance of *Betta splendens* in a radial arm maze. *Animal Learning and Behavior*, **10**, 108–14.

Ronacher, B. and Wehner, R. (1995). Desert ants *Cataglyphis fortis* use self-induced optic flow to measure distances travelled. *Journal of Comparative Physiology A*, **177**, 21–7.

Rosengren, R. (1971). Route fidelity, visual memory and recruitment behaviour in foraging wood ants of the genus *Formica* (Hymenoptera, Formicidae). *Acta Zoologica Fennica*, **133**, 1–106.

Ruttner, F. (1966) The life and flight activity of drones. *Bee World*, **47**, 93–100.

Saunders, R. L. and Gee, J. H. (1964). Movements of young atlantic salmon in a small stream. *Journal of the Fisheries Research Board of Canada*, **21**, 27–36.

Sauvé, J.-P. (1989). L'orientation spatiale: Formalisation d'un modèle de mémorisation égocentrée et expérimentation chez l'homme. Doctoral thesis, University of Aix-Marseille II.

Save, E. (1997). The contribution of visual and inertial mechanisms to navigation in total darkness. *Animal Learning and Behavior*, **25**, 324–34.

Save, E., Cressant, A., Thinus-Blanc, C. and Poucet, B. (1996). Early visual deprivation does not prevent hippocampal place cell firing in the rat. *Society for Neuroscience Abstracts*, **22**, 358.9.

Schäfer, M. and Wehner, R. (1993). Loading does not affect measurement of walking distance in desert ants (*Cataglyphis fortis*). *Verhandlungen der Deutschen Zoologischen Gesellschaft*, **86**, 270.

Schenk, F., Grobéty, M.-C., Lavenex, P. and Lipp, H. P. (1995). Dissociation between basic components of spatial memory in rats. In *Behavioural brain research in naturalistic and semi-naturalistic settings*, Proceedings of the NATO Advanced Study Institute, Acquafredda di Maratea, Italy, September 10–20, 1994 (ed. E. Alleva, A. Fasolo, H.-P. Lipp, L. Nadel and L. Ricceri), pp. 277–300. Kluwer Academic Publishers, Dordrecht.

Schenk, F., Grobéty, M.-C. and Gafner, M. (1997). Spatial learning by rats across visually disconnected environments. *Quarterly Journal of Experimental Psychology*, **50B**, 54–78.

Schifferer, G. (1952). Über die Entfernungsangabe bei den Tänzen der Bienen. Lehramtsarbeit naturwissenschaftliche Fakultät, Universität München.

Schlund, W. (1992). Intra-nasal zinc sulfate irrigation in pigeons: Effects on olfactory capabilities and homing. *Journal of Experimental Biology*, **164**, 171–87.

Schmidt-Koenig, K. (1958). Experimentelle einflussnahme auf die 24-Stunden-Periodik bei Brieftauben und deren Auswirkungen unter besonderer Berücksichtigung des Heimfindevermögens. *Zeitschrift für Tierpsychologie*, **15**, 301–31.

Schmidt-Koenig, K. (1961). Die Sonne als Kompass in Heimorientierungssytem der Breiftauben. *Zeitschrift für Tierpsychologie*, **68**, 221–4.

Schmidt-Koenig, K. and Keeton, W. T. (1977). Sun compass utilization by pigeons wearing frosted contact lenses. *Auk*, **94**, 143–5.

Schmidt-Koenig, K. and Walcott, C. (1978). Tracks of pigeons homing with frosted lenses. *Animal Behaviour*, **26**, 480–6.

Schmidt-Koenig, K., Ganzhorn, J. U. and Ranvaud, R. (1991). The sun compass. In *Orientation in Birds* (ed. P. Berthold), pp. 1–15. Birkhäuser Verlag, Basel.

Schneirla, T. C. (1929). Learning and orientation in ants. *Comparative Psychology Monographs*, **6**, 143.

Schöps, M. and Wiltschko, W. (1994). Orientation of homing pigeons deprived of infrasound. *Journal für Ornithologie*, **135**, 415.

Schüz, E. (1971). *Grundriß der Vogelzugskunde*. Parey, Berlin.

Schwegler, H. and Lipp, H.-P. (1995). Variations in the morphology of the septo-hippocampal complex and maze learning in rodents: correlation between morphology and behaviour. In *Behavioural brain research in naturalistic and semi-naturalistic settings*. Proceedings of the NATO Advanced Study Institute, Acquafredda di Maratea, Italy, September 10–20, 1994 (ed. E. Alleva, A. Fasolo, H.-P. Lipp, L. Nadel and L. Ricceri), pp. 259–76. Kluwer Academic Publishers, Dordrecht.

Scoville, W. B. and Milner, B. (1957). Loss of recent memory after bilateral hippocampal lesions. *Journal of Neurology Neurosurgery and Psychiatry*, **20**, 11–21.

Seeley, T. D. and Towne, W. F. (1992). Tactics of dance choice in honey bees: do foragers compare dances? *Behavioral Ecology and Sociobiology*, **30**, 59–69.

Séguinot, V., Maurer, R. and Etienne, A. S. (1993). Dead reckoning in a small mammal: The evaluation of distance. *Journal of Comparative Physiology A*, **173**, 103–13.

Seyfarth, E.-A. and Barth, F. G. (1972). Compound slit sense organs on the spider leg: Mechanoreceptors involved in kinesthetic orientation. *Journal of Comparative Physiology A*, **78**, 176–91.

Seyfarth, E.-A., Hergenröder, R., Ebbes, H. and Barth, F. G. (1982). Idiothetic orientation of a wandering spider: Compensation of detours and estimates of goal distance. *Behavioral Ecology and Sociobiology*, **11**, 139–48.

Shapiro, M. L. and Olton, D. S. (1994). Hippocampal function and interference. In *Memory systems 1994* (ed. D. L. Schacter and E. Tulving), pp. 87–117. MIT Press, Cambridge, MA.

Sherry, D. F. and Schacter, D. L. (1987). The evolution of multiple memory systems. *Psychological Review*, **49**, 439–54.

Sherry, D. F. and Vaccarino, A. L. (1989). Hippocampus and memory for food caches in black-capped chickadees. *Behavioral Neuroscience*, **103**, 308–18.

Sherry, D. F., Jacobs, L. F. and Gaulin, S. C. (1992). Spatial memory and adaptive specialization of the hippocampus. *Trends in Neurosciences*, **15**, 298–303.

Sherry, D. F., Vaccarino, A. L., Buckenham, K. and Herz, R. S. (1989). The hippocampal complex of food-storing birds. *Brain, Behavior and Evolution*, **34**, 308–17.

Sherry, D. F., Forbes, M. R L., Khurgel, M. and Ivy, G. O. (1993). Females have a larger hippocampus than males in the brood-parasitic brown-headed cowbird. *Proceedings of the National Academy of Science USA*, **90**, 7839–43.

Shimizu, T. and Karten, H. J. (1990). Immunohistochemical analysis of the visual wulst of the pigeon (*Columba livia*). *Journal of Comparative Neurology*, **300**, 346–69.

Shettleworth, S.J. (1995). Comparative studies of storing birds: from the field to the Skinner box. In *Behavioural brain research in naturalistic and semi-naturalistic settings*, Proceedings of the NATO Advanced Study Institute, Acquafredda di Maratea, Italy, Sept. 10–20, 1994, (ed. E. Alleva, A. Fasolo, H.-P. Lipp, L. Nadel and L. Ricceri), pp. 159–92. Kluwer Academic Publishers, Dordrecht, Netherlands.

Smith, G. T., Brenowitz, E., Nalls, B. and Wingfield, J. (1992). Testosterone changes song control region volume in photostimulated male Gambel's sparrows. *Proceedings of the 3rd International Congress of Neuroethology*, 292.

Smith, R. J. F. (1992). Alarm signal in fishes. *Reviews in Fish Biology and Fisheries*, **2**, 33–63.

Smulders, T. V., Sasson, A. D. and Devoogd, T. J. (1995). Seasonal variation in hippocampal volume in a food-storing bird, the black-capped chickadee. *Journal of Neurobiology*, **27**, 15–25.

Solomon, D. J. (1982). Tracking fish with radio tags. *Symposia of the Zoological Society, London*, **49**, 95–105.

Spetch, M. L. (1995). Overshadowing in landmark learning: Touch-screen studies with pigeons and humans. *Journal of Experimental Psychology: Animal Behavior Processes*, **21**, 166–81.

Spetch, M. L. and Edwards, C. A. (1988). Pigeons', *Columba livia*, use of global and local cues for spatial memory. *Animal Behaviour*, **36**, 293–6.

Spetch, M. L. and Mondloch, M. V. (1993). Control of pigeons' spatial search by graphic landmarks in a touch-screen task. *Journal of Experimental Psychology: Animal Behavior Processes*, **19**, 353–72.

Spetch, M. L. and Wilkie, D. M. (1994). Pigeons' use of landmarks presented in digitized images. *Learning and Motivation*, **25**, 245–75.

Spetch, M. L., Cheng, K. and Mondloch, M. V. (1992). Landmark use by pigeons in a touch-screen spatial search task. *Animal Learning and Behavior*, **20**, 281–92.

Spetch, M. L., Cheng, K. and MacDonald, S. E. (1996). Learning the configuration of a landmark array: I. Touch-screen studies with pigeons and humans. *Journal of Comparative Psychology*, **110**, 55–68.

Spetch, M. L., Cheng, K., MacDonald, S. E., Linkenhoker, B., Kelly, D. and Doerkson, S. (1997). Learning the configuration of a landmark array in pigeons and humans, II: Generality across search tasks. *Journal of Comparative Psychology*, **111**, 14–24.

Squire, L. R. (1992). Memory and the hippocampus: a synthesis from findings with rats, monkeys, and humans. *Psychological Review*, **99,** 195–231.

Squire, L. R. (1993). The hippocampus and spatial memory. *Trends in Neuroscience*, **16,** 56–7.

Srinivasan, M. V., Zhang, S. W., Lehrer, M. and Collett, T. S. (1996). Honeybee navigation *en route* to the goal: visual flight control and odometry. *Journal of Experimental Biology*, **199,** 237–44.

Stabell, O. B. (1987). Intraspecific pheromone discrimination and substrate marking by Atlantic salmon (*Salmo salar*). *Journal of Chemical Ecology*, **13,** 1625–43.

Steiner, A. (1932). Die Arbeitsteilung der Feldwespe *Polistes dubia* K. *Zeitschrift für Vergleichende Physiologie,* 17, 101–52.

Stevens, T. A. and J. R. Krebs. (1986). Retrieval of stored seeds by Marsh Tits *Parus palustris* in the field. *Ibis*, **128,** 513–25.

Stradmeyer, L. and Thorpe, J. E. (1987). Feeding behaviour of wild Atlantic salmon parr in mid- to late-summer in a Scottish stream. *Aquaculture and Fish Management*, **18,** 33–49.

Streng, A. and Wallraff, H. G. (1992). Attempts to determine the roles of visual and olfactory inputs in initial orientation and homing of pigeons over familiar terrain. *Ethology*, **91,** 203–19.

Stresemann, E. (1934). Aves. In *Handbuch der Zoologie 7* (ed. W. Kükenthal and T. Krumbach, pp. 1–899. de Gruyter & Co, Berlin.

Suzuki, S. Augerinos, G. and Black, A. (1980). Stimulus control of spatial behavior on the eight-arm maze in rats. *Learning and Motivation*, **11,** 1–18.

Swanson, L. W. (1979). The hippocampus—new anatomical insights. *Trends in Neurosciences*, **2**, 9–12.

Székely, A. D. and Krebs, J. R. (1996). Efferent connectivity of the hippocampal-formation of the zebra finch (*Taenopygia guttata*)—an anterograde pathway tracing study using phaseolus-vulgaris leukoagglutinin. *Journal of Comparative Neurology*, **368,** 198–214.

Székely, A. D., Clayton, N. S. and Krebs, J. R. (1992). Regional distribution of immediate early gene-expression in the avian brain following food-storing behavior. *European Journal of Neuroscience*, **S5,** 149.

Taube, J. S. and Burton, H. L. (1995). Head direction cell activity monitored in a novel environment and during a cue conflict situation. *Journal of Neurophysiology*, **74,** 1953–71.

Taube, J. S., Goodridge, J. P., Golob, E. J., Dudchenko, P. A. and Stackman, R. W. (1996). Processing the head direction cell signal: a review and commentary. *Brain Research Bulletin*, **40,** 477–84.

Teroni, E., Portenier, V. and Etienne, A. S. (1987). Spatial orientation of the golden hamster in conditions of conflicting location-based and route-based information. *Behavioral Ecology and Sociobiology*, **20**, 389–97.

Terrill, S. B. (1990). Ecophysiological aspects of movements by migrants in the wintering quarters. In *Bird migration. Physiology and ecophysiology* (ed. E. Gwinner), pp. 130–43. Springer-Verlag, Berlin.

Terrill, S. B. (1991). Evolutionary aspects of orientation and migration in birds. In *Orientation in birds* (ed. P. Berthold), pp. 180–201. Birkhäuser Verlag, Basel.

Teyke, T. (1989). Learning and remembering the environment in blind cave fish *Anoptichthy jordani*. *Journal of Comparative Physiology A*, **164**, 655–62.

Thinus-Blanc, C. and Gaunet, F. (1997). Space representations in the blind: Vision as a spatial sense? *Psychological Bulletin*, **121**, 20–42.

Thinus-Blanc, C, Bouzouba, L., Chaix, K., Chapuis, N., Durup, M. and Poucet, B. (1987). A study of spatial parameters encoded during exploration in hamsters. *Journal of Experimental Psychology: Animal Behavior Processes*, **13**, 418–27.

Tinbergen, N. (1932). Über die Orientierung des Bienenwolfes (*Philanthus triangulum* Fabr.). *Zeitschrift für Vergleichende Physiologie*, 16, 305–34.

Tinbergen, N. (1972). *The animal in its world*. Harvard Press, Cambridge, MA.

Tögel, A. and Wiltschko, R. (1992). Detour experiments with homing pigeons: Information obtained during the outward journey is included in the navigational process. *Behavioral Ecology and Sociobiology*, **31**, 73–9.

Tolman, E. C. (1948). Cognitive maps in rats and men. *The Psychological Review*, **55**, 189–208.

Tolman, E. C. and Honzick, C. H. (1930). Degrees of hunger, reward and non reward on maze learning in rats. *University of California Publications in Psychology*, **4**, 241–56.

Tomback, D. F. (1977). Foraging strategies of Clark's nutcrackers. *Living Bird*, **16**, 123–61.

Tomlinson, W. T. and Johnston, T. D. (1991). Hamsters remember spatial information derived from olfactory cues. *Animal Learning and Behavior*, **19**, 185–90.

Tully, T. and Quinn, W.G. (1985). Classical conditioning and retention in normal and mutant *Drosophila melanogaster*. *Journal of Comparative Physiology*, **157**, 263–77.

Ueda, H. and Yamauchi, K. (1995). Biochemistry of fish migration. In *Biochemistry and molecular biology of fishes*. (ed. P.W.L. Hochachka and T.P. Mommsen), pp. 265–79. Elsevier Science, Amsterdam.

Ueda, H., Kaeriyama, M., Urano, A., Kurihara, K. and Yamauchi, K. (1995). Homing mechanisms in salmon: roles of vision and olfaction. In *International Symposium on Reproductive Physiology of Fish* (ed. F. W. Goetz), pp. 35–7, Texas.

Vallortigara, G., Zanforlin, M. and Pasti, G. (1990). Geometric modules in animals' spatial representations: A test with chicks (*Gallus gallus domesticus*). *Journal of Comparative Psychology*, **104**, 248–54.

Vander Wall, S. B. (1982). An experimental analysis of cache recovery in Clark's nutcracker. *Animal Behaviour*, **30**, 84–94.

Vannini, M. and Cannicci, S. (1995). Homing behaviour and possible cognitive maps in crustacean decapods. *Journal of Experimental Marine Biology and Ecology*, **193**, 67–91.

Visscher, K. and Seeley, T. D. (1982). Foraging strategy of honeybee colonies in a temperate deciduous forest. *Ecology*, **63**, 1790–801.

Vollbehr, J. (1975). Zur Orientierung junger Honigbienen bei ihrem 1. Orientierungsflug. *Zoologisches Jahrbuch Physiologie,* **79**, 33–69.

Wagner, A. R., Logan, F. A., Haberlandt, K. and Price, T. (1968). Stimulus selection in animal discrimination learning. *Journal of Experimental Psychology*, **76**, 171–80.

Walcott, C. (1991). Magnetic maps in pigeons. In *Orientation in birds* (ed. P. Berthold), pp. 38–51. Birkhäuser Verlag, Basel.

Walcott, C. (1996). Pigeon homing: observations, experiments and confusions. *Journal of Experimental Biology*, **199**, 21–7.

Walker, M. M. (1984). Learned magnetic field discrimination in yellowfin tuna, *Thunnus albacares. Journal of Comparative Physiology A*, **155**, 673–9.

Walker, M. M., Quinn, T. P., Kirschvink, J. L. and Groot, C. (1988). Production of single domain magnetite throughout life by sockeye salmon, *Onchorhynchus nerka. Journal of Experimental Biology*, **140**, 51–63.

Walker, M. M., Montgomery, J. C. and Pankhurst, P. M. (1993). Toward a sensory basis for magnetic navigation by animals. In *Orientation and navigation in birds, humans and other animals*. Paper No. 4. Royal Institute of Navigation, Oxford.

Wallraff, H. G. (1966). Über die Heimfindeleistungen von Brieftauben nach Haltung in Verschiedenartig abgeschirmten Volieren. *Zeitschrift für Vergleichende Physiologie,* **52**, 215–59.

Wallraff, H. G. (1974). *Das navigationssystem der Vögel*. R. Oldenburg, Munich.

Wallraff, H. G. (1980). Does pigeon homing depend on stimuli perceived during displacement? I. Experiments in Germany. *Journal of Comparative Physiology*, **139**, 193–201.

Wallraff, H. G. (1981). The olfactory component of pigeon navigation: Steps of analysis. *Journal of Comparative Physiology*, **143**, 411–22.

Wallraff, H. G. (1989). Simulated navigation based on unreliable sources of information (models on pigeon homing, part 2). *Journal of Theoretical Biology*, **138**, 511–28.

Wallraff, H. G. (1991). Conceptual approaches to avian navigation systems. In *Orientation in birds* (ed. P. Berthold), pp. 128–65. Birkhäuser Verlag, Basel.

Wallraff, H. G. (1993). Correct and false olfactory orientation of homing pigeons as depending on geographical relationships between release site and home site. *Behavioral Ecology and Sociobiology*, **32**, 147–55.

Wallraff, H. G. (1996). Seven theses on pigeon homing deduced from empirical findings. *Journal of Experimental Biology*, **199**, 105–11.

Wallraff, H. G., Kiepenheuer, J. and Streng, A. (1993). Further experiments on olfactory navigation and non-olfactory pilotage by homing pigeons. *Behavioral Ecology and Sociobiology*, **32**, 387–90.

Warburton, K. (1990). The use of local landmarks by foraging goldfish. *Animal Behaviour*, **40**, 500–5.

Weaving, A. J. S. (1989). Nesting strategies in some southern African species of *Ammophila* (Hymenoptera: Sphecidae). *Journal of Natural History*, **23**, 1–16.

Wehner, R. (1972). Dorsoventral asymmetry in the visual field of the bee, *Apis mellifera. Journal of Comparative Physiology A*, **77**, 256–77.

Wehner, R. (1981). Spatial vision in arthropods. In *Handbook of sensory physiology*, Vol. VII/6C (ed. H. Autrum), pp. 287–616. Springer-Verlag, Berlin.

Wehner, R. (1982). Himmelsnavigation bei Insekten. Neurophysiologie und Verhalten. *Neujahrsblatt des Naturforschenden Gesellschaft in Zürich*, **184**, 1–132.

Wehner, R. (1992). Arthropods. In *Animal homing* (ed. F. Papi), pp. 45–144. Chapman & Hall, London.

Wehner, R. and Menzel, R. (1990). Do insects have cognitive maps? *Annual Review of Neuroscience*, **13**, 403–14.

Wehner, R. and Räber, F. (1979). Visual spatial memory in desert ants, *Cataglyphis bicolor* (Hymenoptera: Formicidae). *Experientia*, **35**, 1569–71.

Wehner, R. and Rossel, S. (1985). The bee's celestial compass—a case study in behavioural neurobiology. *Fortschritte der Zoologie*, **31**, 11–53.

Wehner, R. and Srinivasan, M. V. (1981). Searching behaviour of desert ants, genus *Cataglyphis* (Formicidae, Hymenoptera). *Journal of Comparative Physiology A*, **142**, 315–38.

Wehner, R. and Wehner, S. (1990). Insect navigation: use of maps or Ariadne's thread? *Ethology, Ecology and Evolution*, **2**, 27–48.

Wehner, R., Michel, B. and Antonsen, P. (1996). Visual navigation in insects: coupling of egocentric and geocentric information. *Journal of Experimental Biology*, **199**, 129–40.

Whishaw, I. Q. (1985). Formation of a place learning set in the rat: A new procedure for neurobehavioral studies. *Physiology and Behavior*, **26**, 845–51.

Wieraszko, A. and Ball, G. F. (1991). Long-term enhancement of synaptic responses in the songbird hippocampus. *Brain Research*, **538**, 102–6.

Wieraszko, A. and Ball, G. F. (1993). Long-term potentiation in the avian hippocampus does not require activation of the *N*-methyl-D-aspartate (NMDA) receptor. *Synapse*, **13**, 173–8.

Wiltschko, R. (1992). Das Verhalten verfrachteter Vögel. Vogelwarte, **36**, 249–310.

Wiltschko, R. (1996). The function of olfactory input in pigeon orientation: Does it provide navigational information or play another role? *Journal of Experimental Biology*, **199**, 113–9.

Wiltschko, R. and Wiltschko, W. (1995). *Magnetic orientation in animals*. Springer-Verlag, Berlin.

Wiltschko, W. and Wiltschko, R. (1988). Magnetic orientation in birds. In *Current ornithology*, Vol. 5 (ed. R. F. Johnston), pp. 67–121. Plenum Press, New York.

Wiltschko, W. and Wiltschko, R. (1991). Magnetic orientation and celestial cues in migratory orientation. In *Orientation in birds* (ed. P. Berthold), pp. 16–37. Birkhäuser Verlag, Basel.

Wiltschko, W., Wiltschko, R. and Walcott, C. (1987*a*). Pigeon homing: Different effects of olfactory deprivation in different countries. *Behavioral Ecology and Sociobiology*, **21**, 333–42.

Wiltschko, W., Wiltschko, R., Grüter, M. and Kowalski, U. (1987*b*). Pigeon homing: Early experience determines what factors are used for navigation. *Naturwissenschaften*, **74**, 196–8.

Wiltschko, W. Wiltschko, R., Keeton, W. T. and Brown, I. A. (1987*c*). Pigeon homing: The orientation of young birds that had been prevented from seeing the sun. *Ethology*, **76**, 27–32.

Witthöft, W. (1967). Absolute Anzahl und Verteilung der Zellen im Hirn der Honigbiene. *Zeitschrift für Morphologie der Tiere*, **61**, 160–84.

Wittmann, D. (1985). Aerial defence of the nest by workers of the stingless bee *Trigona (Tetragonisca) angustula* (Latreille) (Hymenoptera: Apidae). *Behavioral Ecology and Sociobiology*, **16**, 111–14.

Wittmann, T. and Schwegler, H. (1995). Path integration—a network model. *Biological Cybernetics*, **73**, 569–75.

Wolf, E. (1926). Über das Heimfindevermögen der Bienen. (Erste Mitteilung.). *Zeitschrift für Vergleichende Physiologie*, **3**, 615–91.

Wolf, E. (1927). Über das Heimfindevermögen der Bienen. (Zweite Mitteilung.). *Zeitschrift für Vergleichende Physiologie*, **6**, 221–54.

Zeil, J. (1993*a*). Orientation flights of solitary wasps (*Cerceris*; Sphecidae; Hymenoptera): I. Description of flight. *Journal of Comparative Physiology A*, **172**, 189–205.

Zeil, J. (1993*b*). Orientation flights of solitary wasps (*Cerceris*; Sphecidae; Hymenoptera): II. Similarities between orientation and return flights and the use of motion parallax. *Journal of Comparative Physiology A*, **172**, 207–22.

Zeil, J. and Kelber, A. (1991). Orientation flights in ground-nesting wasps and bees share a common organisation. *Verhandlungen Deutschen Zoologischen Gesellschaft*, **84**, 371–2.

Zeil, J. and Wittmann, D. (1989). Visually controlled station-keeping by hovering guard bees of *Trigona* (*Tetragonisca*) *angustula* (Apidae, Meliponinae). *Journal of Comparative Physiology A*, **165**, 711–18.

Zeil, J., Kelber, A. and Voss, R. (1996). Structure and function of learning flights in bees and wasps. *Journal of Experimental Biology*, **199**, 245–52.

Zhang, S. W., Srinivasan, M. V. and Collett, T. S. (1995). Convergent processing in honeybee vision: Multiple channels for the recognition of shape. *Proceedings of the National Academy of Sciences USA*, **92**, 3029–31.

Zhang, S. W., Bartsch, K. and Srinivasan M. V. (1996). Maze learning by honeybees. *Neurobiology of Learning and Memory*, **66**, 267–82.

Zink, G. (1973–1985). *Der Zug europäischer Singvögel*. Vogelzug-Verlag, Möggingen.

Zola-Morgan, S., Squire, L. and Amaral, D. G. (1986). Human amnesia and the medial temporal region: enduring memory impairment following a bilateral lesion limited to field CA1 of the hippocampus. *Journal of Neuroscience*, **6**, 2950–67.

Index